PROTEIN FOLDING: NEW RESEARCH

PROTEIN FOLDING: NEW RESEARCH

TONY R. OBALINSKY
EDITOR

Nova Science Publishers, Inc.
New York

For permission to use material from this book please contact us:
Telephone 631-231-7269; Fax 631-231-8175
Web Site: http://www.novapublishers.com

LIBRARY OF CONGRESS CATALOGING-IN-PUBLICATION DATA

Protein folding : new research / Tony R. Obalinsky (editor).
p. ; cm.
Includes bibliographical references and index.
ISBN 1-59454-835-8
1. Protein folding. 2. Proteins--Structure.
[DNLM: 1. Protein Folding. 2. Proteins--ultrastructure. QU 55 P966292 2005] I. Obalinsky, Tony R.
QP551.P69582137 2005
572'.633--dc22 2005037618

Published by Nova Science Publishers, Inc. ✣ New York

CONTENTS

PREFACE

Proteins are one of the most basic components of all living cells and therefore serve a vital purpose in the cells of animals, plants and bacteria. They are comprised of chains of amino acids, which are held together by ribosome. These chains have many different patterns, which are known as 'folds.' These folds are complicated, and therefore susceptible to irregularities that are known to be the source of many diseases. Cystic fibrosis, mad cow disease, Alzheimer's disease, emphysema and others are all initiated by improper protein folds. It is clear that, improving our understanding of protein folding is a key to fighting these diseases. This book presents recently performed research from around the world on this important subject.

In chapter one, the author discusses protein misfolding, which is presently considered the main culprit of a number of conformational diseases. The latter are familial or sporadic degenerative conditions whose molecular basis can be traced back to the alteration of the folding or the conformational state of a protein or a peptide. The resulting toxicity can be due to either a loss-of-function (with increased degradation of the non-correctly folded protein) and/or a gain-of-function (with misfolded proteins/peptides undergoing ordered aggregation eventually resulting in toxic fibrous polymers (amyloids and other aggregates); the latter are deposited in the intra- or extracellular spaces of the affected tissues.

Among the conformational diseases, over twenty degenerative conditions affecting the central nervous system or a variety of peripheral tissues appear to result from the deposition of proteins in the form of amyloid fibrils and plaques. These conditions are of enormous importance in the context of present-day human health and welfare as they include Alzheimer's, Parkinson's and the prion diseases, several forms of systemic amyloidoses, and one condition associated with haemodialysis.

Advances in protein folding techniques have revealed that many proteins fold from the denatured states to their native states *via* an intermediate state(s). The number of such folding intermediates and their properties often differ between proteins, even between homologue members that share the same fold. These findings imply that protein folding does not occur randomly, but the process is systematically regulated through a pathway(s). In addition, the existence of multiple folding pathways was demonstrated for some proteins. Detailed information about folding intermediates of a protein characterizes its folding pathways, which is most successfully depicted by the energy landscape model. In contrast, it is not straightforward to describe protein misfolding reactions such as amyloid fibril formation and aggregation by a similar energetic scheme due to a lack of information regarding the amyloid/aggregation-responsible intermediates. Nevertheless, increasing evidence suggests that these misfolding reactions occur through the common folding intermediate states. In chapter two, the authors focus on detailed aspects of intermediate states reported for several proteins, which are responsible for amyloid fibril formation and aggregation. An analogy between these intermediates and folding intermediates is discussed towards the establishment of a model consistent with kinetic and thermodynamic aspects of protein misfolding reactions.

Mechanism of thermal aggregation of protein substrates (bovine lens β_L-crystallin; yeast alcohol dehydrogenase; rabbit skeletal muscles glycogen phosphorylase *b* and glyceraldehydes 3-phosphate dehydrogenase; coat protein of tobacco mosaic virus) has been studied by dynamic light scattering in chapter three. The stage of denaturation of the proteins under study was characterized using differential scanning calorimetry. It has been established that the aggregation process involves a latent stage, its duration (t_0) being determined by the point in time at which the initial increase in the light scattering intensity is observed.

Recently, it has been shown that residual structures are present even in the denatured state of a protein. If these residual structures are related to the initial structures in the folding of the denatured protein, they should affect the protein folding. However, there have been few reports on the effect of the residual structures of a protein on the protein folding. Here, in chapter four, we focus on the relationship between the residual structure in denatured lysozyme and the protein folding.

The protein structure is considered to have at least three basic levels: the primary, secondary and tertiary/quaternary. One of the aims of the post-genomic biology is establishing the definitive links between these levels of protein structure. This is also the task of the classical biophysical research of the protein folding which involves experimental studies of a few model proteins in order to get closer to the principles linking together the these levels of the protein structure. Chapter five concentrates on the roles of the intermediate structural level: the secondary structure. On one hand, biophysical studies of the protein folding suggest that the secondary structure can appear prior or concurrently with the major folding event. On the other hand, bioinformatical analyses, along with the data from computational chemistry presented in the article suggest that the secondary structure might contain considerably more information on the protein's tertiary structure, folding, stability and function than it is currently assumed. In particular, predictions of the tertiary structure of the proteins made exclusively on the base of the secondary structure were unexpectedly successful. The results suggest that the information contained in the secondary structure alone might be sufficient to describe and to predict not only the tertiary structure but also the functional regions in a protein. The new ultra-fast techniques emerging in the modern *in vitro* studies of the protein folding also suggest a unique place for the secondary structure during folding.

Folding of proteins into their native conformation is determined by various extrinsic and intrinsic factors. The most important determinant in folding is the amino acid sequence, yet it is not known how this simple one-dimensional information specifies a complex three-dimensional (3-D) structure. In addition, hydrophobic effects play a major role in protein folding. However, these effects do not adequately explain secondary structural preferences of amino acids. Moreover, they represent the cooperative behavior of systems (protein plus solvent) and reflect the operation of more fundamental processes that are not well understood. Chapter six will discuss how electronic effects play a major role in the fundamental aspects of protein folding. Previously, certain electronic properties of the 20 naturally-occurring amino acids have been characterized, including inductive and field effects, polarizability, and resonance effects. To follow up on this work, the hydrophilicity of amino acids has now been characterized in terms of electronic properties, specifically electron densities. In addition, various electronic properties of dipeptides have been related to secondary structural preferences and to NMR data. Ultimately, a better understanding of the electronic properties of amino acids and proteins will provide insight into protein folding at the atomic level and will allow more accurate prediction of 3-D structure starting from the amino acid sequence.

During the process of protein folding, the amino acid residues along the polypeptide chain interact with each other in a cooperative manner to form the stable native structure. The knowledge about inter-residue interactions in protein structures is very helpful to understand the mechanism of protein folding and stability. The authors classified the inter-residue interactions into short, medium and long range based on a simple geometric approach in chapter seven. The features of these interactions in different structural classes of globular and membrane proteins have been delineated. The application of inter-residue contacts for predicting protein structural class and secondary structure prediction has been evaluated. Further, the relationship between inter-residue contacts and protein folding rates has been highlighted. Moreover, the importance of inter-residue interactions in protein folding kinetics and for understanding the stability of proteins has been discussed. In essence, the information gained from the studies on inter-residue interactions provides valuable insights for understanding protein folding and de novo protein design.

In: Protein Folding: New Research
Editor: Tony R. Obalinsky, pp. 1-50
ISBN 1-59454-835-8

Chapter 1

Molecular Basis, Biological and Clinical Effects of Protein Misfolding and Aggregation

Massimo Stefani*

Department of Biochemical Sciences and Interuniversity Centre for the Study of the Molecular Basis of Neurodegenerative Diseases, University of Florence, Florence, Italy

Abstract

Protein misfolding is presently considered the main culprit of a number of conformational diseases. The latter are familial or sporadic degenerative conditions whose molecular basis can be traced back to the alteration of the folding or the conformational state of a protein or a peptide. The resulting toxicity can be due to either a loss-of-function (with increased degradation of the non-correctly folded protein) and/or a gain-of-function (with misfolded proteins/peptides undergoing ordered aggregation eventually resulting in toxic fibrous polymers (amyloids and other aggregates); the latter are deposited in the intra- or extracellular spaces of the affected tissues.

Among the conformational diseases, over twenty degenerative conditions affecting the central nervous system or a variety of peripheral tissues appear to result from the deposition of proteins in the form of amyloid fibrils and plaques. These conditions are of enormous importance in the context of present-day human health and welfare as they include Alzheimer's, Parkinson's and the prion diseases, several forms of systemic amyloidoses, and one condition associated with haemodialysis.

Much remains to be known about the mechanisms leading the proteins associated with these diseases to aggregate into amyloid or other types of polymers, and the way(s) the latter affect the functions of the organs where they arise. Nevertheless, a great deal of information on such diseases has emerged in recent years allowing a re-examination of a number of fundamental assumptions about the amyloid diseases. For example, recently a

* Correspondence: Prof. Massimo Stefani, Department of Biochemical Sciences, Viale Morgagni 50, 50134 Florence, Italy. Tel: +39.055.4598307; Fax: +39.055.4598905; Email: stefani@scibio.unifi.it

large consensus has been reached about the idea that aggregation into amyloid is a generic property of polypeptide chains, possibly linked to their common peptide backbone, and does not depend on specific amino acid sequences. It also appears that, at least in most cases, even the toxic effects of protein aggregates, mainly in their pre-fibrillar organization, are associated with common structural features and do not depend on specific amino acid sequences.

Indeed, the toxicity of early aggregates of disease-related or unrelated proteins/peptides is likely to result from their intrinsic ability to impair fundamental cellular processes following interaction with cell membranes The subsequent increases in ROS and free Ca^{2+} are considered among the earliest biochemical modifications responsible for the final apoptotic or (less usually) necrotic outcome of the exposed cells.

These data led us and other authors to propose that every polypeptide chain, in itself, possesses a previously unsuspected hidden dark side leading it to transform into a generic toxin to cells under suitable destabilizing conditions. This new way to consider proteins underscores the key importance, in protein evolution, of the negative selection of amino acid sequences with significant tendency to aggregate; it also stresses the significance, in biological evolution, of the development of the complex molecular machineries, including chaperone proteins and the ubiquitin proteasome pathway of protein degradation, aimed at hindering the appearance of misfolded proteins and their toxic early aggregates. Finally, these ideas may represent the rationale leading to suggest that in some cases amyloids may perform significant biological functions and that a higher number of degenerative diseases could, in effect, result from the presence, in the affected tissues, of amyloid aggregates of previously unsuspected proteins. The present review focuses on the most recent reports supporting these ideas and discusses their molecular, biological and clinical significance.

Key words: protein misfolding; protein misfolding diseases; folding and disease; amyloidoses; amyloid

INTRODUCTION

The genetic information within cells encodes not only the specific three-dimensional structures of proteins and their functions, but also the way these structures are attained through the process of protein folding. In the last few years, many key features of protein folding, and the manner in which it is controlled in living systems, have emerged from a combination of theoretical and experimental studies [1]. The information so gained has also raised a number of interesting issues. For example, it has become apparent that protein folding and unfolding are associated with several cellular processes, including molecular trafficking to specific organelles, crossing of cell membranes, cell cycle regulation and immune responses. Such observations have led to conclude that any failure of a specific protein/peptide to fold correctly, or to remain correctly folded (misfolding), is the molecular basis of different types of biological malfunctions and hence of differing forms of disease most often characterized by the presence of ordered protein aggregates in the affected tissues [2].

Indeed, protein misfolding and aggregation is one of the most exciting new frontiers in protein science and in molecular medicine. Presently, it is thought that the knowledge of the molecular basis of protein misfolding and aggregation may help to elucidate the physicochemical features of protein folding; however, it is also expected to shed light on the molecular and biochemical basis of a number of pathological conditions, some of which with severe social impact, such as Alzheimer's and Parkinson's diseases, type 2 diabetes, cystic fibrosis, some forms of emphysema, familial hypercholesterolemia, and others [4,5].

It is well established that 'misfolded' proteins, i.e. proteins partially or completely devoid of the conformation associated with their optimal stability and biological function, are inactive, thus explaining the "loss-of-function" features of the associated pathologies; however, they often aggregate and/or interact inappropriately with other cellular components, impairing cell viability and eventually causing cell death, leading to diseases displaying characteristic "gain-of-function" features. The molecular basis of many diseases, often known as 'protein misfolding diseases' or 'conformational diseases', may ultimately be traced back to the presence, in a living system, of protein or peptide molecules with 'incorrect' structures, different from those found in normally functioning organisms [6]. Such diseases include conditions where a specific protein, or protein complex, fails to fold correctly (e.g. cystic fibrosis, Marfan syndrome, amyotonic lateral sclerosis) or is not sufficiently stable to perform its normal function (e.g. many forms of cancer). They also include conditions where aberrant folding results in the failure of a protein to be correctly trafficked (e.g. familial hypercholesterolemia, α_1-antitrypsin deficiency, and some forms of retinitis pigmentosa) [6].

In particular, in the so-called serpinopathies (including α_1-antitrypsin deficiency, thrombosis, angioedema and familial encephalopathy with neuroserpin inclusion bodies), specific mutations destabilize an exposed mobile flexible loop of serine protease inhibitors including α1-antitrypsin, antithrombin and plasminogen activator inhibitor 1. The loop under normal functioning conditions, is inserted in the active site of the controlled serine protease resulting in enzyme inhibition. As a consequence of any of these mutations, the loop inserts, as an extra beta strand, into the the core beta-sheet of another serpin molecule as a supplemental strand; when propagated, this structural swapping results in the formation of fibrous polymers that are retained inside cells leading to cell impairment by either a loss of function (the lack of active protein) and a toxic gain of function (protein aggregate cytotoxicity) (reviewed in 4]. For example, in α1-antitrypsin deficiency, one out over 70 α1-antitrypsin mutants polymerizes and aggregates into the endoplasmic reticulum of hepatocytes leading to liver disease. Furthermore, lung parenchyma, unprotected against the enzyme neutrophil elastase following the lack of active protein, develops early-onset emphysema (reviewed in 7].

Presently, the main focus of international research is on a group of protein misfolding diseases known as amyloidoses. In these, the failure of specific peptides or proteins to fold, or to remain correctly folded, results in their fibrillar aggregation, the first step of a process eventually giving rise to 'amyloid' deposits in tissue. The polypeptides involved may include full length proteins (e.g. lysozyme, transthyretin, β2-microglobulin, α-synuclein, superoxide dismutase or prion protein), biological peptides (amylin, calcitonin, insulin) or peptide fragments arising from specific processing of larger precursors (Alzheimer β-peptides, ABri/ADan peptides, serum amyloid A) or from aspecific degradation (e.g. polyglutamine stretches cleaved from proteins containing poly(Q) extensions such as huntingtin, ataxins and the androgen receptor). Table 1 lists the peptides and proteins associated with the main known amyloid diseases. Usually the aggregated proteins display wild type sequences, as it happens in the sporadic forms of the diseases; however, in a minority of cases, these are variants resulting from genetic mutations associated with early-onset familial forms of the diseases. Finally, some amyloidoses are transmissible as in the case of the neurodegenerative diseases associated with the prion protein (reviewed in [8]).

Table 1 Main amyloidoses and the aggregated proteins or peptides

Disease	Fibril component (protein/peptide)
Neurodegenerative	
Alzheimer's disease	Aβ peptides (1-40, 1-41, 1-42, 1-43); Tau
Parkinson's disease	α- synuclein (wild-type or mutant)
Spongiform encephalopathies	Prion protein (full length or fragments)
Fronto-temporal dementias	Tau (wild-type or mutant)
Familial Danish dementia	ADan peptide
Familial British dementia	ABri peptide
Hereditary cerebral hemorrage with amyloidosis	Cystatin C (minus a 10-residue fragment); Aβ peptides
Amyotrophic lateral sclerosis	Superoxide dismutase (wild-type or mutant)
Dentatorubro-pallido-Luysian atrophy	Atrophin 1 (polyQ expansion)
Huntington disease	Huntingtin (polyQ expansion)
Cerebellar ataxias	Ataxins (polyQ expansion)
Kennedy disease	Androgen receptor (polyQ expansion)
Spinocerebellar ataxia 17	TATA box-binding protein (polyQ expansion)
Systemic	
Primary systemic amyloidosis	Ig light chains (full length or fragments)
Secondary systemic amyloidosis/ familial Mediterranean fever	Serum amyloid A (fragments)
Senile systemic amyloidosis	Transthyretin (wild-type or fragments)
Familial amyloidotic polyneuropathy I	Transthyretin (over 45 variants or fragments)
Dialysis-related amyloidosis	β2-microglobulin (wild-type)
Familial amyloid polyneuropathy III	Apolipoprotein A-1 (fragments)
Lysozyme systemic amyloidosis	Lysozyme (full length, mutant)
Finnish hereditary systemic amyloidosis	Gelsolin (fragments of the mutant protein)
Type II diabetes	Pro-islet amyloid peptide (fragments)
Medullary carcinoma of the thyroid	Procalcitonin (full length or fragment)
Atrial amyloidosis	Atrial natriuretic factor
Insulin-related amyloidosis	Insulin (full length)
Fibrinogen α-chain amyloidosis	Fibrinogen (α-chain variants and fragments)

Modified from [10].

In general, protein aggregation into amyloid fibrils follows increased synthesis, reduced clearance, specific mutations, misprocessing, proteolysis or deficits in the cellular mechanisms aimed at managing misfolded species. Presently, it is believed that, at least in

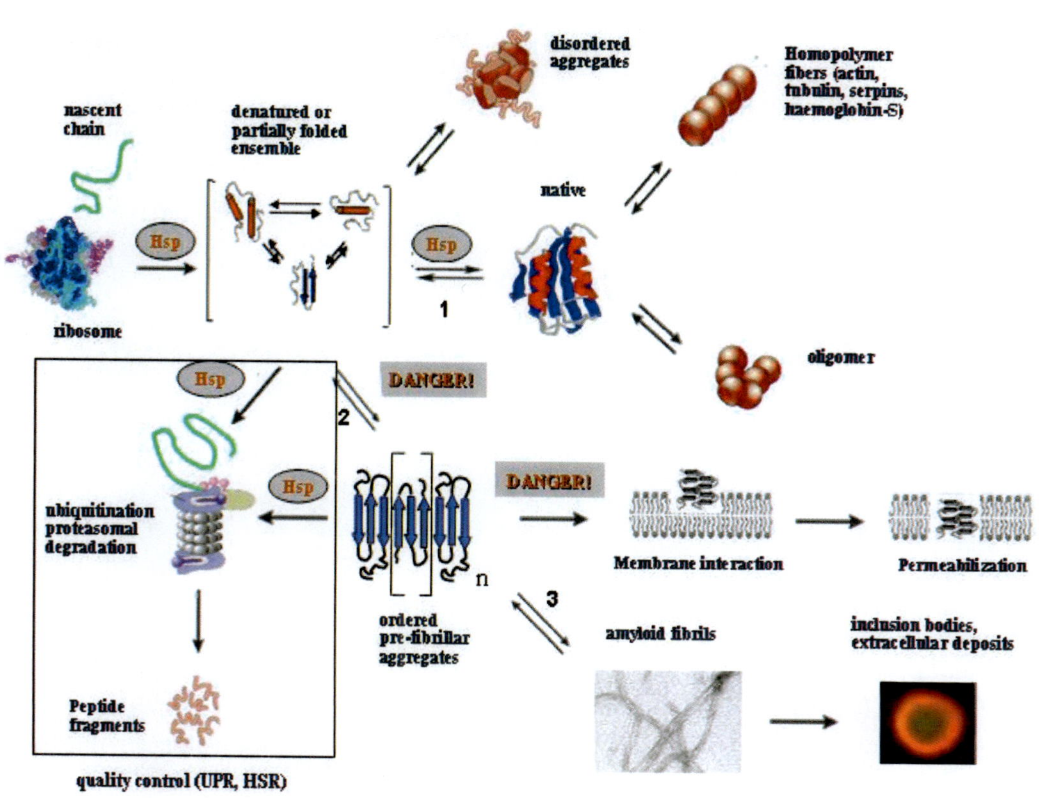

Figure 1. Overview of the possible fates of a newly synthesized polypeptide chain. Usually, equilibrium 1 is strongly shifted to the right except in case of destabilizing mutations, chemical modifications or harsh solution conditions. Under normal conditions, the molecules in the partially or completely unfolded ensemble of structures are degraded by the proteasome; when this clearance mechanism is impaired such species will form disordered aggregates or will shift equilibrium 2 towards the nucleation of pre-fibrillar assemblies that eventually grow into mature fibrils (equilibrium 3 indicates the possibility of a recycling of monomers within fibrils [242]). DANGER! indicates that pre-fibrillar aggregates are considered much more toxic than mature fibrils. Heat shock proteins (Hsp) can suppress the appearance of pre-fibrillar assemblies by reducing the population of free unfolded or partially folded molecules by binding them, by assisting their correct folding or by favouring their degradation by the ubiquitin proteasome pathway.

most cases, both the functional conformation of a protein and that leading to aggregation into amyloid fibrils arise from a common precursor generated in the folding process. Partially folded states may also appear as a consequence of partial denaturation of the native state resulting from misprocessing, specific mutations or any perturbation of the microenvironment (temperature, pH, pressure, metal ion or macromolecular concentration). Under these conditions, the partially unfolded molecules display reduced tertiary structures while retaining or even increasing ordered secondary structure and are able to undergo some structural reorganization leading them to self-assemble into fibrils [3,9]. In such an ensemble of unfolded or partially folded states, hydrophobic groups and main chain amides become exposed to the solvent and can establish the intra- and intermolecular interactions that are the basis for the subsequent formation of large protein aggregates [4]. A balance must therefore exist between protein folding and misfolding that normally favours the former and whose alteration is responsible for the appearance of aggregates (Figure 1).

The existence of familial forms of a number of amyloid diseases has suggested significant clues to the understanding of the molecular origins of these pathologies. For example, there are increasingly strong links between the age of the onset of the familial forms of disease and the increase of the propensity of the mutated proteins to aggregate *in vitro*. Such findings also support the link between protein aggregation and clinical manifestations of the disease (reviewed in 10]. In general, the presence in tissue of proteinaceous deposits is considered a key hallmark of protein deposition diseases, suggesting a causative link between presence of aggregates and clinical symptoms [3,9,11]. However, in some cases a correlation between amount of aggregated material and severity of symptoms is not apparent [12]. At the present time, the causative link between amyloid formation and disease (what is known as "amyloid hypothesis") is widely accepted on the basis of a large number of biochemical and genetic studies. However, the structure of the pathogenic species and the molecular basis of their toxicity to cells are still the subject of intense debate [13-20]. In neurodegenerative disorders, it is very likely that the interaction of protein aggregates with cellular components accounts for the impairment of cellular function [18,20-22] whereas in the systemic diseases the build-up in vital organs of huge amounts of amyloid can be the main culprit of the most severe clinical symptoms [23].

In strictly defined amyloidoses such as Alzheimer's and Creutzfeldt-Jakob diseases, systemic amyloidoses, type-II diabetes and hemodialysis-related amyloidosis, amyloid deposits are mainly extracellular and appear as thread-like fibrillar structures, sometimes assembled further into larger aggregates or plaques. Yet, other components such as collagen, glycosaminoglycans and proteins (e.g. SAP) are often present in the deposits protecting them against degradation [24-26]. Instead, other conditions (Parkinson's and poly(Q) diseases, amyotrophic lateral sclerosis) are characterized by intracellular protein deposits with structural features similar to those shown by the extracellular deposits. Intracellular deposits are found either in the cytoplasm, in the form of specialised aggregates known as aggresomes, in inclusion bodies such as Lewy, Bunina or Russell bodies, or in the nucleus and often arise from deficits of the cell's protective machineries [27].

The tendency of proteins to produce aggregates extremely difficult to dissolve and to refold is well known in other circumstances such as the formation of inclusion bodies during overexpression of heterologous proteins in bacteria and protein precipitation during laboratory purification. Indeed, protein aggregation is well known as one of the major problems associated with protein production and handling in biotechnology and drug development [28].

The studies performed in the last few years have established new milestones in the theme of protein misfolding and aggregation. Presently, there is increasing awareness that protein aggregation is much more widespread than previously believed either in biology and in medicine and that aggregation may involve a higher number of peptides and proteins than those found aggregated in the known amyloid diseases; in some case amyloids with physiological significance have also been described (reviewed in 10] (see later). Indeed, a number of reports indicate that most, possibly all, proteins and peptides (even as short as four residues or amino acid homopolymers) can aggregate into amyloid assemblies under suitable conditions (reviewed in 8] (see later); thus protein aggregation into amyloid is presently considered a pathway alternative to protein folding under conditions favouring intermolecular, rather than intramolecular, interactions involving the peptide backbone, regardless to their amino acid sequences [4].

The view of protein aggregation as a behaviour inherent to the peptide backbone of any polypeptide chain suggests the existence of a previously unconsidered constraint in protein evolution; indeed, the latter must have discarded every functional sequence with any tendency to aggregate under the conditions where its biological function is carried out. The generic tendency of polypeptide chains to aggregate also underscores the biochemical importance and the biological significance of the complex molecular machineries responsible of the quality control of protein folding. These include the molecular chaperones, the ubiquitin-proteasome pathway of protein degradation, the heat shock response in the cytosol and the unfolded protein response in the ER (reviewed in 27,29] (see later). The evolution of such a complex biochemical machinery testifies the key importance, for cells, to isolate and clear as more rapidly and efficiently as possible any potentially aggregating protein or peptide as soon as it appears thus confirming the generic cytotoxicity of these species.

This review focuses on the state-of the-art of the knowledge on the molecular basis of amyloid formation, disposal and toxicity as well as on the new perspectives and ideas raised by the investigation of model proteins not associated with deposition diseases.

PROTEIN MISFOLDING AND AGGREGATION

Fibrous protein polymers are known since long time; besides those endowed with specific biological functions such as collagen and actin fibers, it is well known that haemoglobin S a mutant haemoglobin found in people with sickle cell anaemia, under hypoxia (and hence in the deoxy form) aggregates into polymeric fibers responsible for the characteristic sickle form displayed by the erythrocytes under these conditions. The substitution, in haemoglobin S of a hydrophobic valine residue for the hydrophilic glutamate at position 6 of the β chain is followed by the appearance, in the deoxygenated molecules, of a surface hydrophobic patch that fits a hydrophobic pocket in the alpha chain of another molecule, and so on thus generating an haemoglobin S fiber.

Other protein misfolding diseases are referred to as serpinopathies; these are pathological conditions, including thrombosis, immune hypersensitivity, angioedema as well as emphysema and liver cirrhosis, characterized by the deposition, in the affected tissues, of insoluble polymers of a serpin (serine protease inhibitor) carrying specific mutations (see above). Although the serpinopathies are not classified among the classical amyloidoses and the aggregates do not display the typical cross-β structure of the amyloids (see later), they bear similarities with the amyloid deposition diseases, and the features of protein polymerization underlying these pathologies provide a model for other conformational diseases resulting from aberrant β-linkages. On this view, domain swapping has been proposed as a possible molecular basis of protein aggregation into other types of polymers such as amyloids [31].

The Fate of a Newly Synthesized Polypeptide Chain

Differently from the above mentioned protein deposition diseases, where the monomer proteins maintain their native fold when aggregated, the molecular basis of aggregation in protein deposition diseases of amyloid type is protein misfolding. In the latter, a specific polypeptide chain loses, or is unable to attain, its native, closely packed, three-dimensional structure thus populating unfolded, partially folded or misfolded states in equilibrium with each other. In these non-native states, protein molecules are loosely packed and their hydrophobic cores become exposed to the solvent; the resulting loss of stability enhances the tendency to nucleate initial oligomeric assemblies with increased content of beta structure [3,9,32,33]. Current opinion considers these "seeds" or "aggregation nuclei" appearing after some lag time as a sort of template where other misfolded or partially folded molecules (or natively folded molecules in the case of the infectious prion diseases, see below) are recruited thus increasing the size of the growing assemblies eventually giving rise to fibrillar aggregates (reviewed in [8]). Besides describing protein aggregation into amyloid as a nucleation-polymerization event, this view also suggests that a balance must exist between protein folding and misfolding that normally favours the former and whose alteration is responsible for the appearance of the aggregates (Figure 1).

A polypeptide chain may fail to reach or to maintain its functional three-dimensional structure following differing perturbations, comprising specific mutations, misprocessing, aberrant interactions with metal ions, changes in environmental conditions (e.g. pH or temperature), or chemical modification (e.g. oxidation, proteolysis). Any perturbation in the conformational properties of the polypeptide chain resulting from such phenomena may affect the equilibrium 1 between partially folded states and the correctly folded molecules in Figure 1, thus increasing the population of partially unfolded, or misfolded, species that are much more aggregation-prone than the native state. A fraction of partly unfolded molecules display reduced tertiary structure but still maintain or even increase ordered secondary structure and are able to undergo some structural reorganization leading them to self-assemble into fibrils (reviewed in 8,10]. Such an ensemble of unfolded or partly folded states expose hydrophobic groups and main chain amides to the solvent thus favouring the intra- and intermolecular interactions that pave the way to the formation of large protein aggregates [8,10].

Specific mutations may also enhance aggregation simply by speeding the assembly of the unfolded or partly folded monomers into the early oligomeric nuclei thus reducing the aggregation lag time (equilibrium 2 in Figure 1). Reaction 3 of Figure 1 is considered essentially, but not absolutely, irreversible, and mature fibrils are thought as the final, stable product of the aggregation process. Indeed, a number of findings support a regression of deposits and an arrest of new fibril formation following removal of the supply of fibril precursor proteins [26 and references therein). On this aspect, recent data have shown that general physicochemical features, such as mean hydrophobicity, net charge and propensity to alpha and beta structure formation, affect the tendency of an unfolded or partially folded polypeptide chain to aggregate [34] (see later).

Protein Aggregation May be Favoured by Several Differing Conditions

In addition to specific mutations, the onset of protein aggregation may be triggered by any factor resulting in the rise of the concentration of the amyloidogenic precursor(s); these include mutations, environmental changes or chemical modifications shifting the equilibrium 1 between correctly folded and partially folded molecules in Figure 1 towards the latter or an increase of the expression level of the affected protein and hence its whole equilibrium population comprising partially folded molecules. For example, any change in the macromolecular crowding, the total concentration of macromolecules in a given biological compartment (typically 300-400 mg/ml in cells) is known to perturb the folding and binding of proteins [35]. It has been estimated that an increase in macromolecular crowding from 30% to 33% (the fractional volume of a given space occupied by macromolecules) could result in a rise of molecular binding affinities by as much as one order of magnitude [36], favouring more compact states of macromolecules and increasing the population of aggregated species, including those that nucleate rapid growth of amyloid fibrils. Similar changes in total macromolecular concentration could be associated with alterations in cellular properties as a result of ageing [37] or of the progression through the cell cycle [38]. It is not surprising that cells are equipped with mechanisms designed to maintain or to restore cellular volume, water content and/or turgor pressure in response to modifications of extracellular fluid composition [39].

Increased levels of aggregation-prone species may also occur following enhanced protein synthesis or reduced clearance, particularly in the case of intrinsically unstable or natively unfolded proteins (see below) or of proteins with relatively stable folding intermediates such as β_2-microglobulin. For example, overexpression of the gene for tau protein or α synuclein in the central nervous system of transgenic mouse models results in the appearance of neurological symptoms very similar to those displayed by humans affected by corresponding amyloid diseases [8,40,41]. Patients with Down's syndrome develop a form of Alzheimer's disease by the first decade or two of their life as a result of the enhanced dosage of the gene for the Alzheimer precursor protein (APP) which is present in the supernumerary chromosome 21 [42]. It has recently been reported that, in *Drosophila* models, the gain of toxicity by ataxin-1, a protein commonly associated with poly(Q) expansions, may also result from increased levels of the wild-type protein [43]. More recently, it has been proposed that the appearance in the cytosol of minute amounts of misfolded PrP^c molecules following retrograde transport from the ER and reduced degradation by the proteasome leads to cell death even in the absence of the conversion to the self-propagating PrP^{sc} form that appears not to be the primary toxic species [44].

In the case of amyloid deposits of β_2-microglobulin in patients exposed to long-term dialysis, these seem to result principally from the high levels of this protein in plasma due to the loss of kidney function. β_2-microglobulin folds following a rather complex path in which several phases and a number (at least two) of intermediates are distinguishable one of which is significantly populated at equilibrium and stabilized by copper; the latter appears responsible of the slow folding phase and displays similarities to the amyloidogenic N-terminal truncated protein derivative [45]. Such findings provide clues on the possible origin of the dialysis-related amyloidosis [9] when one considers that, in polydialyzed people, the serum levels of this protein may raise by as much as 100 folds [46] and until recently dialysis membranes leaked copper ions.

A natively folded protein may also misfold and aggregate provided it meets a suitable template favouring a specific conformational modification thus reducing the lag time necessary for the initial nuclei to form, as it is best exemplified by the prion diseases (Creutzfeld-Jakob disease and others) where aggregates of the prion protein (PrP^{sc}) recruit the natively folded PrP^{c} molecules thus propagating the aggregating (PrP^{sc}) structure [47]. This behaviour accounts for the transmissibility of the phenotypes determined by passing among individuals even minute amounts of PrP^{sc} aggregates. Recent data suggest that other proteins/peptides are able to propagate a toxic conformation to the natively folded counterparts [48-50] or even to proteins with low tendency to aggregate (heterogeneous seeding) [48].

Finally, protein aggregation may be favoured under conditions resulting in the impairment or overwhelming of the molecular machineries aimed at performing the quality control of protein folding. The latter comprises the molecular chaperones either of the ER and the cytosol, the ER membrane carriers performing the retrograde transport to the cytosol of the proteins unable to fold in the ER lumen [29], the ATP-dependent proteolytic complexes in mitochondria and the components of the ubiquitin-proteasome pathway [51] (Figure 1). During and soon after intracellular synthesis, both in the cytosol and in the ER, the nascent protein chains are handled by molecular chaperones and enzymes favouring their folding and preventing aggregation. The data reported in the last few years highlight the central role performed by these machineries in ensuring that folding intermediates are promptly bound and refolded by the chaperones or degraded by the ubiquitin-proteasome machinery so as their intracellular steady-state concentration is maintained at negligible levels [29]. Nevertheless, even in normal cells, a large fraction of newly synthesized proteins fail to attain the native conformation and are degraded. As it has recently been reported, about one third of the newly synthesized proteins targeted for export out of the cell do not meet the ER quality control and are rapidly destroyed by the cellular clearing mechanisms without attaining their native structure in the ER [52,53].

Specific Sequence and Physicochemical Features Determine the Aggregability of a Polypeptide Chain

As recalled before, protein aggregation starts from partially unfolded conformers of a protein. The kinetics of the reaction leading an unfolded or partially folded amino acid sequence to modify its conformation so as to undergo the first steps of aggregation must cross an energetic barrier whose height determines the rate of oligomer growth (nucleation). The latter is determined by a number of physicochemical features (mean hydrophobicity, the intrinsic propensity to attain beta, rather than alpha, structure and the net charge) that have recently been described in a rather comprehensive way. This has led us to propose an algorithm suitable to predict the effect on the aggregation rate of any protein/peptide of any mutation with no effect on the conformational stability but modifying quantitatively these parameters [34]. The quantitative effects of these parameters have been found by investigating a large number of mutants of a model protein, acylphosphatase, leading to establish that a significant correlation does exist between aggregation rate and any change of these physicochemical parameters following the presence of a specific non-destabilising mutation. Such a correlation is highly improved when these factors are considered together, implying that their effects are additive.

This algorithm was validated using it on a number of proteins and peptides carrying conformationally neutral mutations linked to specific familial amyloid diseases; for most of these mutations the structural basis of the increased aggregability of the affected protein/peptide had not previously been explained. It has turned out that the algorithm works quite well even on proteins other than acylphosphatase; hence, it can be generalized as a useful tool to predict the effect of any mutation with no effect on the conformational stability of the involved protein/peptide, in terms of increase or decrease of the propensity to aggregate respect to the wild-type form [34]. More recently, this algorithm has been implemented to allow prediction of the intrinsic aggregability of any polypeptide chain from its amino acid sequence [54].

These findings demonstrate that protein aggregation is a general phenomenon resulting from basic physicochemical rules that, in principle, are valid for every polypeptide chain. In addition, the work performed on acylphosphatase is an example of the usefulness of the investigation of a model protein to provide data on the molecular basis of protein unfolding and aggregation that can be of general value.

Amyloid Aggregates Share Basic Structural Features

The problem to determine and to describe in detail the molecular structures of amyloid fibrils has attracted considerable attention and effort in the last several years. Indeed, the knowledge of the structural organization of either amyloid fibrils and their precursors can provide valuable information on the mechanisms of fibrillization and, possibly, on the molecular basis of amyloid disease pathogenesis and on the strategies suitable to prevent amyloidoses. Hence, much effort has also been spent to describe the pathway(s) leading to mature fibril assembly. Nevertheless, due to inherent technical difficulties, complete high resolution structures of both the amyloid fibrils and their precursors have not yet been reported.

In general, detailed structural information on amyloids is not easily attainable with conventional techniques of structural investigation such as NMR in solution and X-ray crystallography. Furthermore, imaging techniques such as transmission and cryo-electron microscopy or atomic force microscopy (AFM) (Figure 2), are able to provide a detailed structural description of those assemblies as a whole, but not structural information at the residue level. To overcome these difficulties, new integrated indirect strategies complementary to those mentioned above including biophysical (solid-state NMR, X-ray and neutron scattering) and biochemical (limited proteolysis coupled to mass spectrometry) approaches together with modeling techniques have been successfully applied to define key features of protein and peptide conformations as well as their supramolecular organization within amyloid fibrils. The body of data so obtained are beginning to shed light on varying structural aspects of amyloid assemblies including the nature of the stabilizing intramolecular interactions, the molecular basis of amyloid fibril polymorphisms, the common basic structural features of amyloid fibrils, the balance between structural order and disorder within them as well as the surface topology of soluble proteins, protein complexes and protein aggregates [55-58]. The initial monomer state from which the aggregates form is also difficult to characterize; in fact, often it is an ensemble of unstable conformations that easily polymerize at the high protein concentrations required for detailed structural investigation by NMR, although recently examples of protein fibrillization starting from native-like protein conformers have been reported [57,58].

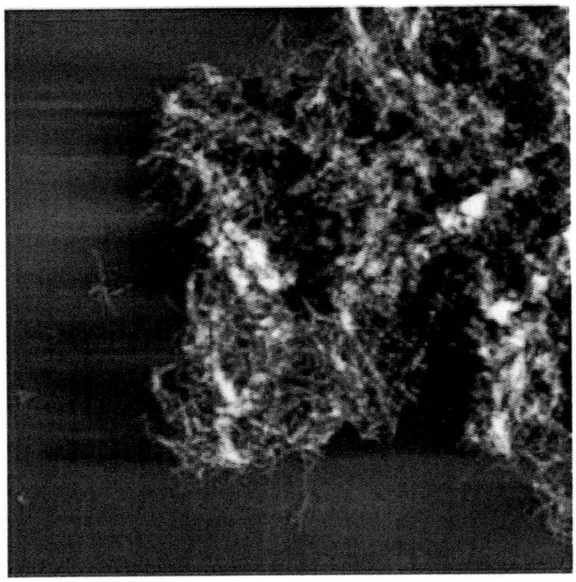

Figure 2. AFM image of a mesh of amyloid fibrils. Single fibrils are 8-10 nm in diameter. Kindly provided by A. Relini, University of Genoa.

Many Protein Folds, One Amyloid Core Structure

Despite the absence of obvious similarities in size, amino-acid composition, sequence or structure among the various peptides and proteins associated with amyloid diseases, the amyloid fibrils into which they convert are surprisingly similar both in morphology and in the core structure (Figure 3). Perhaps the basic structural feature of amyloid fibrils is a high content of β structure, even when the latter is poorly present or is absent at all in the monomeric peptides or proteins. As a consequence, amyloid fibrils display a characteristic X-ray diffraction pattern with main reflections at around 4.8 and 9.6 Å consistent with the presence of an ordered inner core. The latter appears to be made of a double beta-sheet extending parallel to main axis of the fibril whose beta strands, contributed by the monomer polypeptide chains, run parallel or antiparallel to each other and perpendicular to the fibril axis. Such a structure, known as "cross-beta", is the common basic ordered core organization of all amyloid fibrils, although, in some cases, specific supersecondary structure motifs such as β-helices [59,60] or the recently proposed μ-helix [61] may exist. Recently, the Pauling and Corey's α-pleated sheet as been proposed as a shared structure of the conformational intermediate resulting in amyloids [62]. Instead, no detailed information is available on the structural features of the polypeptide segments joining the beta strands and wrapped, in some way around the beta-sheet core.

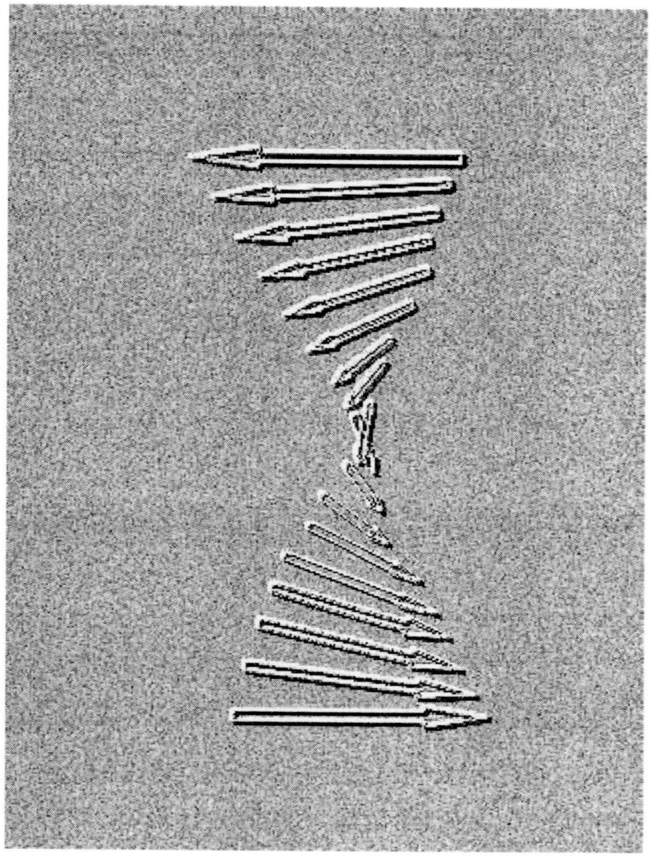

Figure 3. Schematic model of the cross beta structure of a protofilament. The parallel β-sheet shown here is matched by another one where the two strands of each layer are connected by less structured or unstructured parts of the monomers. The double sheet extends along the protofilament axis and each β-strand runs perpendicular to it. A mature fibrils is made of two or more twisted protofilaments.

Models of Amyloid Fibril Structure

Despite the lack of detailed structure at the molecular level of any amyloid fibril, investigations by electron and atomic force microscopy show that they are typically long (as much as around 1.0 μm), straight and unbranched. The fibrils are typically 6-12 nm in diameter and usually consist of 2-6 'protofilaments', each of diameter about 2 nm twisted around each other to form rope-like assemblies [57,63,64]. It seems possible that there may be significant differences in the way the strands are assembled depending on the characteristics of the polypeptide chain involved [59,65]. Factors including length, sequence (and in some cases the presence of disulphide bonds or post-translational modifications such as glycosylation) may also be important in determining details of the fibril structure.

Several recent papers report structural models of amyloid fibrils containing different polypeptide chains, including the Aβ_{40} peptide, insulin and fragments of the prion protein, based on data from techniques such as cryo-electron microscopy and solid state NMR spectroscopy [57,63,64,66]. These models share many structural features, suggesting that the structures of different fibrils are likely to be variations on a common theme [60]. It is also emerging that there may be some common and highly organised assemblies of amyloid protofilaments that are not simply extended threads or ribbons. For example, in some cases large closed loops [67,68] or doughnut-shaped small assemblies [69-71] can be formed.

An important aspect of the amyloid structures is the specific mechanism by which they are formed from their soluble precursors. It is clear from studies of a variety of different systems that several steps are involved in the assembly process [67,69-73]. In most studies, electron micrographs or AFM images show the presence of aggregates often called "amorphous aggregates", pre-fibrillar aggregates or sometimes "micelles". These are heterogeneous populations of small, roundish particles, either isolated or connected in bead-like chains, tubular assemblies or annular rings 2.5-5.0 nm in diameter [67,70,71,73]. Such assemblies appear, at least in most cases, to be precursors of curvy protofibrils, whereas longer protofilaments and mature fibrils usually appear after longer periods of time. These "early aggregates" may be very important for understanding the nature and origins of the pathological properties of amyloid structures associated with disease, and particularly with neurodegenerative conditions.

A recent report provides evidence that the soluble pre-fibrillar aggregates (but not mature fibrils) of a number of structurally different peptides and proteins including Aβ peptides, lysozyme, insulin, amylin, α-synuclein, the 106-126 prion peptide and poly(Q) stretches are recognised by a polyclonal antibody raised against a molecular mimic of soluble pre-fibrillar A$\beta_{1\text{-}40}$ or A$\beta_{1\text{-}42}$ oligomers [74]. This finding indicates that pre-fibrillar aggregates of different proteins and peptides share common structural features that are recognised by the same antibody and are different from those displayed by the monomer/oligomer or fibrillar counterparts. It has been proposed that the α-pleated sheet structure is the only backbone conformation that may explain the different recognition, by the same antibody, of soluble oligomeric and insoluble fibrillar amyloids [62].

Amyloid Aggregates May be Recognized by Several Spectroscopic Features

The apparent shared structural organization of amyloid fibrils matches their specific tinctorial properties with reagents such as thioflavin T (ThT) and Congo red (CR). In the presence of these stains, the supramolecular assemblies of amyloid type display common responses such as the enhancement of the ThT fluorescence at 480 nm [75] and a characteristic red shift of the maximum of absorbance of the CR spectrum [76]; furthermore, samples stained with CR display a characteristic green birefingence under polarized light. The formation of amyloid aggregates can also be monitored by circular dichroism, where usually an increase of the signal at 215-218 nm characteristic of β-structure is displayed by monomers preceding their oligomerization. Finally, the presence of β-structure in soluble or insoluble amyloid aggregates may be investigated by Fourier transform infrared spectroscopy leading to discriminate between ordered and amorphous aggregates that are of pathway of fibril formation.

However, none of these assays is, in itself, fully indicative of the presence of aggregates characterized by the cross beta structure. As it has recently pointed out, morphological imaging of the aggregates by TEM or AFM and, in particular, X-ray characterization are necessary to assess with proper confidence the presence of aggregated material of amyloid type [77].

FIBRILLIZATION IS A GENERIC PROPERTY OF POLYPEPTIDE CHAINS

The data reported above on the physicochemical features of a polypeptide chain underlying its propensity to aggregate into amyloid assemblies were found by investigating acylphosphatase, a protein not associated with any amyloid disease. Indeed, in the past the formation of amyloid aggregates *in vivo* was thought to be primarily triggered by proteolysis after it was ascertained that lysosomal enzymes, at acidic pH were able to convert amyloidogenic proteins into amyloid fibrils [78]. However, over ten years ago it was reported that it was possible to get amyloid fibrils from transthyretin *in vitro* following acid-induced conformational change [79]. This finding showed for the first time that an alteration of a protein's three-dimensional structure was sufficient to populate aggregation-prone conformers. A similar behaviour was subsequently demonstrated for a large number of proteins known to aggregate *in vivo*. These data supported strongly the idea that the molecular basis of protein aggregation was some unusual structural feature of the few peptides and proteins found to be associated with the amyloid diseases, and that the underlying conformational changes were closely associated with their specific amino acid sequences.

Aggregation is a Tendency Inherent to the Peptide Backbone of Proteins

This view was first challenged in 1998, when observations made by chance demonstrated that a couple of proteins not associated with any amyloid disease were able to aggregate *in vitro* into fibrillar assemblies closely similar to the amyloid fibrils produced from disease-associated peptides and proteins [80,81]. These reports were soon reinforced by others showing that a similar structural conversion could be achieved deliberately for other proteins by a rational choice of appropriate solution conditions [82,83]. Presently, these data have been repeatedly confirmed by a large number of studies (reviewed in [8]) even on peptides, both fragments of natural proteins, artificially designed sequences, peptides with as few as 4-6 residues and amino acid homopolymers [84-86]. In general, full-length proteins aggregate into amyloid fibrils under destabilising solution conditions (such as lack of specific ligands, high temperature, low pH, moderate concentrations of salts or of co-solvents such as trifluoroethanol) suitable to partially or completely disrupt the native structure but still maintaining, at least partially, secondary interactions such as hydrogen-bonding (reviewed in [8]).

The possibility of peptides and proteins to form amyloid fibrils has profound consequences for understanding the fundamental origins of the deposition of proteins in diseases. It also has very great practical relevance as it increases dramatically the number of proteins and peptides that can be investigated to discover the general features underlying the mechanisms of protein misfolding and aggregation. Such a knowledge has prompted a more general discussion about the various conformational states a polypeptide can adopt following its synthesis *in vivo* and the way the living world has set up to favour those with minimal aggregation potential through evolutionary processes. Thus, for example, protein translocation across membranes involves unfolded or partially folded states similar to those that are populated during the folding process through which the native state is achieved. Moreover, the evolution of the highly cooperative structures of native proteins appears to be a critical step in allowing proteins to escape aggregation for significant lengths of time [66]. Notwithstanding this, the functional state of a polypeptide chain is always in dynamic equilibrium with other states including aggregate precursors that, at any time, can nucleate rapid aggregate formation following changes in polypeptide chain features and medium conditions (see above).

Protein Aggregation Reflects an Ancestral Tendency of All Polypeptide Chains

All the above considerations provide strong support to the idea that protein aggregation is a generic property inherent to any polypeptide chain possibly linked to the structure of the shared peptide backbone, thus explaining the structural properties of the amyloid fibril core [4]. This contrasts with the large number of different compact folds found in native proteins, whose structures are dictated primarily by side-chain interactions that differ for each protein sequence.

The evolved amino acid sequences of natural proteins must therefore possess structural features favouring their biological activity but also their folding over aggregation under the conditions where each protein must perform its function. Hence, the evolution of the highly cooperative nature of the functional protein structures appears to be a critical step in the appearance of proteins stable against their inherent tendency to aggregate for lengths of time consistent with their intracellular half-lives and with the overall reproductive life span of an individual [4]. Protein evolution must therefore have selected specific amino acid sequences suitable to attain folds able not only to perform efficiently specific biological functions but also to segregate at their interior the main chain atoms, thus avoiding their inherent tendency to interact with other polypeptide chains and to aggregate.

The exposure of the main chain atoms of polypeptide chains under partially destabilizing conditions would favour such a primordial behaviour leading to the intermolecular interactions found in the amyloid aggregates. Natural proteins can therefore be thought as a special group of evolved polymers where the specific interactions among side-chains dictate the globular structure, whereas amyloid fibrils may be seen as the expression of the ancestral generic tendency of the polypeptide chains to organize into polymers stabilized by beta structure-based intermolecular interactions arising from their peptide backbone [87] (Figure 4]. On this view, the properties of the side-chains are not important in determining the core structure of amyloids although they are associated with the tendency to aggregate of a protein/peptide and defining the conditions were such a tendency can manifest. Clearly, the presence of different side-chains can influence the aggregation conditions and the details of amyloid structures, particularly the assembly of protofibrils, giving rise to the variations on the common structural theme discussed above.

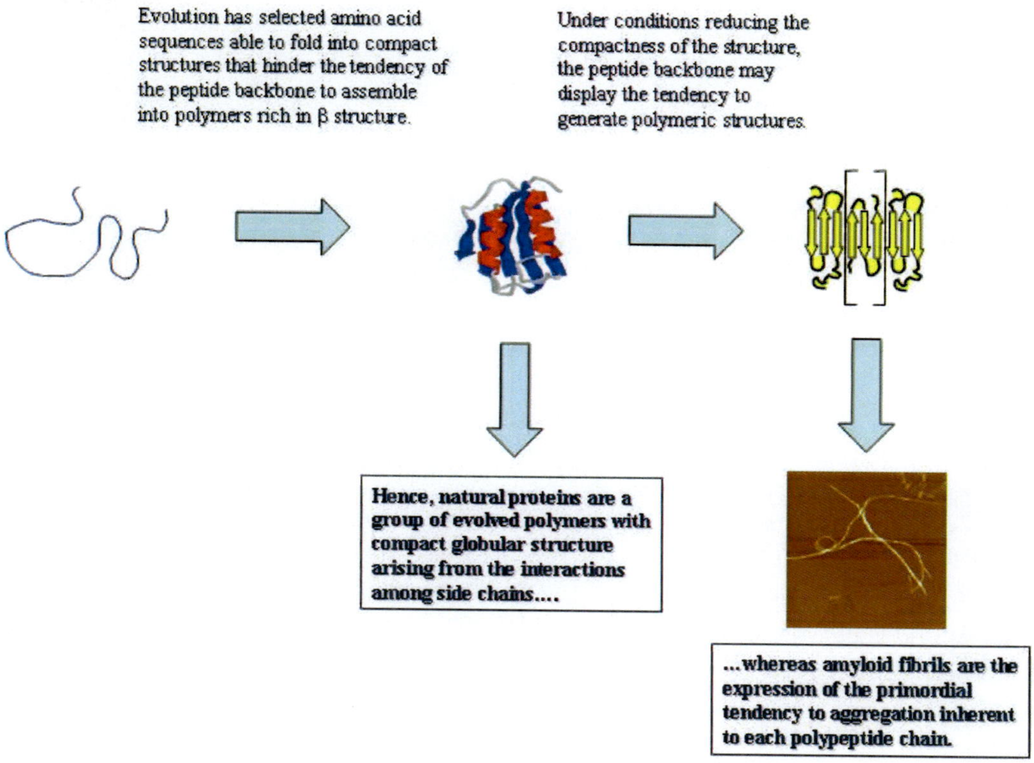

Figure 4. Aggregation into amyloid is a property inherent to most, possibly all, polypeptide chains.

The potential aggregability of many, possibly all, polypeptide chains contrasts with the evidence that, under physiological conditions, only a very limited number of peptides or proteins are found as amyloid aggregates in tissues. Therefore, besides the adaptations favoring folding into compact states. previously unsuspected negative constraints must exist in protein evolution that have selected against the appearance of sequences endowed with intrinsic propensity to aggregate. Recent database searches have highlighted a number of strategies natural beta-sheet proteins have developed to avoid intermolecular association of β-strands in their native states and hence to reduce their tendency to aggregate at least to levels compatible with their managing by the cellular machineries. These strategies involve mostly the edge strands and are aimed at disfavoring their interaction with the corresponding strands of another monomer protein thus avoiding oligomerization through sheet extension [88]. Other surveys have shown that, in general, nature disfavors the presence, in proteins, of stretches of several consecutive hydrophobic residues or of alternating polar and non polar residues, both enhancing the tendency of a protein to aggregate prior to becoming completely folded [89,90]. It has therefore been suggested that these constraints considerably limit the content of information in natural polypeptide chains respect to that allowable with a 20-letter alphabet. Very recently, a database search in 28 full proteomes has hoghlighted a previously undescribed strategy in protein evolution to avoid natural protein aggregation and to favour the recognition by chaperones of unfolded sequences [90a].

Protein Aggregation in the Living World May Happen more Frequently than Previously Suspected

The aggregation potential inherent to polypeptide chains suggests that protein aggregation *in vivo* might be not as rare as previously believed and that one of the main functions of the molecular chaperones and the ubiquitin proteasome pathway could be to favour refolding or, alternatively, unfolding and degradation of misfolded proteins as soon as they appear inside cells [27]. It also suggests that, in addition to the known amyloidoses, other protein aggregation diseases could exist, whose molecular basis can be traced back to any unbalance between the rate of aggregate appearance and the efficiency of the clearing machineries. Therefore, it is conceivable to expect that in the near future other degenerative conditions will be shown to where deposition of aggregates of proteins presently not associated with disease will be found. Indeed, an increasing number of reports in the last few years describe new degenerative diseases where amyloid deposits of proteins previously not associated to disease have been found in the affected tissues (see later). Finally, the intrinsic tendency of polypeptide chains to aggregate makes also it likely that nature has exploited this property in certain biological systems by producing specific protein aggregates to perform specialized functions (see later).

Amyloid Fibrils or Their Precursors May Perform Specific Biological Functions

In the last few years, an increasing number of reports has appeared showing that, at least (but not only) in the microbial world, amyloid aggregates of specific proteins or their precursors may perform specific physiological functions (Table 2). This hypothesis stems also from the similarity of some early amyloid aggregates with the pores resulting from oligomerization of a number of bacterial toxins and pore-forming eukaryotic proteins (reviewed in [10]).

In 2002 it was first shown that the β-sheet rich highly aggregated fibers known as curli produced by *Escherichia coli* and deposited at the cell surface were indeed amyloid fibrils morphologically identical to those described in amyloid diseases [91]. These fibrils arise from a protein, curlin, by a nucleation-precipitation process involving chaperone-like and nucleator proteins encoded by the *csgAB* and *csgDEFG* operons; the function of the encoded proteins is possibly to prevent curlin polymerization within the cell whilst accelerating it at the cell surface [92], were curli favours cell adhesion to the substrate in the colonization of inert surfaces and mediates binding to various host proteins.

This finding raises the possibility that the proteinaceous filaments found at the cell surfaces of other micro-organisms may be amyloid in nature. Indeed, it has been claimed that aerial hyphae produced by *Streptomyces coelicolor* require the assembly into amyloid-like fibrils of a novel class of secreted hydrophobic, highly surface-active proteins (chaplins) [93].

The latter enable hyphae to grow into the air and also provide the aerial structures with a hydrophobic coat. It is possible that in other fungal systems hyphae may be coated with amyloid-like fibrils with the same functional significance as chaplins. For example, the hydrophobins of filamentous fungi are a group of proteins assembled into highly insoluble films composed of a mosaic of amyloid-like fibrils that help hyphae to breach the water-air interface by the same mechanism as chaplins [94]. It has also been suggested that in the filamentous fungus *Podospora anserina*, the HET-s prion protein aggregating into amyloid fibrils performs some function associated with heterokaryon incompatibility and hence with self/non-self recognition [95].

Table 2 Recognized physiological functions of amyloids in biological systems°

Protein	Source	Function
Microorganisms		
Curlin	*E. coli*	Substrate adhesion
Chaplins	*S. coelicolor*	Aerial hyphae formation
HET-s prion	*P. anserina*	Self/non-self recognition
Hydrophobins?	Fungi	Fungal coat
Higher organisms		
Chorion proteins	Silkmoth	Egg and embryo protection
Fibroin?	Spiders, silkworms	Silk constituent
Crystallins	Mammals	Refractive index of the lens
SAA?	Mammals	Cell killing
Aβ peptides	Human	Small cerebral vessel sealing
Pmel17 (fragment)	Human	Melanine polymerization

A question mark indicates polymeric systems not proven to be true amyloids.
Modified from [10].

Some bacterial pore-forming toxins assemble into pore-like oligomers that kill the target cell by permeabilizing its plasma membrane. In some cases, protein insertion into the plasma membrane is accompanied by a conformational rearrangement with changes in secondary structure elements. As an example, perfringolysin inserts into the plasma membrane of the target cell upon conversion of six alpha-helices in domain 3 into four amphipathic beta-strands [96]. It is not known whether such a change may be equivalent to those leading other proteins to assemble into pre-fibrillar amyloid structures, however it depicts an overall mechanism similar to that proposed for the toxic effects of pre-fibrillar amyloid aggregates (see later).

Possible physiological functions of amyloids have also been reported in higher organisms such as insects and mammals. For example, a peptide from the A- and B-family of the silkmoth chorion proteins has been found to account for 30% of the material found as amyloid aggregates in the eggshell, leading to suggest that silkmoth chorion is a natural amyloid with protective properties necessary for the oocyte and the embryo [97,98]. There is also evidence that the natural silk spinning process in spiders and silkworms involves the nucleation of β-sheet oligomers from a concentrated solution of fibroin stored in a liquid crystalline state [99]

In mammals, several reports indicate that the major proteins in normal mammalian lens exist predominantly as β-pleated sheets *in vivo* and that in normal lenses a positivity to the classical amyloidophilic stains such as Congo red and thioflavine T does exist, supporting the idea that in the interior fiber cells of the lens, β-sheet arrays of proteins are physiologically organized in an amyloid-like supramolecular order [100] thus exploiting the inherent high stability of amyloids to ensure the long-term structural integrity and transparency of the lens.

Acute-phase isoforms of human and murine serum amyloid A (SAAp and SAA2.2, respectively) have been found in solution as hexameric assemblies with a central pore able to permeabilize synthetic and biological membranes [101]. The dramatic increase of SAA concentration in plasma during acute and chronic inflammation [102] is believed to contribute to the possible development of the reactive amyloidosis characterized by the presence, in the kidney, liver and spleen, of amyloid deposits of the whole protein and its 1-76 N-terminal fragment (AA) [102]. The toxic effects of the SAA and AA aggregates could be a drawback of the proposed physiological function of the hexameric assemblies: killing the invading bacteria by forming toxic channels in their cell membranes [101].

A specific protective role in the organism has been proposed for a folding variant of the milk protein α-lactalbumin formed at low pH and trapped by an associated oleic acid molecule. This form of the protein displays molten-globule-like features and bactericidal activity [103]. It is also able to trigger apoptosis selectively in tumoural cells while leaving fully differentiated cells unaffected providing evidence for its importance in protecting infants from certain types of cancer [103]. These data have led to propose a protective effect of breastfeeding against childhood tumours and the use of this folding variant of α-lactalbumin as a possible new anti-cancer molecule [103]. The findings on α-lactalbumin show clearly that different conformational states of a protein can have very different biological properties and may perform specific biological functions. Indeed, 15 years ago it was first proposed that molten globules are biologically important conformational states in allowing proteins to cross cell membranes [104], suggesting that protein conformational states that are currently believed to be precursors of amyloid aggregates may, at least in some instances, exploit biological functions.

A large wealth of data support the idea that Aβ aggregates are key elements in the process of sealing capillaries and arterioles in the central nervous tissue or in maintaining regional integrity following traumatic insults (reviewed in 105]. Indeed, the rapid deposition of Aβ following severe head trauma highlights the possible involvement of these aggregates in maintaining vascular integrity thus protecting brain parenchyma against haemorrhage. These data question the opportunity to remove Aβ from brain as in some immunologic approaches against Alzheimer's disease [105].

Finally, very recent findings show that melanine production in melanosomes and melanosome biogenesis require the presence, in the latter, of intralumenal fibrous striations. These are formed by the polymerization of a luminal domain fragment specifically cleaved from the resident membrane protein Pmel17 by a furin-like convertase. Pmel-17 cleavage regulates melanosome biogenesis by exploiting its fibrillogenic potential and, upon aggregation into amyloid fibers, provides a template onto which melanine polymerization may occur [106]. It has been proposed that such a mechanism could help to clarify some of the molecular mechanisms governing the biogenesis of other cellular organelles as well as their unique structural features [106].

BIOCHEMICAL FEATURES OF CELL IMPAIRMENT BY THE TOXIC AGGREGATES

The data reported since 1998 clearly indicate that the ability to produce amyloid aggregates is inherent to the peptide backbone of every polypeptide chain. But how about aggregate toxicity? Can this be associated with specific amino acid sequences of the aggregated units or it is also a basic property of all aggregates that can be traced back to the presence, in the latter, of a specific "toxic fold"? Recent reports show that pre-fibrillar aggregates of disease-unrelated proteins such as the SH3 domain of the bovine PI_3 kinase, the N-terminal domain of the bacterial hydrogenase maturation factor HypF (HypF-N), human endostatin and apomyoglobin display cytotoxic effects very similar to those reported for similar aggregates of peptides and proteins associated with amyloid diseases [107-110]. Even in these cases the assemblies endowed with the highest toxicity are the protofibrils whereas protofilaments and mature fibrils appear much less toxic or non-toxic.

Amyloid Aggregate Toxicity Seems Related to a Basic "Toxic Fold"

These data clearly indicate that, similarly to protein aggregation, even aggregate toxicity, at least in most cases, can be traced back to the presence, in protein aggregates, of basic common structural features. This conclusion is supported by a recent paper showing that antibodies raised against pre-fibrillar aggregates of a mimic of Aβ peptides are able to reduce their toxicity to cultured cells as well as that of similar aggregates of differing peptides and proteins associated with specific amyloidoses [74]. This result implies that amyloid cytotoxicity arises from shared features of the supramolecular structure of the aggregates rather than from specific physicochemical properties of the amino acid sequences of the monomer polypeptides. These findings are in direct contrast with the properties of native proteins, whose amino acid sequences determine completely both the native structure and its biological activity. Such an otherwise remarkable result in fact follows from the conclusion discussed above that the specific interactions of the side-chains need not to determine directly the structure, and hence the properties, of species other than the native state.

Further studies on a wider range of peptides and proteins are required to explore the generality of these observations, however it could well be that the cytotoxicity of these types of aggregate is generic [109], arising from the "misfolded" nature of the aggregated species and their precursors with exposure of regions (e.g. hydrophobic residues and the polypeptide main-chain) that are buried in the native state of the protein. As many of these regions are likely to be aggregation-prone (or "sticky") they may interact with membranes and other cellular components [109,110] thus triggering the complex cascade of biochemical events eventually leading to cell death.

Indeed, in an ensemble of small aggregates containing misfolded polypeptide chains there will be a vast array of exposed amino acid clusters, some of which may mimic regions present at the surfaces of native proteins. Such aggregates might be able to interact inappropriately with the binding partners or receptors of a wider range of different proteins. The intrinsic instability of pre-fibrillar species enabling them to assemble further and organise into more highly ordered structures reflects by itself the existence of accessible regions of the structures able to interact with other cellular components.

Cell Membranes May Be the Primary Target of the Toxic Aggregates

Indeed, pre-fibrillar assemblies have been shown to interact with synthetic phospholipid bilayers [69,72,111-115] and with cell membranes [69,101,116], modifying their permeability, destabilising them and impairing the function of specific membrane-bound proteins and signalling pathways [117,118]. Pre-fibrillar amyloid aggregates may interact with cell membranes in a way that is reminiscent of the action of prokaryotic or eukaryotic peptides or proteins (e.g. some bacterial toxins) that oligomerise into the membranes of the target cells forming pore-like assemblies that destabilise the plasma membrane and impair ion balance across it (see later). In most cases, the interaction of a misfolded species with a membrane is likely to occur via a two-step mechanism involving the electrostatic interaction of the positively charged residues with negatively charged or polar lipid head groups followed by the insertion of hydrophobic regions inside the membrane [119].

The hypothesis that proteins and peptides able to destabilize cell membranes are endowed with intrinsic cytotoxicity depicts membrane damage as a common key event leading to malfunctioning and impairment of viability in cells exposed to cytotoxic peptides such as those present in venoms, antimicrobial secretions, the mammalian immune system, antibacterial toxins, viral proteins, misfolded proteins or early amyloid aggregates [118-121]. This scenario is supported by the findings mentioned above concerning the toxic effects on tumoural cells of a partially unfolded state of α-lactalbumin at acidic pH [122], and the proposed mechanism of membrane insertion and toxicity of bacterial toxins such as perfringolysin and diphtheria toxin (see above). This idea has now been supported by the finding that pre-fibrillar aggregates, whose exposed hydrophobic surfaces may bear similarities to those of molten globules, are able to interact and associate with cell membranes.

The importance of membranes and, more generally, of biological surfaces in protein aggregation and aggregate toxicity stems from a number of observations indicating that these surfaces may recruit protein/peptide monomers increasing significantly their local concentrations, favouring specific conformational changes and hence promoting aggregate nucleation, in most cases the rate-limiting step of fibrillogenesis [123,124]. Lipid membrane composition appears particularly important. On this regard, the role of cholesterol, gangliosides and anionic phospholipids has been investigated in some detail. A preferential localization of APP and secretases into ganglioside and cholesterol-rich lipid rafts has been reported [125-127] and aggregation of soluble Aβ peptides has been proposed as a raft-associated process [126]. It has also been reported that break of cholesterol homeostasis could be the unifying primary cause of differing neurodegenerative diseases [127]. Aβ appears able to regulate lipid synthesis in brain neurons [128]; in addition, Aβ aggregates have been shown to localize at the surface of the plasma membrane and interaction of Aβ with cell surface, particularly at sites rich in cholesterol, appears to be an important requirement for neurotoxicity [129]. It is known that AD patients have reduced brain cholesterol [130] possibly following down regulation of seladin-1, the neuronal enzyme responsible for the conversion of 7-dehydrocholesterol into cholesterol [131], and that low brain cholesterol leads to neurodegeneration [132]. Finally, recent reports indicate that loss of membrane cholesterol enhances amyloid peptide generation [133] and that enrichment in cholesterol of membranes of cultured cells exposed to toxic pre-fibrillar aggregates reduces aggregate interaction with the plasma membrane and cytotoxicity [134]. Although requiring more extensive research, most of these data support the idea that a higher membrane rigidity following increased cholesterol content is protective against aggregate interaction with cell membrane.

The role of acidic phospholipids in aggregate toxicity has also been investigated. In the past, several candidate cell surface proteins have been considered as possible receptors of amyloid aggregates, notably those made from Aβ peptides; however, increasing evidence suggests that additional neuronal binding sites must be involved in the interaction of amyloid aggregates made from different peptides and proteins with the plasma membrane [135-137] and that increasing the content of negatively charged lipids increases channel formation in synthetic lipid bilayers [138]. It has also been proposed that negative membrane surfaces are potent inductors of beta-sheet structures by acting as conformational catalysts for amyloids [138,139]. Recently, it has been reported that phosphatidylserine (PS)-containing liposomes are able to induce *in vitro* amyloid aggregation of a variety of proteins such as lysozyme, glyceraldehyde-3-phosphate dehydrogenase, insulin, myoglobin, transthyretin, cytochrome c, histone H1, α-lactalbumin and endostatin [136]; moreover, annexin-5 has been shown to protects against Aβ-peptide cytotoxicity by competing at a common PS-rich site [140]. Anionic membrane phospholipids such as PS and phosphatidylglycerol (PG) have also been shown to interact with amyloid aggregates possibly by recognizing a shared fold [139]. Such phospholipid-target hypothesis suggests a differential toxicity of aggregates when they are produced into cells or outside cells, considering that PS is almost exclusively found at the cytosolic plasma membrane leaflet in all cells other than cancer cells, vascular endothelial cells in tumours and apoptotic cells, where it moves to the outer leaflet [141,142].

This finding could explain the selective antitumoural specificity of either endostatin [135,139] and folding variants of some proteins such as α-lactalbumin (see above) and apoptin [143]. It must also be reminded that amyloid formation accompanies a wide variety of malignancies [135], suggesting that anti-tumoural proteins such as endostatin might perform their effects through formation of toxic aggregates at the surface of cancer cells and vascular endothelial cells in tumours; in this case, aggregation would be favoured by the presence of PS at the outer membrane surface of cancer cells. Accordingly, it has been observed that a number of antimicrobial peptides known to target PG in microbial membranes are also able to kill cancer cells [144].

Amyloid Pores May Play a Key Role in Aggregate Toxicity

A large body of information on the molecular, biochemical and biological features of cell impairment following exposure to amyloid aggregates has appeared in the last few years altough much remains to be understood on this topic. In the past five years a central role has been proposed for pre-fibrillar assemblies [70-73] that, in most cases, appear endowed with the highest toxicity, whereas mature fibrils are much less toxic and are mainly considered substantially harmless reservoirs of the toxic aggregates [18,73,145-147].

Much interest has recently been raised by the possibility that a subpopulation of protofibrils, notably the amyloid pores, may account for the toxicity of the amyloid aggregates, as it has been shown for the aggregates of several different peptides and proteins, thus envisaging a basically common early biochemical mechanism of aggregate toxicity [119]. In 1993, the "channel hypothesis" of amyloid toxicity was first proposed, whereby the toxic aggregated species form non-specific pore-like channels in the membranes of the exposed cells [148] (Figure 5). This proposal is supported by studies carried out both on synthetic phospholipid bilayers and on cell membranes, where the function of specific membrane proteins appears to be impaired by the interaction with misfolded species or their oligomers [119,145] (see above).

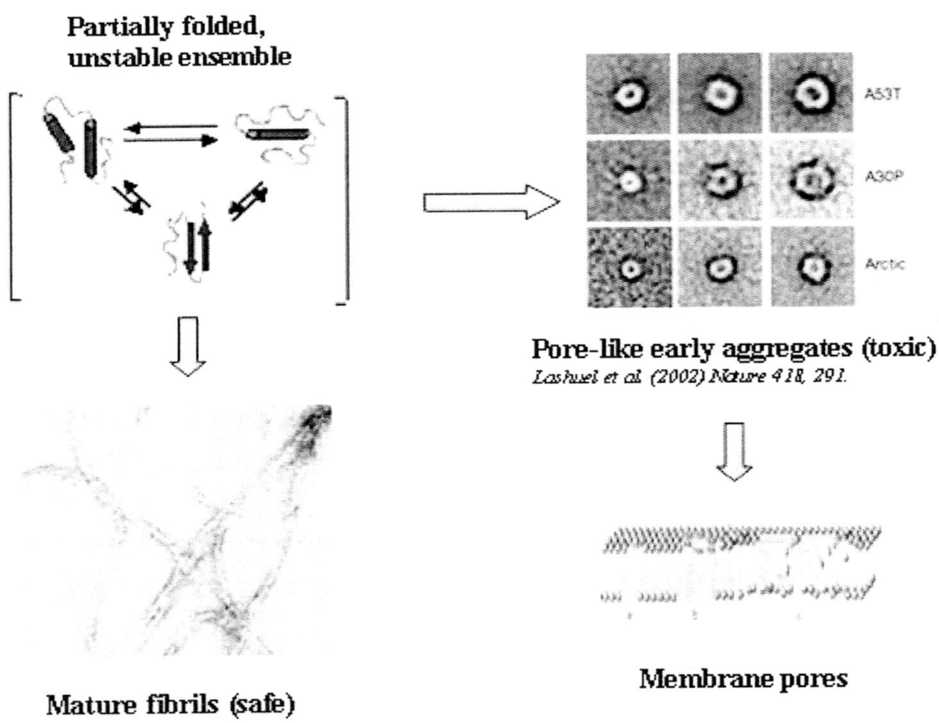

Figure 5. Pore-like early oligomeric amyloid aggregates may permeabilize cell membranes similarly to a number of other systems such as bacterial pore toxins or eukaryotic pore forming protein complexes.

According to this hypothesis, the cytotoxicity induced by misfolding of proteins would be a direct consequence of the exposure of hydrophobic regions, favouring the interaction of the misfolded species with cell membranes and leading to disruption of membrane integrity via the formation of non-specific ion channels (Figure 5). These channels, or pores, have been described *in vitro* for a number of peptides and proteins associated with amyloid disease including Aβ peptides [19,69,117,145] and their fragments [149], α-synuclein [111], islet-amyloid polypeptide [114], the 106-126 fragment of the prion protein [150], poly(Q) stretches [61], the C-type natriuretic peptide [112], β_2-microglobulin [72], transthyretin [151], murine serum amyloid A [101] and a the N-terminal peptide of an acute phase isoform variant of human serum amyloid A1.1 (SAAp) [101]. These channels have also been characterized primarily by recording ion currents across biological or reconstituted membranes, but 'doughnuts' or channel-like assemblies of pre-fibrillar aggregates of $A\beta_{1-42}$, α-synuclein, transthyretin and serum amyloid A have also been observed by electron and atomic force microscopy [69,70,73,152].

In general, heterogeneity of amyloid intermediates, including globules, chains, doughnuts, protofibrils and protofilaments can result in differing potency of toxicity since the varying types of intermediates may act in differing ways on membranes as a consequence of the different extent of exposure of large patches of hydrophobic groups; the latter are likely to be particularly significant in making such assemblies unstable and in favouring their interaction with cell membranes [104,111,117-119,153]. Interactions of this type are likely to lead to the impairment of the function and integrity of the involved membranes, giving rise to a loss of regulation of the intracellular ion balance and redox status, and eventually to cell death. In addition, misfolded proteins will undoubtedly interact inappropriately with other cellular components, potentially giving rise to the impairment of a range of other biological processes.

For example, the size-dependent permeabilization of artificial vesicles by protofibrillar α-synuclein suggests that permeabilization may occur mainly as a result of a specific membrane perturbation via the formation of pores at least 2.5 nm in diameter [70]. In such a case, the "pores" coexist with fibrils under conditions of molecular crowding [154], raising the possibility that, at the conditions found in the cytoplasm, "pores" may be stable enough to be the true pathogenic species in Parkinson's disease [70]. Should this be proven true, then inhibition of "pore" production would represent a suitable therapeutic strategy for several amyloidoses, although it is not easy to imagine a drug molecule able to distinguish specifically among chain protofibrils, annular protofibrils and mature fibrils.

In addition to several bacterial pore-forming toxins (see above), eukaryotic counterparts of pore forming proteins are also described; these include, in mammals, perforin, the C5b-8/9 complement assembly in the membrane attack complex and the BCL-2 family of pro-apoptotic proteins [155-157]. Although the amyloid nature of these channels has not been assessed, these similarities suggest the evolution, in the living world of a death mechanism whereby protein oligomers act as biological "bullets" killing the target cells by forming non-specific membrane pores resulting in unbalance of the ion content. Overall, when considered together with the findings on pore-forming proteins, the channel hypothesis of amyloid toxicity could be considered as an undesired side-effect of a mechanism of cell death conserved from bacteria to mammals.

Biochemical Impairment of Cells Exposed to Toxic Aggregates

A growing body of data support the idea that amyloid aggregates of differing peptides and proteins, mainly in their pre-fibrillar organization, not only share the same basic structural features, but in most cases cause, in cells facing them, early alterations of the same biochemical parameters, notably the free calcium concentration and the intracellular redox status. From these reports it results that a significant increase of free calcium together with a sharp oxidative stress are among the earliest biochemical modifications in cells exposed to pre-fibrillar aggregates of protein/peptides either associated or not associated with amyloid diseases [42,110,158-168]. In most cases, the free calcium increase appears a consequence of the interaction of the early aggregates with the plasma membrane with subsequent membrane derangement and loss of selective permeability; in particular, the presence, among the early aggregates, of annular rings with a central pore (see above) could account for the formation, in the plasma membrane, of aspecific channels leading to intracellular ion homeostasis unbalance. However, the loss of membrane selective permeability may result from a less specific physical alteration of the membrane that does not necessarily require the interaction with pre-formed pores. Free calcium elevation in exposed cells may be a primary factor in determining the final apoptotic outcome of exposed cells (see below)

Oxidative stress is another early modification in cells exposed to pre-fibrillar toxic aggregates. Unbalance of the redox status is measured by the increased levels of reactive oxygen species (ROS) and reactive nitrogen species (RNS) and the consequent rise of the intracellular levels of carbonylated and nitrated proteins as well as of oxidized membrane lipid products including malonyldialdehyde and alkenals such as 4-hydroxynonenal. In particular, it has been proposed that the oxidative stress following exposure to protein aggregates impairs the activity of membrane ion pumps thus providing another possible way to account for the rise of the intracellular free Ca^{2+} [169]. Indeed, oxidative stress appears one of the key events affecting viability in cells suffering from the exposure to toxic aggregates of peptides and proteins [159-166], and is confirmed by the protective effects of antioxidants such as reduced glutathione, lipoic acid and vitamin E [166].

Although oxidative stress is one of the early events accompanying protein aggregation both *in vivo* and *in vitro*, it is not clear why protein aggregation is followed by ROS production. Various hypotheses have been put forward in the last few years on this regard. In the case of $A\beta_{42}$, an involvement of Met35 has been claimed [170]. More generally, an important role of metal ions such as iron, zinc and copper in ROS generation upon protein aggregation has been proposed, for example in generating hydroxide radicals from hydrogen peroxide by Fenton reaction [171,172]. Metal ion co-ordination to the amyloidogenic protein/peptide could also involve oxygen binding possibly as a peroxy bridge that would be destabilized and released as superoxide following structural reorganization into amyloid aggregates [172].

Dysregulation of membrane protein such as receptors and pumps [173] following cell membrane destabilization by the toxic aggregates could also result in oxidative stress. Indeed, microglia and cortical neurons exposed to $A\beta$ aggregates display increased activity of hydrogen peroxide-producing enzymes such as NADPH oxidase and cytochrome P450 reductase in the plasma membrane and in the ER, respectively, [174,175]. Recent data support the idea that intracellular ROS elevation following exposure to amyloid aggregates could be a consequence of calcium entry into the cells followed by the activation of oxidative metabolism aimed at providing the ATP needed to support the activity of membrane ion pumps to clear the excess calcium [169,176]. On turn, ROS elevation would impair ion pumps either by direct oxidation and by inactivating calmodulin, whose oxidized form is no more able to activate Ca^{2+}-ATPases. Ca^{2+} pump impairment would result in alteration of intracellular ion (notably free calcium) homeostasis, thus leading to Ca^{2+} increase mainly in the ER and in mitochondria with reduction of membrane potential and release of pro-apoptotic factors [176, reviewed in [177].

Beside playing a well-recognized role in oxidative stress and in apoptosis, mitochondria are also able to regulate calcium levels and ROS production in neural and non-neural cells, particularly in synapses [178]. Indeed, the impairment of mitochondrial function followed by the opening of mitochondrial permeability transition pores by calcium entry and by the release of cytochrome c, a strong inducer of apoptosis, could be a key event in the appearance of oxidative stress and cell sufferance eventually leading to cell death [179].

The findings on the early biochemical modifications in cells affected by toxic aggregates provide the rationale of possible therapeutic interventions, although they cannot, probably, be extended to all amyloid diseases, in some of which they may also impair differing cellular machineries [180,181]. In addition, the clinical signs of systemic amyloidoses point to a tissue or organ damage that is considered the effect of the deposition of huge amounts of fibrillar aggregates bound to serum amyloid P (SAP); these deposits in some cases, reach the order of kilograms, disrupting tissue structure and leading to tissue or organ failure [26]. SAP is a plasma protein that combines with amyloid aggregates in peripheral tissues protecting them from degradation, thus contributing to the pathogenesis of peripheral amyloidoses [102]. In these cases, treatment with synthetic molecules able to deplete SAP could be beneficial [102]. Clinical trials are also currently underway in AD patients in which the beneficial effects of long-term treatment with antioxidants and non-steroidal anti-inflammatory drugs are investigated. The latter, besides modulating the APP processing favouring the production of the less toxic $Abeta_{40}$ peptide, could also enhance the expression of molecular chaperones of the Hsp family, thus reducing the overload of the ubiqiuitin-proteasome system [182,183] (see below).

Cells Are Protected against Misfolded or Aggregated Proteins

The generic toxicity of pre-fibrillar aggregates discussed above further highlights the significance of the evolutionary development of the complex machinery responsible for the unfolded protein response in the ER and the heat shock response in the cytosol; these cellular pathways undoubtedly prevent the intracellular accumulation of potentially toxic materials such as misfolded proteins or their early aggregates [184-195]. In addition, other protective tools may be present at the cell membrane or outside cells; these comprise proteases such as nephrilysin and the insulin degrading enzyme (IDE), that are able to digest Aβ peptides and other aggregate precursors in their soluble or even aggregated form [196-198] and chaperones, such as clusterin, found in the extracellular fluid [199]

Indeed, a major step forward in understanding many aspects of cell biology was made when it was realized that the molecular chaperones perform key roles not only in favouring protein folding but also in the normal 'housekeeping' processes that are inherent in healthy cells [200,201]. Many data reported in the last few years underscore the fundamental importance of the molecular chaperones (Hsps and many other chaperones such as crystallins, prefoldin, Hsc70 in the cytosol, BiP, Grp94 and calnexin in the ER) and of the ubiquitin-proteasome pathway in enabling cells to clear misfolded or damaged proteins, thus avoiding formation of toxic aggregates (reviewed in [27]).

Interestingly, the ideas of molecular chaperones emerged from the study of the effects of heat shock, where expression of this type of proteins is increased to prevent the effects of protein unfolding and aggregation. The role of the molecular chaperones in enhancing protein folding emerged from the realisation that they are essential in normally functioning cells, where they are estimated to account for about 1% of the total protein content [202]. This observation is also important for their role in reducing the harmful effects of misfolded and aggregation-prone species. When molecular chaperone binding capacity is overwhelmed following the increase of misfolded/unfolded species, the resulting "chaperone overload" results in intracellular accumulation of unchaperoned misfolded proteins thus favouring their aggregation. This process is likely to further impair proteasome activity leading to the appearance, in the centrosome region of the cell, of inclusion bodies (aggresomes) rich of aggregated proteins, Hsps, ubiquitin and proteasome subunits [201].

The key role of molecular chaperones (notably Hsp90 and the Hsp70/40 system) in preventing the appearance of misfolded proteins and protein aggregates has been shown both in cultured cells [44,45,185] and in model organisms such as yeast, transgenic mice and *Drosophila* [191-193,203]. Increasing evidence indicates that any malfunctioning of the Hsp and ubiquitin-proteasome systems is important for the development of a range of neurodegenerative conditions including Parkinson's and Alzheimer's diseases [193,204,205], poly(Q) diseases [194,195], several forms of retinitis pigmentosa [206], pseudoexfoliation syndrome [207], heredo-oto-ophthalmo-encephalopathy [208] and, possibly, systemic amyloidoses [209] as well as many forms of cataract [210,211].

A number of neurological or systemic familial degenerative diseases have recently been associated to genotypes carrying mutations resulting in any impairment of the activity of specific chaperones (reviewed in [212]). These "chaperonepathies", rare inherited diseases caused by mutations in, or abnormal expression of, the genes encoding molecular chaperones, further underscore the protective role of the latter against protein aggregation. Abnormal levels of molecular chaperones have recently been found in the brains of AD patients [213], suggesting the opportunity to search for abnormalities in the regulation of the genes for molecular chaperones in protein deposition diseases [212].

Finally, progress in understanding the key role of the ubiquitin-proteasome system in intracellular proteolysis has advanced rapidly in the last few years, indicating that this pathway is central to the regulation of cellular homeostasis. In effect, many major human degenerative diseases may be indicated as "ubiquitin protein catabolic disorders" to stress the fact that the progression of these diseases is caused or contributed by anomalous protein turnover following defects in the ubiquitin-proteasome system through a reduction of the activity of ubiquitin, ubiquitinating or deubiquitinating enzymes and the proteasome itself [203-205,214,reviewed in [215]); the failure of the quality control mechanisms that ensure proper maturation of proteins in the ER may also be involved in other cases.

Consequences of the Generic Toxicity of Protein Aggregates

As mentioned above, the generic amyloidogenic potential and aggregate toxicity of natural and synthetic peptides and proteins suggest that, in spite of the evolutionary adaptations of protein evolution, protein aggregation in human tissues may be a more frequent event than previously thought. This general hypothesis is made more intriguing in the light of the recent data on the human genome sequence, whose exons have been shown to contain about 60,000 single nucleotide polymorphisms (an average of 1-2 per gene) [216]. At least some of these variations are likely to impair the ability of the involved proteins to fold efficiently to the stable native structure; in fact, at 37 °C, the $\Delta G_{U \rightarrow F}$ for a typical protein is in the 5-15 kcal/mol range and a destabilisation of the native structure by as little as 2 kcal/mol can easily be attained by single mutations or chemical modifications such as oxidation or altered glycosylation. It has been calculated these reduced energetic shifts would, on a simple two-state model, enhance the equilibrium concentration of the unfolded molecules by a factor of more than 30, thus increasing the probability of aggregate nucleation by a factor of more than 10^5 [217]. The possibility that the risk of acquiring Parkinson's disease is influenced by genetic polymorphisms has previously been investigated [218].

Another consideration involves the "natively unfolded proteins" or "natively unstructured proteins" (NUPs), a large family of apparently unrelated proteins including many transcription factors, ribosomal proteins and also signalling proteins involved in cell cycle control. The three-dimensional structures of these proteins are in part or totally disordered *in vitro* and probably in many cases even in the cellular environment, although many undoubtedly are able to adopt specific structures upon interaction with their specific targets proteins [219,220]. NUPs are easily recognizable from the amino acid content as they generally display a low mean hydrophobicity and a high net charge. These characteristics, although essential to allow these proteins to remain unfolded in the absence of partners are also able to reduce their intrinsic tendency to aggregate in the highly crowded intracellular milieu. Despite these structural adaptations, the propensity of NUPs to aggregate can be significant; for example, the aggregation of α-synuclein and tau, both natively unfolded, is associated with Parkinson's disease and Alzheimer's disease, respectively (see Table 1). A recent search in the Swiss Protein Database has led to predict that over 15,000 proteins could contain disordered regions of as many as 40 consecutive residues and over 1000 proteins could be completely disordered [221]. This observation indicates that significant segments of the eukaryotic genomes encode long stretches of amino acid residues that, at least under some conditions, are likely to be unfolded or to adopt non-globular loose structures.

Finally, it is increasingly recognised that epigenetics, the complex chemical changes such as DNA methylation or histone acetylation, that do not affect the DNA sequence but modulate gene expression, may play an important role in the development of common diseases, and its importance in cancer is well established [222]. Differences in the complex chemical modifications of the genome on an individual basis could help to explain why most amyloid diseases appear late in our lifespan; considering that ageing is accompanied by changes in DNA methylation, the latter could lead, in some cases, to up-regulate the expression of specific proteins, stimulating their build-up and aggregation into cells.

Protein Deposition Diseases Might be much more Frequent than Previously Suspected

Overall the above considerations suggest the possibility that even minute deposits of aggregates of as yet unidentified peptides or proteins might accumulate within cells as a consequence of the ageing process. These aggregates could result from impairment of specific cellular functions, such as the ability to clear misfolded proteins or protein aggregates, or from changes in the intracellular environment such as a decrease in pH or in the antioxidant defences or an increase in the macromolecular crowding (see above). The presence, in cells, of minute amounts of early aggregates could perhaps account for subtle impairments of cellular function and viability in the absence of a clear amyloid phenotype in neurological disorders that presently are not associated with amyloid deposition [109]; this can also be the case of prion disease elicited by certain prion protein variants [223].

This consideration may, in part, explain the association, particularly in the developed countries, between the increasing prevalence of protein deposition diseases in human and the increasingly higher life expectancy. Proteins are not necessarily optimized to maintain their correctly folded states under progressively declining environmental conditions and impaired biological safety mechanisms as it happens during ageing. Therefore, it is likely that presently we are challenging the work of protein evolution in optimizing the resistance of proteins against aggregation to the biological lifetime by which during evolution humans have passed their genes to the progeny. On the basis of these considerations and of those discussed in the preceding section, it is conceivable to expect that not only the incidence of well known amyloidoses, but also the number of degenerative diseases one can trace back to the appearance of amyloid aggregates will rise in the near future.

Presently, an increasing number of reports demonstrate that several degenerative diseases of previously unknown origin display the presence, in the affected tissues, of aggregates of known proteins (or of proteins that have not yet been identified) previously unsuspected to be able to deposit in amyloid assemblies) (reviewed in [10]) (Table 3). For instance, the presence of protein deposits of amyloid type in varying organs and tissues with unknown origin and clinical significance has been described in the basement membrane and lamina propria of the gastrointestinal tract, in the walls of the gastrointestinal blood vessels, in the seminal vesicles, in the pituitary of elderly people and in the liver [224-226].

Indeed, the number of diseases associated with protein misfolding and aggregation is increasing steadily (reviewed in [10]). These comprise a number of degenerative diseases where deposits of amyloid type of proteins previously unknown to be associated with disease have been described. In most cases, these aggregated proteins are rare mutants of the wild type counterparts and the underlying pathologies are rare genetic forms. However, there are a number examples of protein aggregates, such as those found in atherosclerosis and in many types of cancer, where the deposits involve wild type forms of specific proteins such as apo B-100 and p53, respectively [227-229].

Such new degenerative diseases with amyloid aggregates affect eye tissues (several forms of retinitis pigmentosa, retinal and corneal dystrophies, as well as inherited and sporadic cataract, pseudoexfoliation syndrome and heredo-oto-ophthalmo-encephalopathy), epithelial tissues (hypotrichosis simplex of the scalp, junctional epidermolysis bullosa, cutaneous lichen amyloidosis), lungs (pulmonary alveolar proteinosis), skeletal muscle (oculopharyngeal muscular dystrophy, sporadic inclusion-body myositis) and nervous tissue (familial encephalopathy with neuroserpin inclusion bodies, indeed a serpinopathy, DFNA9, Charcot-Marie-Tooth-related disorders) (reviewed in [10]).

Table 3. Other degenerative diseases with amyloid aggregates

Disease	Aggregated protein	Tissue/cell
Cronic lung diseases	Surfactant protein C	Lung
Retinal dystrophies	Rhodopsin	Retina
Cataract (sporadic/congenital)	γ-crystallins	Lens
Familial corneal amyloidosis	Lactoferrin	Cornea
Inherited corneal dystrophies	βig-h3	Cornea
Lattice corneal dystrophies	Kerato-epithelin	Cornea
Pseudoexfoliation syndrome	?	Aqueous humor
Heredo-oto-ophthalmo encephalopathy	?	Retinal vessels
Oculopharyngeal muscular dystrophy	PAPB2	Skeletal muscle
Sporadic inclusion-body myositis	APP, Abeta	Skeletal muscle
Hypotrichosis simplex of the scalp	Corneodesmosin	Hair follicle
Atherosclerosis	LDL/ApoB100	Vessel walls
DFNA9	Cochlin	Inner ear
Hirschprung disease/	RET	Enteric nervous system
Cutaneous lichen amyloidosis	RET	Papillary dermis
Charcot-Marie-Tooth-like diseases	Myelin protein 22/0	Peripheral nerve tissue
Short-chain acylCoA DH deficiency	SCAD	Skeletal muscle, brain
Aging pituitary	Prolactin	Pituitary
Aortic medial amyloidosis	Lactadherin (fragment)	Aortic wall
Cancers	p53	Tumoural tissues

Modified from [10].

Overall, the findings appeared mainly in the last five years support the idea that a number of degenerative diseases, both sporadic and familial, of unknown molecular origin and many types of cancers may be considered as amyloidoses or amyloid-related diseases. Although the above survey may not be exhaustive of all most recent reports on this topic, it supports the concept that protein deposition diseases are much more widespread than previously believed and may account for a quite large number of degenerative conditions.

The Dark Side of the Protein World

The generic ability of peptides and proteins unrelated to disease to form amyloid aggregates with specific cytotoxic effects in their pre-fibrillar organization increases largely the number of molecular structures one can investigate to describe the general structural and physicochemical features underlying the molecular mechanisms of protein folding, misfolding and aggregation as well as the biochemical modifications in cells exposed to these aggregates. It has also important consequences for an in-depth understanding of the fundamentals of the origin of protein deposition diseases as well as very important practical outcomes. For example, protein engineers must take into account this constraint when designing new or modified peptides and proteins. Moreover, the pharmacological strategies aimed at treating the various amyloidoses must re-consider, in part, their targets in order to develop molecules aimed at reducing the toxicity of pre-fibrillar aggregates or their formation, and hence the build-up of misfolded proteins, rather than at simply hindering the growth of mature fibrils (less toxic or even harmless).

Overall, the aggregability and aggregate toxicity of most (possibly all) proteins shed a new light on the protein world. Indeed, it is becoming clear that protein and peptide molecules besides being the fundamental molecular tools of the living world, also possess a "dark side" leading them to transform into dangerous toxins able to kill cells (Figure 6). Nevertheless, nature has exploited this fundamental behaviour of all polypeptide chains to perform specific functions that, in part, appear related to the basic toxic potential of amyloid aggregates (see above).

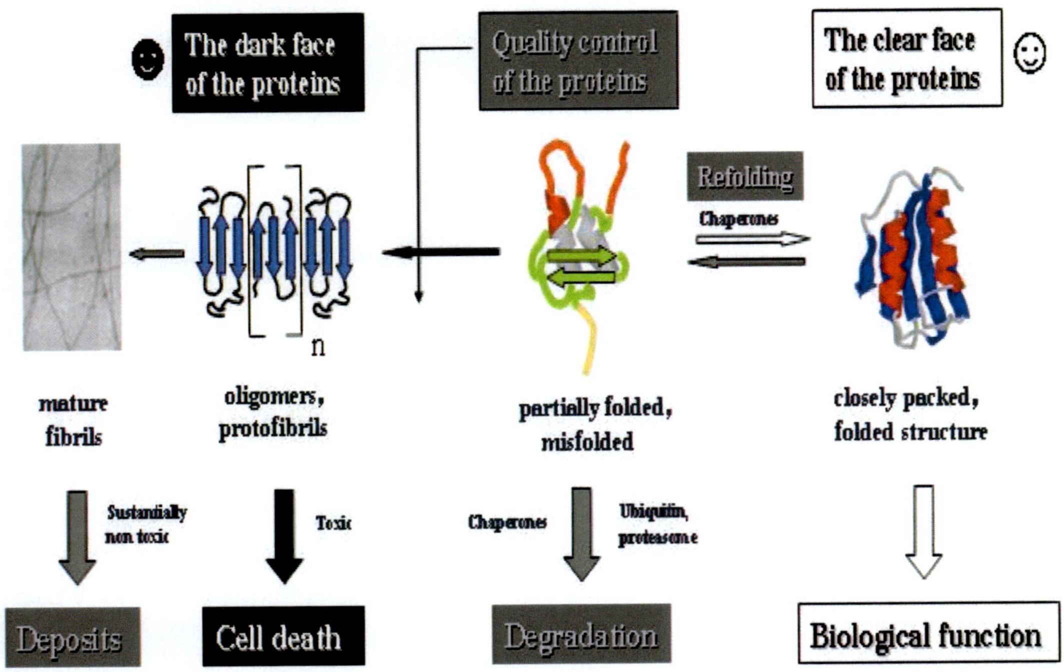

Figure 6. The dark side of the protein world.

The Molecular Consequences of Biological Evolution

The potential cytotoxicity of many aggregated proteins suggests that, in addition to providing cells with mechanisms to clear unfolded and misfolded proteins and to minimise their ability to induce toxicity, evolution must also have operated to eliminate protein sequences with a high intrinsic propensity to aggregate [6]. Thus, mutations that are neutral with respect to protein function could be selected against because they enhance the tendency of proteins to aggregate under physiological conditions. The recent studies of the ways in which structural adaptations of proteins can minimise their tendency to misfold and aggregate mentioned above show, however, that polypeptides are far from being optimised in their ability to resist aggregation. One reason is that sequences must encode many features of proteins, such as their need to fold and to bind to other species. Another reason is that sequences selected by evolution will, in general, only be optimised to an extent that allows a particular organism to function efficiently during its normal life span [87]. In addition, as mentioned above, the physicochemical features favouring folding and aggregation are essentially the same.

It is interesting to note that most of the polypeptide chains associated with aggregation diseases are secreted or membrane-bound proteins or fragments thereof. It could be that such proteins are more easily able to escape the mechanisms that protect cells against protein misfolding and aggregation. It is also possible that processing of polypeptide chains in the ER prior to secretion or their retrograde translocation to the cytosol when they have failed the quality control tests in the ER [230] represent additional steps associated with folding in which errors could occur or accumulate. Indeed, several amyloidoses are associated with deposition of peptides aberrantly produced following mutations of specific membrane proteins, such as the Alzheimer precursor protein (APP), gelsolin and Bri, and impairment of the secretory pathway responsible of their processing upon proteolytic cleavage [231].

Recent work has highlighted the central importance of the ER in the quality control of the folding of secretory proteins [29]. The high efficiency of such a control allows a significant percentage of the proteins maturating in the ER to be cleared before they can properly fold [52,53]. This may be beneficial, for example by improving the promptness of the immune response against viral infections [53] but may also have adverse effects. For example, the most common mutant of the CFTR chloride channel associated with cystic fibrosis (ΔF508CFTR) displays impaired folding leading the ER quality control machinery to clear it before it reaches the correct fold even though, when folded, it could properly function as ion channel at the cell surface ([230] and references therein).

Conclusions and Perspectives

The data reported in the last few years strongly suggest that the conversion into amyloid fibrils of normally soluble proteins and the cytotoxicity of small aggregates appearing during the early stages of fibrillization are generic features of polypeptide chains. The molecular and biochemical basis of such a toxicity also appears to display common features in the different systems that have been studied so far. The ability of many, perhaps all, natural polypeptides to "misfold" and to convert into toxic aggregates under suitable conditions suggests that one of the main driving forces in protein evolution must have been the negative selection against amino acid sequences with significant tendency to aggregate. Nevertheless, since protein folding is a stochastic, and hence not completely infallible, process in competition with misfolding and aggregation, misfolded proteins or folding intermediates in equilibrium with the natively folded molecules are likely to continuously appear within cells. As it has recently been pointed out by the one-hit model of cell death due to aggregate formation, the fate of a cell is determined when nuclei of aggregates of a given protein/peptide start to appear into it following a process that is substantially stochastic in nature [232] and cannot be easily reversed by the cell. Thus mechanisms to deal with aggregation-prone species must have co-evolved with proteins. Indeed, it is clear that misfolding. and the associated tendency to aggregate, is kept under control by molecular chaperones, that render the resulting species harmless by assisting their refolding, or by triggering their degradation by the cellular clearance machineries [187-194].

However, it may happen that protein/peptide aggregates may build-up within the cell due to the increase of incompletely folded or misfolded species or to their enhanced propensity to aggregate. This may occur as the result of the expression of mutational variants of proteins, of the overproduction of some types of proteins, of other genetic factors or of perturbations to the cellular environment that generate conditions, such as heat shock or oxidative stress, favouring aggregation. Finally, the accumulation of misfolded or aggregated proteins can arise from any impairment of the chaperones or the clearance mechanisms as a result of specific mutant phenotypes or of the general effects of ageing [194,195].

The above considerations on the biological roles of molecular chaperones have recently led to the hypothesis that they can act as capacitors of morphological evolution due to their ability to mask and hence to render harmless, by their binding, mutations that could otherwise be damaging to the cell [233]. Evidence for this idea has come from studies of *Drosophila* [233,234], yeast [235] and *Arabidopsis* [236] and could well be important even in humans. The latter function of molecular chaperones could be of very considerable importance as it would reduce the constraints on protein evolution resulting from random mutations imposed by the intrinsic potential of many such variations to increase the aggregation potential.

Extension of these ideas has led to the hypothesis that a higher number of degenerative diseases and other diseases than is presently known could result from the presence in cells of even minute amounts of aggregates that could produce significant impairment of cell viability even without a clear amyloid phenotype [109]. The presence of such aggregates could result, for example, from general effects of ageing where the cellular clearance machinery may become less efficient and the propensity to aggregate enhanced by processes such as chemical modification (e.g. as a result of oxidative stress). Indeed, the number of diseases found to be associated with misfolding and aggregation is increasing steadily (reviewed in [10]).

The increasing prevalence of amyloid diseases is undoubtedly associated with recent increases in human life expectancy, particularly in highly developed countries. One can consider that we are beginning to see the limits of the proteins being optimised to resist aggregation simply as a result of evolutionary pressure [87], that is limited by the reproductive period of every species. It is also interesting, however, that several outbreaks of transmissible amyloid diseases, associated with prions, such as bovine spongiform encephalopathy (BSE), have occurred in recent times. The BSE epidemic is almost universally considered as the result of unnatural feeding of the cattle with the remains of dead individuals. Such a situation is analogous to the outbreak of kuru in Papua New Guinea in the 1950s that was associated with ritual cannibalism, and of Creutzfeldt-Jakob disease in individuals treated in the past with contaminated growth hormone purified from human cadavers. The prion diseases are thought to be triggered by the introduction in the organism of aggregated material in tissue, and the circumstances of such outbreaks result from the violation of practices to which evolutionary pressure has applied [87].

Indeed, the amyloid conditions have been called 'civilisation' or 'post evolutionary' diseases [237] as their present prevalence is the result of our recent abilities to prolong our life spans or of the introduction of new medical and agricultural practices [87,237,238]. This chapter has focussed on the nature and origins of misfolding and aggregation diseases. Although it is beyond the scope of this chapter, attention must be drawn to the development of a wide range of new therapeutic strategies many of which are firmly based on the rapidly evolving knowledge of the diseases that have been outlined [26,238-241]. It can be expected that the knowledge gained from the large number of recent studies on protein folding/aggregation and amyloid toxicity will give new insights into the nature of amyloid diseases and will help to provide a more rational basis for novel therapeutic strategies. We can therefore be optimistic that the rapidly developing scientific and medical skills will find ways leading to prevent or to treat many of these conditions in the near future.

REFERENCES

[1] Levinthal, C. (1968) Are there pathways for protein folding? *J. Chem. Phys.* 85:44-45.

[2] Radford, S.E. and Dobson, C.M. (1999) From computer simulations to human disease: emerging themes in protein folding. *Cell* 97:291-298.

[3] Kelly, J.W. (1998) Alternative conformation of amyloidogenic proteins and their multi-step assembly pathways. *Curr. Opin. Struct.Biol.* 8:101-106.

[4] Dobson, C.M. (2003) Protein folding and misfolding. *Nature* 426:884-890.

[5] Selkoe, D.J. (2003) Folding proteins in fatal ways. *Nature* 426:900-904.

[6] Thomas, P.J., Qu. B.-H. and Pedersen, P.L. (1995) Defective protein folding as a basis of human disease. *Trends Biochem. Sci.* 20:456-459.

[7] Lomas, D.A. and Carrell, R.W. (2002) Serpinopathies and the conformational dementias. *Nat. Rev. Genet.* 3:759-768.

[8] Stefani, M. and Dobson, C.M. (2003) Protein aggregation and aggregate toxicity: new insights into protein folding, misfolding diseases and biological evolution. *J. Mol. Med.* 81:678-699.

[9] Dobson, C.M. (2001) The structural basis of protein folding and its links with human disease *Phil. Trans. R. Soc. Lond.* B 356:133-145.

[10] Stefani, M. (2004) Protein misfolding and aggregation: new examples in medicine and biology of the dark side of the protein world. *Biochim. Biophys.* Acta 1739:5-25.

[11] Reilly, M.M. (1998) Genetically determined neuropathies *J. Neurol.* 245:6-13.

[12] Dickson, D.W. (1995) Correlation of synaptic and pathological markers with cognition of the elderly. *Neurobiol. Aging* 16:285-298.

[13] Lambert, M.P., Barlow, A.K., Chromy, B.A., Edwards, C., Freed, R., Liosatos, M., Morgan, T.E., Rozovsky, I., Trommer, B., Viola, K.L., Wals, P., Zhang, C., Finch, C.E., Krafft, G.A. and Klein, W.L. (1998) Diffusible nonfibrillar ligands derived from Aβ-42 are potent central nervous system neurotoxins. *Proc. Natl. Acad. Sci. USA* 95:6448-6453.

[14] Hartley, D., Walsh, D.M., Ye, C.P., Diehl, T., Vasquez, S. and Vassilev, P.M (1999) Protofibrillar intermediates of amyloid β-protein induce acute electrophysiological changes and progressive neurotoxicity in cortical neurons. *J. Neurosci.* 19:8876-8884.

[15] Walsh., D.M., Hartley, D.M., Kusumoto, Y., Fezoui, Y., Condron, M.M., Lomakin, A., Benedek, G.B., Selkoe, D.J. and Teplow, D.B. (1999) Amyloid β-protein fibrillogenesis. Structure and biological activity of protofibrillar intermediates. *J. Biol.Chem.* 274:25945-25952.

[16] Monji, A., Yoshida, I., Tashiro,K.-I., Hayashi, Y., Matsuda, K. and Tashiro, N. (2000) Inhibition of Aβ fibril formation and Aβ-induced cytotoxicity by senile plaque-associated proteins. *Neurosci. Lett.* 278:81-84.

[17] Goldberg, M.S. and Lansbury, P.T (2000) Is there a cause-and-effect relationship between alpha-synuclein fibrillization and Parkinson's disease? *Nature Cell Biol.* 2:E115-E119.

[18] Conway, K.A., Lee, S.-J., Rochet, J.C., Ding, T.T., Williamson, R.E. and Lansbury, P.T. (2000) Acceleration of oligomerization not fibrillization is a shared property of both alpha-synuclein mutations linked to early-onset Parkinson's disease. Implication for pathogenesis and therapy *Proc. Natl. Acad. Sci. USA* 97:571-576.

[19] Lin, H., Zhu, Y.J.. and Lal, R. (1999) Amyloid β protein (1-40) forms calcium-permeable Zn^{2+}-sensitive channel in reconstituted lipid vesicles. *Biochemistry* 38:11189-11196.

[20] Walsh, D.M., Klyubin, I.,Fadeeva, J.V., Cullen, W.K., Anwyl, R., Wolfe, M.S., Rowan, M.J. and Selkoe, D.J. (2002) Naturally secreted oligomers of amyloid β protein potently inhibit hippocampal long-term potentiation *in vivo*. *Nature* 416:535-539.

[21] Lorenzo, A. and Yankner, B.A. (1994) β-Amyloid neurotoxicity requires fibril formation and is inhibited by Congo red. *Proc. Natl. Acad. Sci. USA* 91:12243-12247.

[22] Thomas, T., Thomas, G., McLendon, C., Sutton, T. and Mullan, M. (1996) β-Amyloid-mediated vasoactivity and vascular endothelial damage. *Nature* 380:168-171.

[23] Pepys, M.B. in *Oxford Textbook of Medicine* (edsWheaterall, D.J., Ledingham, J.G. and Warrel, D.A.) 3rd Edition, 1512-1524 (Oxford Univ. Press, Oxford, 1995).

[24] van Horssen, J., Wilhelmus, M.M., Heljasvaara, R., Pihlajaniemi, T., Wesseling, P., de Waal, R.M. and Verbeek, M.M. (2002) Collagen XVIII: a novel heparan sulfate proteoglycan associated with vascular amyloid. depositions and senile plaques in Alzheimer's disease brains. *Brain Pathol* 12:456-462.

[25] Diaz-Nido, J., Wandosell, F. and Avila, J. (2002) Glycosaminoglycans and beta-amyloid, prion and tau peptides in neurodegenerative diseases. Peptides 23:1323-1332.

[26] Pepys, M.B., Herbert, J., Hutchinson, W.L., Tennent, G.A., Lachmann, H.J., Gallimore, J.R., Lovat, L.B., Bartfal, T., Alanine, A., Hertel, C., Hofmann, T., Jakob-Roetne, R., Norcross, R.D., Kemp, J.A., Yamamura, K., Suzuki, M., Taylor, G.W., Murray, S., Thompson, D., Purvis, A., Kolstoe, S., Wood, S.P. and Hawkins, P.N. (2002) Targeted pharmaceutical depletion of serum amyloid P component for treatment of human amyloidosis. *Nature* 417:254-259.

[27] Sherman, M.Y. and Goldberg, A.L. (2001) Cellular defenses against unfolded proteins: a cell biologist thinks about neurodegenerative diseases. *Neuron* 29:15-32.

[28] Clark, E.D.B. (1998) Refolding of recombinants proteins. *Curr. Opin. Biotechnol.* 9:157-163.

[29] Sitia, R. and Braakman, I. (2003) Quality control in the endoplasmic reticulum protein factory. *Nature* 426:891-894.

[30] Huntington, J.A., Pannu, N.S., Hazes, B., Read, R.J., Lomas, D.A. and Carrell, R.W. (1999) A 2.6 Å structure of a serpin polymer and implications for conformational disease. *J. Mol. Biol.* 293:449-455.

[31] Newcomer, M.E. (2002) Protein folding and three-dimensional domain swapping: a strained relationship? *Curr. Opin Struct. Biol.* 12:48-53.

[32] Booth, D.R., Sunde, M., Bellotti, V., Robinson, C.V., Hutchinson, W.L., Fraser, P.E., Hawkins, P.N. Dobson, C.M., Radford, S.E., Blake, C.F. and Pepys, M.B. (1997) Instability, unfolding and aggregation of human lysozyme variants underlying amyloid fibrillogenesis. *Nature* 385:787-793.

[33] Dumoulin, M., Last, A., Desmyter, A., Decanniere, K., Canet, D., Larsson, G., Spencer, A., Archer, D.B., Sasse, J., Muyidermans, S., Wyns, L., Redfield, C., Matagne, A., Robinson, C. and Dobson, C.M. (2003) A camelid antibody fragment inhibits the formation of amyloid fibrils by human lysozyme. *Nature* 424:783-788.

[34] Chiti, F., Stefani, M., Taddei, N., Ramponi, G. and Dobson, C.M. (2003) Rationalization of the effects of mutations on peptide and protein aggregation rates. *Nature* 424:805-808.

[35] Minton, A.P. (1994) Influence of macromolecular crowding on intracellular association reactions: possible role in volume regulation. In *Cellular and Molecular Physiology of cell volume regulation* (Strange K. Ed.) pp. 181-190, CRC Press, Boca Raton, Fl.

[36] Ellis, R.J. (2001) Macromolecular crowding: an important but neglected aspect of the intracellular environment. *Corr. Opin. Struct. Biol.* 11:114-119.

[37] Nagy, I.Z., Nagy, K. and Lustyik, G. (1982) Protein and water content of aging brain. *Exp Brain Res. Suppl.* 5:118-122.

[38] Conlon, I.J., Dunn, G.A., Mudge, A.W. and Raff, M.C. (2001) Extracellular control of cell size. *Nat. Cell. Biol.* 3:918-921.

[39] Al-Habori, M. (2001) Macromolecular crowding and its role as intracellular signalling of cell volume regulation. *Int. J. Biochem. Cell Biol.* 33:844-864.

[40] Kirik, D., Rosenblad, C., Burger, C., Lundberg, C., Johansen, T.E., Muzyczka, N., Mandel, R.J. and Bjorklund, A. (2002) Parkinson-like neurodegeneration induced by targeted overexpression of alpha-synuclein in the nigrostriatal system. *J.Neurosci.* 22:2780-2791.

[41] Trojanowski, J.Q., Ishihara, T., Higuchi, M., Yoshiyama, Y., Hong, M., Zhang, B., Forman, M.S., Zukareva, V. and Lee, V.M. (2002) Amyotrophic lateral sclerosis/parkinsonism dementia complex: transgenic mice provide insights into mechanisms underlying a common tauopathy in an ethnic minority on Guam. Exp. *Neurol.* 176:1-11.

[42] Selkoe, D.J. (2001) Alzheimer's disease: genes, proteins, and therapy *Physiol. Rev.* 81:741-766.

[43] Fernando-Funez, P., Nino-Rosales, M.L., de Gouyon, B., She, W.-C., Luchak, J.M., Martinez, P., Turiegano, E., Benito, J., Capovilla, M., Skinner, P.J., McCall, A., Canal, I., Orr, H.T., Zoghbi, H.Y. and Botas, J. (2000) Identification of genes that modify ataxin-1-induced neurodegeneration. *Nature* 408:101-106.

[44] Ma, J., Wollmann, R. and Lindquist, S. (2002) Neurotoxicity and neurodegeneration when PrP accumulates in the cytosol. *Science* 298:1781-1785.

[45] Morgan, C.J., Gelfrand, M., Atreya, C. and Miranker, A. (2001) Kidney dialysis-associated amyloidosis: a molecular role for copper in fiber formation. *J. Mol.Biol.* 309:339-345.

[46] Floege, J. and Ehlerding, G. (1996) β2-Microglobulin associated amyloidosis. *Nephron* 72:9-26.

[47] Prusiner, S.B. (1998) Prions. *Proc. Natl. Acad. Sci. USA* 95 :13363-13383.

[48] Xing, Y., Nakamura, A., Korenaga, T., Guo, Z., Yao, J., Fu, X., Matsushita, T., Kogishi, K., Hosokawa, M., Kametani, F., Mori, M. and Higuchi, K. (2002) Induction of protein conformational change in mouse senile amyloidosis. *J. Biol. Chem.* 277:33164-33169.

[49] Lundmark, K., Westermark, G.T., Nyström, S., Murphy, C.L., Solomon, A. and Westermark, P. (2002) Transmissibility of systemic amyloidosis by a prion-like mechanism. *Proc. Natl. Acad. Sci. USA* 99:6979-6984.

[50] Giasson, B.I., Forman, M.S., Higuchi, M., Golbe, L.I., Graves, C.L., Kotzbauer, P.T., Trojanowski, J.Q. and Lee, V. M.-Y. (2003) Initiation and synergistic fibrillization of tau and alpha-synuclein. Science 300:636-640.

[51] Goldberg, A.L. (2003) Protein degradation and protection against misfolded or damaged proteins *Nature* 426: 895-899

[52] Schubert, U., Antòn, L.C., Gibbs, J., Orbyry, C.C., Yewdell, J.W. and Bennink, J.R. (2000) Rapid degradation of a large fraction of newly synthesized proteins by proteasomes. *Nature*, 404:770-774.

[53] Reits, E.A.J., Vos, J.C., Grommé, M. and Neefjes, J. (2000) The major substrates for TAP in vivo are derived from newly synthesized proteins. *Nature* 404:774-778.

[54] DuBay, K.F., Pawar, A.P., Chiti, F., Zurdo, J., Dobson, C.M. and Vendruscolo, M. (2004) Prediction of the absolute aggregation rate of amyloidogenic polypeptide chains. *J. Mol. Biol.* 341:1317-1326.

[55] Sirangelo, I., Dal Piaz, F., Malmo, C., Casillo, M., Birolo, L., Pucci, P., Marino, G. and Irace, G. (2003) Hexafluoroisopropanol and acid destabilized forms of apomyoglobin exhibit structural differences. *Biochemistry* 42:312-319.

[56] Monti, M., Principe, S., Giorgetti, S., Mangione, P., Merlini, G., Clark, A., Bellotti, V., Amoresano, A. and Pucci, P. (2002) Topological investigation of amyloid fibrils obtained from beta2-microglobulin. *Prot. Sci.* 11:2362-2369.

[57] Petkova, A.T., Ishii, Y., Balbach, J.J., Antzutkin, O.N., Leapman, R.D., Delaglio, F. and Tycko, R. (2002) A structural model for Alzheimer's β-amyloid fibrils based on experimental constraints from solid state NMR. *Proc. Natl. Acad. Sci. USA* 99:16742-16747.

[58] Tycko, R. (2004) Progress towards a molecular-level structural understanding of amyloid fibrils. *Curr. Opin. Struct. Biol.* 14:96-103.

[59] Jiménez, J.L., Guijarro, J.I., Orlova, E., Zurdo, J., Dobson, C.M., Sunde, M. and Saibil, H.R. (1999) Cryo-electron microscopy structure of an SH3 amyloid fibril and model of the molecular packing. *EMBO J.* 18:815-821.

[60] Wetzel, R. (2002) Ideas of order for amyloid fibril structure. Structure 10:1031-1036.

[61] Monoi, H., Futaki, S., Kugimyia, S., Minakata, H. and Yoshihara, K. (2000) Poly-L-glutamine forms cation channels: relevance to the pathogenesis of the polyglutamine diseases. *Biophys. J.* 78:2892-2899.

[62] Armen, R.S., DeMarco, M.L., Alonso, D.O. and Daggett, V. (2004) Pauling and Corey's α-pleated sheet structure may define the prefibrillar amyloidogenic intermediate in amyloid disease. *Proc. Natl. Acad. Sci. USA* 101:11622-11627.

[63] Serpell. L.S. (2000) Alzheimer's amyloid fibrils: structure and assembly. *Biochim. Biophys. Acta* 1502:16-30.

[64] Jiménez, J.L., Nettleton, E. J., Bouchard, M., Robinson, C.V., Dobson, C.M. and Saibil, H.R. (2002) The protofilament structure of insulin amyloid fibrils. *Proc. Natl.Acad. Sci. USA* 99:9196-9201.

[65] Chamberlain, A.K., MacPhee, C.E., Zurdo, J., Morozova-Roche, L.A., Hill, H.A., Dobson, C.M. and Davis, J.J. (2000) Ultrastructural organization of amyloid fibrils by atomic force microscopy. *Biophys. J.* 79:3282-3293.

[66] Dobson, C.M. (1999) Protein misfolding, evolution and disease. *Trends Biochem. Sci.* 24:329-332.

[67] Relini, A., Torrassa, S., Rolandi, R., Ghiozzi, A., Rosano, C., Canale, C., Bolognesi, M., Plakoutsi, G., Bucciantini, M., Chiti, F. and Stefani, M. (2004) Monitoring the process of HypF fibrillization and liposome permeabilization by protofibrils *J. Mol. Biol.* 338:943-957.

[68] Malisauskas, M., Zamotin, V., Jass, J., Noppe, W., Dobson, C.M. and Morozova-Roche, L.A. (2003) Amyloid protofilaments from the calcium-binding protein equine lysozyme: formation of ring and linear structures depends on pH and metal ion concentration. *J. Mol Biol.* 330:879-90.

[69] Lin, H., Bhatia, R. and Lal, R. (2001) Amyloid β protein forms ion channels: implications for Alzheimer's disease pathophysiology. *FASEB J.* 15:2433-2444.

[70] Lashuel, H.A., Petre, B.M., Wall, J., Simon, M., Nowak, R.J., Walz, T and Lansbury, P.T. (2002) α-Synuclein, especially the Parkinson's disease-associated mutants, forms pore-like annular and tubular protofibrils. *J. Mol. Biol.* 322:1089-1102.

[71] Poirier, M.A., Li, H., Macosko, J., Cail, S., Amzel, M. and Ross, C.A. (2002) Huntingtin spheroids and protofibrils as precursors in polyglutamine fibrillization. *J. Biol. Chem.* 277:41032-41037.

[72] Hirakura, Y and Kagan, B.L. (2001) Pore formation by beta-2-microglobulin: a mechanism for the pathogenesis of dialysis-associated amyloidosis. *Amyloid* 8:94-100.

[73] Quintas, A., Vaz, D.C., Cardoso, I., Saraiva, M.J.M. and Brito, R.M.M. (2001) Tetramer dissociation and monomer partial unfolding precedes protofibril formation in amyloidogenic transthyretin variants. *J. Biol. Chem.* 276:27207-27213.

[74] Kayed, R., Head, E., Thompson, J.L., McIntire, T.M., Milton, S.C., Cotman, C.W. and Glabe, C.G. (2003) Common structure of soluble amyloid oligomers implies common mechanisms of pathogenesis. *Science* 300:486-489.

[75] LeVine, H. (1993) Thioflavine T interaction with synthetic Alzheimer's disease beta-amyloid peptides: detection of amyloid aggregation in solution. *Protein Sci.* 2:404-410.

[76] Klunk, W.E., Pettegrew, J.W. and Abraham, D.J. (1989) Quantitative evaluation of congo red binding to amyloid-like proteins with a beta-pleated sheet conformation. *J. Histochem. Cytochem.* 37:1273-1281.

[77] Bousset, L., Thomson, N.H., Radford, S.E. and Melki, R. (2002) The yeast prion Ure2p retains its native alpha-helical conformation upon assembly into protein fibrils in vitro. *EMBO J.* 21:2903-2911.

[78] Glenner, G.G., Ein, D., Eanes, E.D., Bladen, H.A., Terry, W. and Page, D.L. (1971) Creation of amyloid fibrils from Bence Jones proteins *in vitro*. *Science* 174:712-714.

[79] Colon, W. and Kelly, J.W. (1992) Partial denaturation of transthyretin is sufficient for amyloid fibril formation *in vitro*. *Biochemistry* 31:8654-8660.

[80] Gujiarro, J.I., Sunde, M., Jones, J.A., Campbell, I.D. and Dobson, C.M. (1998) Amyloid fibril formation by an SH3 domain. *Proc. Natl. Acad. Sci.* 95:4224-4228.

[81] Litvinovich, S.V., Brew, S.A., Aota, S., Akiyama, S.K., Haudenschild, C. and Ingham, K.C. (1998) Formation of amyloid-like fibrils by self-association of a partially unfolded fibronectin type III module. *J.Mol.Biol.* 280:245-258.

[82] Chiti, F., Webster, P., Taddei, N., Clark, A., Stefani, M., Ramponi, G. and Dobson, C.M. (1999) Designing conditions for in vitro formation of amyloid protofilaments and fibrils. *Proc. Natl. Acad. Sci. USA* 96:3590-3594.

[83] Chiti, F., Bucciantini, M., Capanni, C., Taddei, N., Dobson, C.M. and Stefani, M. (2001) Solution conditions can promote formation of either amyloid protofilaments or mature fibrils from the HypF N-terminal domain. *Protein Sci.* 10:2541-2547.

[84] Tjernberg, L., Hosia, W., Bark, N., Thyberg, J. and Johansson, J. (2002) Charge attraction and β propensity are necessary for amyloid fibril formation from tetrapeptides. *J.Biol.Chem.* 277:43243-43246.

[85] Lopez De La Paz, M., Goldie, K., Zurdo, J., Lacroix, E., Dobson, C.M., Hoenger, A. and Serrano, L. (2002) De novo designed peptide-based amyloid fibrils. *Proc. Natl.Acad. Sci. USA* 99:16052-16057.

[86] Fandrich, M. and Dobson, C.M. (2002) The behaviour of poly amino acids reveals an inverse side chain effect in amyloid structure formation. EMBO J. 21: 5682-5690.

[87] Dobson C.M. (2003) Getting out of shape. *Nature* 418:729-730.

[88] Richardson, J.S. and Richardson, D.C. (2002) Natural β-sheet proteins use negative design to avoid edge-to-edge aggregation. *Proc. Natl. Acad. Sci. USA* 99:2754-2759.

[89] Broome, B.M. and Hecht, M.H. (2000) Nature disfavours sequences of alternative polar and non-polar amino acids: implications for amyloidogenesis. *J. Mol. Biol.* 296:961-968.

[90] Schwarz, R., Istrail, S. and King, J. (2001) Frequencies of amino acid strings in globular protein sequences indicate suppression of blocks of consecutive hydrophobic residues. *Protein Sci.* 10:1023-1031.

[90a]Rousseau, F., Serrano, L. and Schymkowits, J.W.H. (2006) How evolutionary pressure against protein aggregation shaped chaperone specificity. *J. Mol. Biol.* 356:1037-1047.

[91] Chapman, M.R., Robinson, L.S., Pinkner, J.S., Roth, R., Heuser, J., Hammar, M., Normark, S. and Hultgren, S.J. (2002) Role of *Escherichia coli* curli operons in directing amyloid fiber formation. *Science* 295:851-855.

[92] Vidal, O., Longin, R., Prigent-Combaret, C., Dorel, C., Hooreman, M., Lejeune, P., Vidal, O., Longin, R., Prigent-Combaret, C., Dorel, C., Hooreman, M. and Lejeune, P. (1998) Isolation of an *Escherichia coli* K-12 mutant strain able to form biofilms on inert surfaces: involvement of a new ompR allele that increases curli expression. *J. Bacteriol.* 180:2442-2449.

[93] Claessen, D., Rink, R., de Jong, W., Siebring, J., de Vreungd, P., Hiddee Borsma, F.G., Dijkhuizen, L. and Wösten, H.A.B. (2003) A novel class of secreted hydrophobic proteins is involved in aerial hyphae formation in *Streptomyces coelicolor* by forming amyloid-like fibrils. *Genes Dev.* 17:1714-1726.

[94] Butko, P., Buford, J.P., Goodwin, J.S., Stroud, P.A., McCormick, C.L. and Cannon, G.C. (2001) Spectroscopic evidence for amyloid-like interfacial self-assembly of hydrophobin Sc3. *Biochim. Biophys. Res. Commun.* 280:212-215.

[95] Dos Reis, S., Coulary-Salin, B., Forgel, V., Lascu, I., Bégueret, J. and Saupe, S.J. (2002) The HET-s prion protein of the filamentous fungus *Podospora anserina* aggregates *in vitro* into amyloid-like fibrils. *J. Biol. Chem.* 277:5703-5706.

[96] Hotze, E.M., Heuck, A.P., Czajkowsky, M., Shao, Z., Johnson, A.E. and Tweten, R. (2002) Monomer-monomer interactions drive the prepore to pore conversion of a β-barrel-forming cholesterol-dependent cytolysin. *J. Biol. Chem.* 277:11597-115605.

[97] Iconomidou, V.A., Vriend, G. and Hamodrakas, S.J. (2000) Amyloids protect the silkmoth oocyte embryo. *FEBS Lett.* 479:141-145.

[98] Iconomidou, V.A., Cryssikos, G.D., Gionis, V., Vriend, G., Hoenger, A. and Hamodrakas, S.J. (2000) Amyloid-like fibrils form a 18-residue analogue of a part of the central domain of the B-family of silkmoth chorion proteins. *FEBS Lett.* 499:268-273.

[99] Li, G., Zhou, P., Shao, Z., Xie, X., Chen, X., Wang, H., Chunyu, L. and Yu, T. (2001) *Eur. J. Biochem.* 268:6600-6606.

[100] Frederikse, P.H. (2000) Amyloid-like protein structure in mammalian ocular lenses. *Curr. Eye Res.* 20:462-468.

[101] Hirakura, Y., Carreras, I., Sipe, J.D. and Kagan, B.L. (2002) Channel formation by serum amyloid A: a potential mechanism for amyloid pathogenesis and host defense. *Amyloid* 9:13-23.

[102] Gillmore, J.D., Lovat, L.B., Persey, M.R., Pepys, M.B. and Hawkins, P.N. (2001) Amyloid load and clinical outcome in AA amyloidoses in relation to circulating concentration of serum amyloid A protein. *The lancet* 358:24-29.

[103] Svanborg, C., Agerstam, H., Aronson, A., Bjerkvig, R., Duringer, C., Fischer, W., Gustafsson, L., Hallgren, O., Leijonhuvud, I., Linse, S., Mossberg, A.-K., Nilsson, H., Pettersson, J. and Svensson, M. (2003) HAMLET kills tumor cells by an apoptosis-like mechanism –cellular, molecular, and therapeutic aspects. *Adv. Cancer Res.* 88:1-29.

[104] Bychkova, V.E., Pain, R.H., and Ptitsyn, O.B. (1988) The molten globule state is involved in the translocation of protein across membranes. *FEBS Lett.* 238:231-234.

[105] Craig, S., Bowen, R.L., Smith, M.A. and Perry, G. (2003) Cerebrovascular requirement for sealant, anti-coagulant and remodelling molecules that allow for the maintenance of vascular integrity and blood supply *Brain Res. Rev.* 41:164-178.

[106] Berson, J.F., Theos, A.C., Harper, D.C., Tenza, D., Raposo, G. and Marks, M.S. (2003) Preprotein convertase cleavage liberates a fibrillogenic fragment of a resident glycoprotein to initiate melanosomes biogenesis. *J. Cell. Biol.* 16:521-533.

[107] Kranenburg, O., Kroon-Batenburg,L.M.J., Reijerkerk, A., Wu, Y.-P., Voest, E.E. and Gebbink, M.F.B.G. (2003) Recombinant endostatin forms amyloid fibrils that bind and are cytotoxic to murine neuroblastoma cells *in vitro*. *FEBS Lett.* 539:149-155.

[108] Sirangelo, I., Malmo, C., Iannuzzi, C., Mezzogiorno, A., Bianco, M.R., Papa, M. and Irace, G. (2004) Fibrillogenesis and cytotoxic activity of the amyloid-forming apomyoglobin mutant W7FW14F. *J. Biol. Chem.* 279:13183-13189.

[109] Bucciantini, M., Giannoni, E., Chiti, F., Baroni, F., Formigli, L., Zurdo, J., Taddei, N., Ramponi, G., Dobson, C.M. and Stefani, M. (2002) Inherent toxicity of aggregates implies a common mechanism for protein misfolding diseases. *Nature* 416:507-511.

[110] Bucciantini, M., Calloni, G., Chiti, F., Formigli, L., Nosi, D., Dobson, C.M. and Stefani, M. (2004) Pre-fibrillar amyloid protein aggregates share common features of cytotoxicity. *J. Biol. Chem.* 279:31374-31382.

[111] Volles, M.J. and Lansbury, P.T. (2001) Vesicle permeabilization by protofibrillar α-synuclein: comparison of wild-type with Parkinson's disease linked mutants and insights in the mechanisms. *Biochemistry* 40:7812-7819.

[112] Kourie, J.I. (1999) Synthetic C-type mammalian natriuretic peptide forms large cation selective channels. *FEBS Lett.* 445:57-62.

[113] Ariste, N,, Pollard, H.B. and Rojas, E. (1993) Giant multilevel cation channels formed by Alzheimer disease amyloid beta-protein [A beta P-(1-40] in bilayer membranes. *Proc. Natl. Acad. Sci. USA* 90:10573-10577.

[114] Mirzabekov, T.A., Lin, M.C. and Kagan, B.L. (1996) Pore formation by the cytotoxic islet amyloid peptide amylin. *J. Biol. Chem.* 271:1988-1992.

[115] Lin, M.C., Mirzabekov, T. and Kagan, B.L. (1997) Channel formation by a neurotoxic prion protein fragment. *J. Biol. Chem.* 272:44-47.

[116] Ding, T.T., Lee, S.-J., Rochet, J.-C. and Lansbury, P.T. (2002) Annular α-synuclein protofibrils are produced when spherical protofibrils are incubated in solution or bound to brain-derived membranes. *Biochemistry* 41:10209-10217.

[117] Zhu, Y.J., Lin, H. and Lal, R. (2000) Fresh and nonfibrillar amyloid β protein (1-40) induces rapid cellular degeneration in aged human fibroblasts: evidence for AβP-channel-mediated cellular toxicity. *FASEB J.* 14:1244-1254.

[118] Kourie, J.I. and Shorthouse, A.A. (2000) Properties of cytotoxic peptide-induced ion channels. *Am. J. Physiol. Cell Physiol.* 278:C1063-C1087.

[119] Kourie, J.I. and Henry, C.L. (2002) Ion channel formation and membrane-linked pathologies of misfolded hydrophobic proteins: the role of dangerous unchaperoned molecules. *Clin. Exp. Pharmacol. Physiol.* 29:741-753.

[120] Kayed, R., Sokolow, Y., Edmonds, B., McIntire, T.M., Milton, S.C., Hall, J.E. and Glabe, C.G. (2004) Permeabilization of lipid bilayers is a common conformation-dependent activity of soluble amyloid oligomers in protein misfolding diseases. *J. Biol. Chem.* 279:46363-46366.

[121] Demuro, A., Mina, E., Kayed, R., Milton, S.C., Parker, I. and Glabe, C.G. (2005) Calcium dysregulation and membrane disruption as a ubiquitous neurotoxic mechanism of soluble amyloid oligomers. *J. Biol. Chem.* 280:17294-17300.

[122] Svensson, M., Sabharwal, H., Hakansson, A., Mossberg, A.-K., Lipniunas, P., Leffler, H., Svanborg, C. and Linset, S. (1999) Molecular characterization of α-lactalbumin folding variants that induce apoptosis in tumor cells. *J.Biol. Chem.* 274:6388-6396.

[123] Zhu, M., Souillac, O., Ionescu-Zanetti, C., Carters, S.A. and Fink, A.L. (2002) Surface-catalyzed amyloid fibril formation. *J. Biol. Chem.* 277:50914-50922.

[124] Sethyraman, A. and Belfort, G. (2005) Protein structural perturbation and aggregation on homogeneous surfaces. *Biophys. J.* 88:1322-1333.

[125] Lee, S.J., Liyanage, U., Bickel, P.E., Xia, W., Lansbury, P.T. and Kosik, K.S. (1998) A detergent-insoluble membrane compartment contains Aβ in vivo. *Nature Med.* 4:730-734.

[126] Ehahalt, R., Keller, P., Haass, C., Thiele, C. and Simons, K. (2003) Amyloidogenic processing of the Alzheimer beta-amyloid precursor protein depends on lipid rafts. *J. Cell Biol.* 160:113-123.

[127] Kakio, A., Nishimoto, S.-L., Kozutsumi,, Y. and Matsuzaki, K. (2003) Formation of membrane-active form of amyloid β-protein in raft-like model membranes. *Biochim. Biophys. Res. Commun.* 303:514-518.

[128] Koudinov, A.L. and Koudinova, N.V. (2005) Cholesterol homeostasis failure as a unifying cause of synaptic degeneration. *J. Neurol. Sci.* 229-230:233-240.

[129] Kakio, A., Nishimoto, S.-L., Yanagisawa, K., Kozutsumi,, Y. and Matsuzaki, K. (2002) Interaction of amyloid β-protein with various gangliosides in the raft-like membranes: importance of GM1 ganglioside-bound form as an endogenous seed for Alzheimer amyloid. *Biochemistry* 41:7385-7390.

[130] Mason, R.P., Shoemaker, W.J., Shajenko, L., Chambers, T.E. and Herbette, L.G. (1992) Evidence for changes in the Alzheimer's disease brain cortical membrane structure mediated by cholesterol. *Neurobiol. Aging* 13:413-419.

[131] Iivonen, S., Hiltunen, M., Alafuzoff, L., Mannermaa, A., Kerokoski, P., Puolivati, J., Salminen, A. and Helisalmi, S. (2002) Seladin-1 transcription is linked to neuronal degeneration in Alzheimer's disease. *Neuroscience* 113:301-310.

[132] Arispe, N. and Doh, M. (2002) Plasma membrane cholesterol controls the cytotoxicity of Alzheimer's disease Aβ(1-40) and (1-42) peptides. *FASEB J.* 16:1526-1536.

[133] Abad-Rodriguez, J., Ledesma, M.D., Craessaerts, K., Perga, S., Medina, M., Delacourte, A., Dingwall, C., De Strooper, B. and Dotti, C.G. (2005) Neuronal membrane cholesterol loss enhances amyloid peptide generation. *J. Cell Sci.* 167:953-960.

[134] Cecchi, C., Baglioni, S., Fiorillo, C., Pensalfini, A., Liguri, G., Nosi, D., Rigacci, S., Bucciantini, M. and Stefani, M. (2005) Insights into the molecular basis of the differing susceptibility of varying cell types to the toxicity of amyloid aggregates. *J. Cell Sci. in press.*

[135] Zhao, H., Jutila, A., Nurminen, T., Wickström, S.A., Keski-Oja, J. and Kinnunen, P.K.J. (2005) Binding of endostatin to phosphatidylserine-containing membranes and formation of amyloid-like fibers. *Biochemistry* 44:2857-2863.

[136] Kazlauskaite, J., Sanghera, N., Sylvester, I., Vénien-Bryan, C. and Pinheiro, T.J.T. (2003) Structural changes of the prion protein in lipid membranes leading to aggregation and fibrillization. *Biochemistry* 43:3295-3304.

[137] Lin, M.-c.A. and Kagan, B. (2002) Electrophysiologic properties of channels induced by Aβ25-35 in planar lipid bilayers. *Peptides* 23:1215-1228.

[138] Jayakumar, R., Jayaraman, M., Koteeswarl, D. and Gomath, K. (2004) Cytotoxic and membrane perturbation effects of a novel amyloid forming model, peptide poly(leucine-glutamic acid). *J. Biochem.* (Tokyo) 136:457-462.

[139] Zhao, H., Tuominen, E.K.J. and Kinnunen, P.K.J. (2004) Formation of amyloid fibers triggered by phosphatidylserine-containing membranes. Biochemistry 43:10302-10307.

[140] Lee, G., Pollard, H.B. and Arispe, N. (2002) Annexin 5 and apolipoprotein E2 protect against Alzheimer's amyloid-β-peptide cytotoxicity by competitive inhibition at a common phosphatidylserine interaction site. *Peptides* 23:1249-1263.

[141] Utsugi, T., Schroit, A.J., Connor, J., Bucana, C.D. and Fidler, I.J. (1991) Elevated expression of phosphatidylserine inn the outer membrane leaflet of human tomor cells and recognition by activated human blood monocytes. *Cancer Res.* 51:3062-3066.

[142] Ran, S. and Thorpe, P.E. (2002) Phosphatodylserine is a marker of tumor vasculature and a potential target for cancer imaging and therapy. *Int. J. Radiat Oncol Biol. Phys.* 54:1479-1484.

[143] Zhang, Y.-H., Leliveld, S.R., Kooistra, K., Molenaar, C., Rohn, J.L., Tanke, H.J., Abrahams, J.P. and Noteborn, M.H.M. (2003) Recombinant apoptin multimers kill tumor cells but are non-toxic and epitope-shielded in a normal-cell-specific fashion. *Exp. Cell Res.* 289:36-46.

[144] Hancock, R.E.W. % Scott, M.G. (2000) The role of antimicrobial peptides in animal defences. *Proc. Natl. Acad. Sci. USA* 97:8856-8861.

[145] Bhatia, R., Lin, H. and Lal, R. (2000) Fresh and nonfibrillar amyloid β protein(1-42) induces rapid cellular degeneration in aged human fibroblasts: evidence for AβP-channel-mediated cellular toxicity. *FASEB J.* 14:1233-1243.

[146] Nilsberth, C., Westlind-Danielssnon, A., Eckman, C.B., Condron, M.M., Axelman, K., Forsell, C., Stenh, C., Luthman, J., Teplow, D.B., Younkin, S.G., Naslund, J. and Lannfelt, L. (2001) The "arctic" APP mutation. (E693G) causes Alzheimer's disease by enhanced Aβ protofibril formation. *Nature Neurosci.* 4:887-893.

[147] Sousa, M.M., Cardoso, I., Fernandes, R., Guimaraes, A. and Saraiva, M.J. (2001) Deposition of transthyretin in early stages of familial amyloidotic polyneuropathy. *Am. J.Pathol.* 159:1993-2000.

[148] Arispe, N., Rojas, E. and Pollard, H.D. (1993) Alzheimer's disease amyloid beta protein forms calcium channels in bilayer membranes: blockade by tromethamine and aluminium. *Proc. Natl Acad. Sci. USA* 89:10940-10944.

[149] Mattson, M.P., Begley, J.G., Mark, R.J. and Furukawa, K, (1997) Aβ25-35 induces rapid lysis of red blood cells: contrast with Aβ1-42 and examination of underlying mechanisms. Brain Res. 771:147-153.

[150] Kourie, J.I., Farrelly, P.V. and Henry, C.L. (2001) Channel activity of deamidated isoforms of prion protein fragment 106-126 in planar lipid bilayers. *Neurosci. Res.* 66:214-220.

[151] Azimov, R., Azimova, R., Hirakura, Y. and Kagan, B.L. (2001) Ion channels with different selectivity formed by transthyretin. *Biophys. J.* 80:129a.

[152] Wang, L., Lashuel, H.A., Walz, T. and Colòn, W. (2002) Murine apolipoprotein serum amyloid A in solution forms a hexamer containing a central channel. *Proc.Natl. Acad. Sci. USA* 99:15947-15952.

[153] D'Silva, PR and Lala, AK (2000) Unfolding of diphtheria toxin in membranes. A hydrophobic photolabeling study. *J. Biol. Chem.* 275:11771-11777.

[154] Shtilerman, M.D., Ding, T.T. and Lansbury, P.T. (2002) Molecular crowding accelerates fibrillization of alpha-synuclein: could an increase in the cytoplasmic protein concentration induce Parkinson's disease? *Biochemistry* 41:3855-3860.

[155] Fraser, S.A., Karimi, R., Michalak, M. and Hudig, D. (2000) Perforin lytic activity is controlled by calreticulin. *J. Immunol.* 164:4150-4155.

[156] Morgan, B.P. (1999) Regulation of the complement membrane attack pathway. *Crit. Rev. Immunol.* 19:173-198.

[157] Reed, J.C. (2000) Mechanisms of apoptosis. *Am. J. Pathol.* 157:1415-1430.

[158] Kourie, J.I. (2001) Mechanisms of amyloid β protein-induced modification in ion transport systems: implications for neurodegenerative diseases. *Cell. Mol. Neurobiol.* 21:173-213.

[159] Butterfield, A.D., Drake, J., Pocernich, C. and Castegna, A. (2001) Evidence of oxidative damage in Alzeimer's disease brain: central role for amyloid β-peptide. *Trends Mol. Med.* 7:548-554.

[160] Milhavet, O. and Lehmann S. (2002) Oxidative stress and the prion protein in transmissible spongiform encephalopathies. *Brain Res. Rev.* 38:328-339.

[161] Hyun, D.-H., Lee, MH., Hattori, N., Kubo, S.-I., Mizuno, Y., Halliwell, B. and Jenner, P. (2002) Effect of wild-type or mutant parkin on oxidative damage, nitric oxide, antioxidant defenses, and the proteasome. *J. Biol. Chem.*277:28572-28577.

[162] Wyttenbach, A., Sauvageot, O., Carmichael, J., Diaz-Latoud, C., Arrigo, A.-P. and Rubinsztein, D.C. (2002) Heat shock protein 27 prevents cellular polyglutamine toxicity and suppresses the increase of reactive oxygen species caused by Huntingtin. *Hum. Mol. Gen.* 11:1137-1151.

[163] Guentchev, M., Voigtlander, T., Haberler, C., Groschup, M.H. and Budka, H. (2000) Evidence for oxidation stress in experimental prion disease. *Neurobiol. Dis.*, 7:270-273.

[164] Choi, Y.G., Kim, J.L., Lee, H.P., Jin, J.K., Choi, E.K., Carp. R.I. and Kim, Y.S. (2000) Induction of heme oxygenase-1 in the brain of scrapie-infected mice. *Neurosci. Lett.* 11:173-176.

[165] Zhang, L., Xing, G.q, Barker, J.L., Chang, Y., Maric, D., Ma, W., Li, B.-s, and Rubinow, D.R. (2001) α-Lipoic acid protects rat cortical neurons against cell death induced by amyloid and hydrogen peroxide through the Akt signalling pathway. *Neurosci. Lett.* 312:125-128.

[166] Lee, D.W., Sohn, H.O., Lim, H.B., Lee, Y.G., Kim, Y.S., Carp, R.J. and Wisnievski, H.M. (1999) Alteration of free radical metabolism in the brain of mice infected with scrapie agent. *Free Rad. Res.* 30:499-507.

[167] Kawahara, M., Kuroda, Y., Arispe, N. and Rojas, E. (2000) Alzheimer's β-amyloid, human islet amylin, and prion protein fragment evoke intracellular free calcium elevation by a common mechanism in a hypopthalamic GnRH neuronal cell line. *J. Biol. Chem.* 275:14077-14083.

[168] Varadarajan, S., Yatin, .S., Aksenova, M. and Butterfield, D.A. (2000) Alzheimer's amyloid β-peptide-associated free radical oxidative stress and neurotoxicity. *J. Struct. Biol.* 130:184-208.

[169] Squier, T.C. (2001) Oxidative stress and protein aggregation during biological aging. *Exp. Gerontol.* 36:1539-1550.

[170] Kanski, J., Varadarajan, S., Aksenova, M. and Butterfield, D.A. (2001) Role of glycine-33 and methionine-35 in Alzheimer's amyloid β-peptide 1-42-associated oxidative stress and neurotoxicity. *Biochim. Biophys. Acta* 1586:190-198.

[171] Turnbull, S., Tabner, B.J., El-Agnaf, O.M.A., Moore, S., Davies, Y. and Allsop, D. (2001) α-Synuclein implicated in Parkinson's disease catalyzes the formation of hydrogen peroxide *in vitro*. *Free Rad. Biol. Med.* 30:1163-1170.

[172] Tabner, B.J., Turnbull, S., El-Agnaf, O.M.A. and Allsop, D. (2002) Formation of hydrogen peroxide and hydroxyl radicals from Aβ and α-synuclein as a possible

mechanism of cell death in Alzheimer's disease and Parkinson's disease. *Free Rad. Biol. Med.* 32:1076-1083.

[173] Mattson, M.P. (1999) Impairment of membrane transport and signal transduction systems by amyloidogenic proteins. *Methods Enzymol.* 309:733.768.

[174] Pappolla, M.A., Omar, R.A., Chyan, Y.-J., Ghiso, J., Hsiao, K., Bozner, P., Perry, G., Smith, M.A. and Cruz-Sanchez, F. (2001) Induction of NADPH cytochrome P450 reductase by the Alzheimer β-protein. Amyloid as a "foreign body". *J. Neurochem.* 78:121-128.

[175] Qin, L., Liu, Y., Cooper, C., Liu, B., Wilson, B. and Hong, J.-S. (2002) Microglia enhance β-amyloid peptide-induced toxicity in cortical and mesencephalic neurons by producing reactive oxygen species. *J. Neurochem.* 83:973-983.

[176] Bucciantini, M. Rigacci, S., Berti, A., Pieri, L., Cecchi, C., Nosi, D., Formigli, L., Chiti, F. and Stefani, M. (2005) Patterns of cell death triggered in two different cell lines by HypF-N prefibrillar aggregates. *FASEB J.* 19: 437-439.

[177] Schröder, M. and Kaufman, R.J. (2005) ER stress and the unfolded protein response. *Mutation Res.* 569:29-63.

[178] Mattson, M.P., Chan, S.L. and Duan, W. (2002) Modification of brain aging and neurodegenerative disorders by genes, diet, and behavior. *Physiol. Rev.* 82:637-672.

[179] Moreira, P.I., Santos, M.S., Moreno, A., Rego, A.C. and Oliveira, C. (2002) Effect of amyloid beta-peptide on permeability transition pore: a comparative study. *J. Neurosci. Res.* 15:257-267.

[180] Ross, C.A. (2002) Polyglutamine pathogenesis: emergence of unifying mechanisms for Huntington's disease and related disorders. *Neuron* 35:819-822.

[181] Alvarez, A., Toro, R., Caceres, A. and , Maccioni, R.B. (2001) Inhibition of tau phosphorylating protein kinase cdk5 prevents β-amyloid-induced neuronal death. *FEBS Lett.* 459:421-426.

[182] Lim, G.P., Yang, F., Chu, T., Gahtan, E., Ubeda, O., Beech, W., Overmier, J.B., Hsiao-Ashe, K., Frautschy, S.A. and Cole, G.M. (2001) Ibuprofen effects on Alzheimer pathology and open field activity in APPsw transgenic mice. *Neurobiol. Aging* 22:983-991.

[183] Fawcett, T.W., Xu, Q. and Holbrook, N.J. (1997) Potentiation of heat stress-induced hsp70 expression *in vivo* by aspirin. *Cell Stress Chaper.* 2:104-109.

[184] David, D.C., Layfield, R., Serpell, L., Narain, Y., Groedert, M. and Spillantini, M.G. (2002) Proteasomal degradation of tau protein. *J. Neurochem.* 83:176-185.

[185] Tofaris, G.K., Layfield, R. and Spillantini, M.G. (2001) α-Synuclein metabolism and aggregation is linked to ubiquitin-independent degradation by the proteasome. *FEBS Lett.* 509:22-26.

[186] Trinh, C.H., Smith, D.P., Kalverda, A.P., Phillips, S.E.V. and Radford, S. (2002) Crystal structure of monomeric human β-2-microglobulin reveals clues to its amyloidogenic properties. *Proc. Natl. Acad. Sci. USA* 99:9771-9776.

[187] Waelter, S., Boeddrich, A., Lurz, R., Scherzinger, E., Lueder, G., Lebrach, H. and Wanker, E.E. (2001) Accumulation of mutant huntingtin fragments in aggresome-like inclusion bodies as a result of insufficient protein degradation. *Mol. Biol. Cell* 12:1393-1407.

[188] McNaught, K.S.P., Mytilinieou, C., JnoBaptiste, R., Yabut, J., Shashidharan, P., Jenner, P. and Olanov, C.W. (2002) Impairment of the ubiquitin-proteasome system causes dopaminergic cell death and inclusion body formation in ventral mesencephalic cultures. *J. Neurochem.* 81:301-306.

[189] Fonte, V., Kapulkin, V., Taft, A., Fluet, A., Friedman, D. and Link, C.D. (2002) Interaction of intracellular β amyloid peptide with chaperone proteins. *Proc. Natl. Acad. Sci. USA* 99:9439-9444.

[190] Bonini, N.M. (2002) Chaperoning brain degeneration.*Proc. Natl. Acad. Sci. USA* 99 Suppl. 4:16407-11.

[191] Muchowski, P.J., Schaffar, G., Sittler, A., Wanker, E.E., Hayer-Hartl, M.K. and Hartl, U. (2000) Hsp70 and Hsp40 chaperones can inhibit self-assembly of polyglutamine proteins into amyloid-like fibrils. *Proc. Natl. Acad. Sci. USA* 97:7841-7846.

[192] Zoghbi, H.Y. and Botas, J. (2002) Mouse and fly models of neurodegeneration. *Trends Gen.* 18:463-471.

[193] Auluck, P.K., Chan, H.Y.E., Trojanowski, J.Q., Lee, V.M.-Y. and Bonini, N.M. (2002) Chaperone suppression of α-synuclein toxicity in a *Drosophila* model for Parkinson's disease. *Science* 295:865-868.

[194] Bence, N.F., Sampat, R.M. and Kopito, R.R. (2001) Impairment of the ubiquitin-proteasome system by protein aggregation. *Science* 292:1552-1555.

[195] Sakahira, H., Breuer, P., Hayer-Hartl, M.K. and Hartl, F.U. (2002) Molecular chaperones as modulators of polyglutamine protein aggregation and toxicity. *Proc.Natl. Acad. Sci. USA 99* Suppl 4:16412-8.

[196] Ling, Y., Morgan, K. and Kalsheker, N. (2003) Amyloid precursor protein (APP) and the biology of proteolytic processing: relevance to Alzheimer's disease. *Int J Biochem Cell Biol.* 35:1505-35.

[197] Edland, S.D. (2004) Insulin-degrading enzyme, apolipoprotein E, and Alzheimer's disease. *J Mol Neurosci.* 23:213-7.

[198] Kanemitsu, H., Tomiyama, T. and Mori, H. (2003) Human neprilysin is capable of degrading amyloid beta peptide not only in the monomeric form but also the pathological oligomeric form. *Neurosci Lett.* 2003 350:113-116.

[199] DeMattos, R.B., Cirrito, J.R., Parsadanian, M., May, P.C., O'Dell, M.A., Taylor, J.W., Harmony, J.A., Aronow, B.J., Bales, K.R. Paul S.M. and Holtzman, D.M. (2004) ApoE and Clusterin Cooperatively Suppress Abeta Levels and Deposition. Evidence that ApoE Regulates Extracellular Abeta Metabolism In Vivo. *Neuron* 41:193-202.

[200] Pelham, H.R. (1986) Speculations on the functions of the major heat shock and glucose-regulated proteins. *Cell* 46:959-961.

[201] Ellis, R.J., van der Vies, S.M. and Hemmingsen, S.M. (1989) The molecular chaperone concept. *Biochem. Soc. Symp.*55:145-53.

[202] Kopito, R.R. (2000) Aggresomes, inclusion bodies and protein aggregation. *Trends Cell Biol.* 10:524-530.

[203] Shimura, H., Schlossmacher, M.G., Hattori, N., Frosch, M.P., Trockenbacher, A., Schneider, R., Mizuno, Y., Kosik, K.S. and Selkoe, D.J. (2001) Ubiquitination of a new form of α-synuclein by Parkin from human brain: implications for Parkinson's disease. *Science* 293:263-269.

[204] Keller, J.N., Hanni, K.B. and Markesbery, W.R. (2000) Impaired proteasome function in Alzheimer's disease. *J. Neurochem.* 75:436-439.

[205] McNaught, K.St.P. and Jenner, P. (2001) Proteasomal function is impaired in substantia nigra in Parkinson's disease. *Neurosci. Lett.* 297:191-194.

[206] Chappie, J.P., Grayson, C. Hardcastle, A.J., Saliba, R.S., van der Spuy, J. and Cheetham, M.E. (2001) Unfolding retinal dystrophies: a role for molecular chaperones? *Trends Mol.Med.* 7:414-421.

[207] Berlau, J., Lorenz, P., Beck, R., Makovitzky, J., Schlotzer-Schrehardt, U., Thiesen, H.J. and Gauthoff, R. (2001) Analysis of aqueous humor proteins of eyes with and without pseudoexfoliation syndrome. Graefes Arch. Clin. Exp. *Ophthalmol.* 239:743-746.

[208] Bek, T. (2000) Ocular changes in heredo-oto-ophthalmo-encephalopathy. *Br. J. Ophthalmol.* 84:1298-1302.

[209] Dul, J.L., Davis, D.P., Williamson, E.K., Satevens, F.J. and Argon, Y, (2001) Hsp70 and antifibrillogenic peptides promote degradation and inhibit intracellular aggregation of amyloidogenic light chains. *J. Cell. Biol.* 19:705-715.

[210] Sandilands, A., Hutcheson, A.M., Long, H.A., Prescott, A.R., Vrensen, G., Löster, J., Klopp, N., Lutz, R.B., Graw, J., Masaki, S., Dobson, C.M., MacPhee, C.E. and Quinlan, R.A. (2002) Altered aggregation properties of mutant γ-crystallins cause inherited cataract. *EMBO J.* 21:6005-6014.

[211] Kosinski-Collins, M. and King, J. (2003) In vitro unfolding, refolding, and polymerization of human γD crystallin, a protein involved in cataract formation. *Protein Sci.* 12:480-490.

[212] Macario, A.J.L. and de Macario E.C. (2002) Sick chaperones and ageing: a perspective. *Ageing Res. Rev.* 1:295-311.

[213] Yoo, B.C., Kim, S.H., Cairns, N., Fountoulakis, M. and Lubec, G. (2001) Deranged expression of molecular chaperones in brains of patients with Alzheimer's disease. *Biochim. Biophys. Res. Commun.* 280:249-258.

[214] Tanaka, Y., Engelender, S., Igarashi, S., Rao, R.K., Wenner, T., Tanzi, R.E., Sawa, A., Sawson, V.L., Dawson, T.M. and Ross, C.A. (2001) Inducible expression of mutant α-synuclein decreases proteasome activity and increases sensitivity to mitochondria-dependent apoptosis *Hum. Mol. Gen.* 10:919-926.

[215] Layfield, R., Alban, A., Mayer, R.J. and Lowe, J. (2001) The ubiquitin protein catabolic disorders. Neuropathol. *Appl. Neurobiol.* 27:171-179.

[216] The international SNP map working group (2001) A map of human sequence variation containing 1.4 million single nucleotide polymorphisms. *Nature* 409:928-933.

[217] Perutz, M.F., Pope, B.J., Owen, D., Wanker, E.E. and Scherzinger, E. (2002) Aggregation of proteins with expanded glutamine and alanine repeats of the glutamine-rich and asparagine-rich domains of Sup35 and of the amyloid β-peptide of amyloid plaques. *Proc. Natl. Acad. Sci. USA* 99:5596-5600.

[218] Checkoway, H., Farin, F.M. Costa-Mallen, P., Kirchner, S.C. and Costa, L.G. (1998) Genetic polymorphisms in Parkinson's disease. *Neurotoxicology* 19:635-643.

[219] Wright, P.E. and Dyson, H.J. (1999) Intrinsically unstructured proteins: reassessing the protein structure-function paradigm. *J. Mol. Biol.* 293:321-331.

[220] Uversky, V.N. and Fink, A.L. (2004) Conformational constraints for amyloid fibrillation: the importance of being unfolded. *Biochim Biophys Acta.* 1698:131-153.

[221] Romero, P., Obradovich, Z., Kissinger, C., Villafranca, J.E., Garner, E., Guilliot, S. and Bunker, A.K. (1998) Thousands of proteins likely to have long disordered regions. *Pac. Symp. Biocomput.* 3:437-448.

[222] Dennis, C. (2003) Altered States. *Nature* 421:686-688.

[223] Hegde, R.S., Tremblay, P., Groth, D., DeArmond, S.J., Prusiner, S.B. and Lingappa, V.R. (1999) Transmissible and genetic prion diseases share a common pathway of neurodegeneration. *Nature* 402:822-826.

[224] Tsutsumi, Y., Serizawa, A. and Hori, S. (1996) Localized amyloidosis of the seminal vesicle: identification of lactoferrin immunoreactivity in the amyloid material. *Pathol. Int.* 46:491-497.

[225] Westermark, P., Eriksson, L., Engström, U., Eneström, S. and Sletten, K. (1997) Prolactin-derived amyloid in the aging pituitary gland. *Am. J. Pathol.* 150:67-73.

[226] Demirhan, B., Bilezikci, B., Kiyici, H, and Boyacioglu, S. (2002) Globular amyloid deposits in the wall of the gastrointestinal tract: report of six cases. *Amyloid* 9:42-46.

[227] Ursini, F., Davies, K.J.A., Maiorino, M., Parasassi, T. and Sevanian, A. (2002) Atherosclerosis: another protein misfolding disease? *Trends Mol. Med.* 8:370-374.

[228] Moll, U.M., Ostermeyer, A.G., Haladay, R., Winkfield, B., Frazier, M. and Zambetti, G. (1996) Cytoplasmic sequestration of wild-type p53 protein impairs the G1 checkpoint after DNA damage. *Mol. Cell Biol.* 16:1126-1137.

[229] Ostermeyer, A.G., Runko, E., Winkfield, B., Ahn, B. and Moll, U.M. (1996) Citoplasmically sequestered wild-type p53 protein in neuroblastoma is relocated to the nucleus by a C-terminal peptide. *Proc. Natl. Acad. Sci. USA* 93:15190-15194.

[230] Plemper, R.K. and Wolf, D.H. (1999) Retrograde protein translocation: ERADication of secretory proteins in helth and disease. *Trends Biochem. Sci.* 24:266-270.

[231] Huff, M.E., Balch, W.E. and Kelly, J.W. (2003) Pathological and functional amyloid formation orchestrated by the secretory pathway. *Curr. Opin. Struct. Biol.* 13:674-682.

[232] Clarke, G., Collins, R.A., Leavitt, B.R., Andrews, D.F., Hayden, M.R., Lumsden, C.J. and McInnes, R.R. (2000) A one-hit model of cell death in inherited neuronal degeneration. *Nature* 406:195-199.

[233] Rutherford, S.L. and Lindquist, S. (1998) Hsp90 as a capacitor for morphological evolution. *Nature* 396:336-342.

[234] Roberts, S.P. and Fader, M.E. (1999) Natural hyperthermia and expression of the heat shock protein Hsp70 affect developmental abnormalities in *Drosophila melanogaster. Oecologia* 121:323-329.

[235] True, H.L. and Lindquist, S. (2000) A yeast prion provides a mechanism for genetic variation and phenotypic diversity. *Nature* 407:477-483.

[236] Queiltsch, C. Sangster, T.A. and Lindquist, S. (2002) Hsp90 as a capacitor of phenotypic variation. *Nature* 417:618-624.

[237] Csermely, P. (2001) Chaperone overload is a possible contributor to "civilization diseases". *Trends Gen.* 17:701-704.

[238] Dodart, J.C., Bales, K.R., Bales, K.R. and Paul, S.M. (2003) Immunotherapy for Alzheimer's disease: will vaccination work? *Trends Mol. Med.* 9:85-87.

[239] Dobson C.M. (2003) Protein folding and disease: a view from the first Horizon Symposium. *Nat. Rev. Drug. Discov.* 2:154-160.

[240] Hardy, J. and Selkoe, D.J. (2002) The amyloid hypothesis of Alzheimer's disease: progress and problems on the road to therapeutics. *Science* 297:353-356.

[241] Hammarström, P., Wiseman, R.L., Powers, E.T. and Kelly, J.W. (2003) Prevention of transthyretin amyloid disease by changing protein misfolding energetics. *Science* 299:713-716.
[242] Crulla, N., Caddy, G.L., Hall, D.R., Zurdo, J., Gairi, M., Feliz, M., Giralt, E., Robinson, C. and Dobson, C.M. (2005) Molecular recycling within amyloid fibrils. *Nature* 436:554-558.

In: Protein Folding: New Research
Editor: Tony R. Obalinsky, pp. 51-87

ISBN 1-59454-835-8

Chapter 2

FOLDING INTERMEDIATES: TURNING POINTS TO THE NATIVE STATE, AMYLOID FIBRILS AND AGGREGATION

***Masaru Hoshino*[1], *Yuji O. Kamatari*[2] *and Satoshi Ohnishi*[3*]**
[1] Graduate School of Pharmaceutical Sciences, Kyoto University, Kyoto, Japan
[2] Center for Emerging Infectious Diseases, Gifu University, Yanagido Gifu, Japan
[3] RIKEN Genomic Sciences Center, Yokohama, Japan

ABSTRACT

Advances in protein folding techniques have revealed that many proteins fold from the denatured states to their native states *via* an intermediate state(s). The number of such folding intermediates and their properties often differ between proteins, even between homologue members that share the same fold. These findings imply that protein folding does not occur randomly, but the process is systematically regulated through a pathway(s). In addition, the existence of multiple folding pathways was demonstrated for some proteins. Detailed information about folding intermediates of a protein characterizes its folding pathways, which is most successfully depicted by the energy landscape model. In contrast, it is not straightforward to describe protein misfolding reactions such as amyloid fibril formation and aggregation by a similar energetic scheme due to a lack of information regarding the amyloid/aggregation-responsible intermediates. Nevertheless, increasing evidence suggests that these misfolding reactions occur through the common folding intermediate states. In this review, we focus on detailed aspects of intermediate states reported for several proteins, which are responsible for amyloid fibril formation and aggregation. An analogy between these intermediates and folding intermediates is discussed towards the establishment of a model consistent with kinetic and thermodynamic aspects of protein misfolding reactions.

Protein Folding and Intermediates

Introduction

While structural aspects of proteins draw worldwide attention in this post-genome era, we would like to review "protein folding" problems; i.e., questions how polypeptide chains fold into their native forms. Protein is not a solid rock, but a dynamic chain folded in a compact form. An unbranched chain of a protein polypeptide uniquely folds into its native form to play the specific role in cell metabolism, and thus protein function is closely related to its tertiary structure. However, proteins do not always maintain their active forms in cells. Folding and unfolding of proteins are ubiquitous in the vital processes.

What is the major factor that controls protein function and its native structure? Christian Anfinsen gave the first answer for this question through his extensive studies on ribonuclease A (RNaseA), staphylococcal nuclease, and other proteins in the 1950s-1970s, which are best summarized in a milestone paper [1]. The conclusion from his observations is now known as the Anfinsen's dogma; that is, protein native structure is encoded by its amino acid sequence. Subsequently, numerous studies have been conducted toward the understanding of mechanisms of how polypeptide chains of proteins spontaneously find their native conformations.

To date, many fundamental and detailed aspects in the protein folding phenomena have been revealed, which is, probably, most remarkably reflected by rapid growth of the field of computational prediction/design of protein structure/function. Computer algorithms often succeed in predicting the three dimensional structure of a protein with strikingly high accuracy, if its amino acid sequence has a significant homology to proteins whose structures are known (the 6th community wide experiment on the Critical Assessment of Techniques for Protein Structure Prediction (CASP-6), *http://predictioncenter.llnl.gov/casp6/Casp6.html*). The successful algorithms are designed based on the accumulating knowledge regarding protein folding and related physicochemistry, and, without doubt, such computational approaches would play an important role in the comprehension of numerous protein-protein linkages and their molecular biology with atomic resolution. Nevertheless, it should be noted that we are still distant from a complete understanding of protein folding mechanisms. The success in the CASP is limited only for small proteins of which homologue structures are known, and structural prediction of proteins without prior information of homologue structures remains challenging. The situation is similar for a computer-based design of proteins. Although there are a limited number of cases reporting success in designing *de novo* functions on existing proteins [2-6], computer-based protein design, in general, remains extremely challenging. David Baker, one of the leaders in the field of computational protein modeling, succeeded in designing a *de novo* protein from scratch with an artificially designed fold [7]. And yet at the same time, he notes that the success was achieved by optimizing the sequence for maximum protein stability, which is not the case for naturally occurring proteins that are thermodynamically inferior. Indeed, the native structure of a protein is only marginally stable, and a polypeptide chain unfolds and refolds repeatedly in its lifetime. Some proteins lose their native structure due to various stresses, such as heat and acid, and another

* Corresponding Author. Phone: +81-45-503-9317, Fax: +81-45-503-9643; Email: ohnishi@gsc.riken.jp

unfolds to travel across lipid bilayers. In some cases, however, a protein fails to find the correct structure and folds into a "misfolded" form causing serious diseases. These dynamic natures of proteins are highly related to their functions and/or protein transportation. To gain a better understanding of cellular and molecular biology, dynamic aspects of proteins should be further studied. In fact, findings of intermediate states in the process of the conformational conversion have dug deeper into the protein folding problems. Not only stable intermediates that are easily detectable by classical procedures, but also only transiently populated intermediates in the folding reaction have become detectable with progresses in technology as well as methodology. Throughout this chapter, we aim to marshal our thoughts on protein folding with special focus on folding intermediates.

Equilibrium Folding Intermediates

As implied by the Anfinsen's dogma, many denatured, small globular proteins indeed refold into the native structure by adjusting solvent conditions to near physiological. In many cases, such a conformational change between the native form and the denatured form is reversible, and the conformational transition can be described by the two-state mechanism. The experimental criteria for the simple two-state mechanism are: (1) The signal monitoring protein conformation changes in a cooperative manner with a single transition. Typically, a plot of such signals obtained under various denaturing strengths exhibits a sigmoidal curve. (2) The changes in multiple spectroscopic signals are consistent. For instance, the far-ultraviolet (UV) circular dichroism (CD) signal, a measure for the regular secondary structures, should change in concert with the near-UV CD signal, a measure for the rigid tertiary structure around aromatic residues. Fluorescence signals from aromatic rings should also change in parallel with these CD signals. (3) Overlaid spectra of a protein recorded under various degrees of denaturing conditions should show isosbestic points, where the native form and the denatured form exhibit the same signal intensity. (4) The differential scanning calorimetry (DSC) measurement *per se* provides an index for the two-state mechanism; the directly measured enthalpy value (ΔH_{cal}), calculated from the area of the transition peak with a proper baseline, should match with the van't Hoff enthalpy value (ΔH_{vH}), obtained by curve fitting the thermal denaturation profile under the assumption of the two-state transition.

In a wide range of studies on protein denaturation process, however, it has been long known that some proteins do not satisfy the above criteria. This implies the presence of thermostable intermediate state(s) that is different from both the native state and the fully denatured ones. The longer the protein polypeptide is, the more likely intermediate states of the protein are observable. A boundary appears in the molecular size around 10-15 KDa, above which most proteins exhibit stable intermediate states.

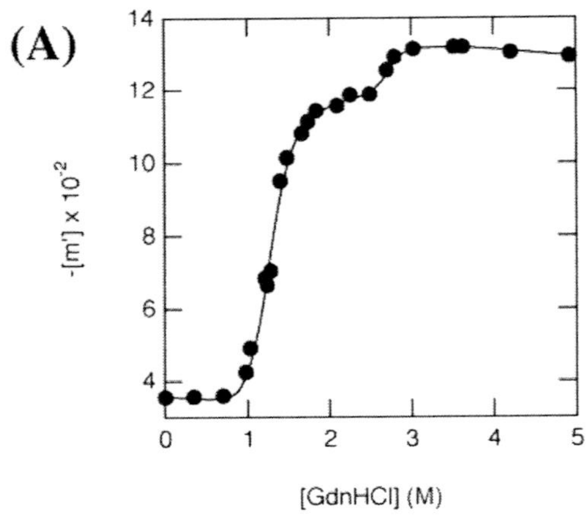

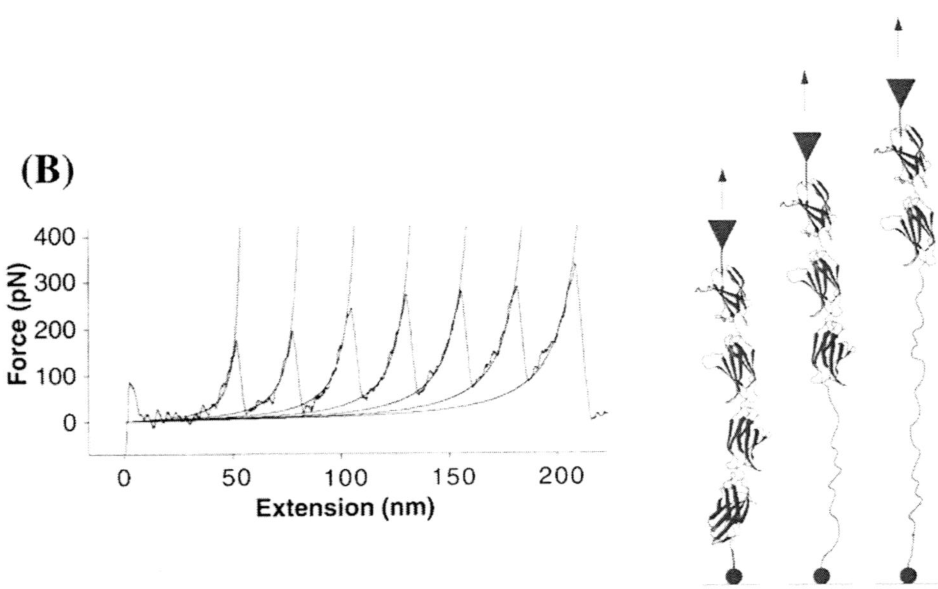

Figure 1. (A) Biphasic denaturation profile of Bence Jones protein. The protein was denatured by the addition of guanidine hydrochloride (GdnHCl), and the conformational change was monitored by optical rotation [m']. Data are taken from Azuma et al. [8] (B) Mechanical unfolding of titin. Characteristic saw-tooth patterns are seen in the force-extension curve, in which each force peak corresponds to sequential unfolding of a single immunoglobulin-like domain. The left panel is reprinted with permission from *Science*, 276, Rief, M., Gautel, M., Oesterhelt, F., Fernandez, J. M., and Gaub, H. E., Reversible unfolding of individual titin immunoglobulin domains by AFM. 1109-1112 [9]. Copyright (1997) AAAS. Schematic picture in the right panel shows the stepwise unfolding events in mechanical unfolding of titin.

Multi-domain Proteins

A large protein often consists of multiple globular domains, in which contiguous segments of the polypeptide chain fold into independent units connected in tandem by flexible linkers. Each domain typically consists of 50~150 amino acids, and such domains can often be separated by a proteolytic cleavage at the linker regions without disrupting structure and function. From these observations, there has been a general acceptance of the concept that domains are structurally independent of each other, and they act as units of folding. Consequently, the conformational transition curve of a tandem protein, typically shows a multi-step profile that reflects a difference in stability between the domains. Such an example is shown in the denaturation profile of the Bence Jones protein that consists of two distinct immunoglobulin domains (C_L and V_L) connected by a linker [8] (Figure 1A). The biphasic profile indicates that a stable intermediate state(s) is present in the process of its denaturation, in which one of the domains is denatured, but the other still has the native structure. Recently, the similar stepwise unfolding events were more directly demonstrated by a newly developed single-molecular method using atomic force microscopy (AFM). Mechanical stretchings of titin, a multiple immunoglobulin domain repeat demonstrated that sequential unfolding of each domain occurs independently in a cooperative and reversible manner [9] (Figure 1B).

The multi-step denaturation is reported not only for necklace-like proteins with multiple domains, but also for some relatively large proteins that consist of directly packed multiple domains without a linker. For example, a sulfhydryl protease papain has two distinct lobes separated by a cleft, and it denatures in a biphasic manner, suggesting that each domain denatures independently [10]. The gastric aspartic proteinase pepsin also has two globular domains connected by a hinge, and the N-terminal domain unfolds prior to the denaturation of the C-terminal domain [11]. Despite no obvious domain separation in the protein structure, α1-antichymotrypsin provides another example of a multistep denaturation [12].

Molten Globule State

In the 1980s, characteristic aspects of an intermediate state observed under moderately denaturing conditions at acidic pH were competitively reported for several proteins [13-16]. This intermediate state is called as "molten globule state" or "A-state", and has been assumed to be a general intermediate state in the process of folding reaction. Common features of the molten globule state are; a compact size of overall molecule, a significant amount of the native-like secondary structures, and little organization of the tertiary structure. One of the well-known examples of the molten globule state is that of cytochrome c, which populates at acidic pH (~ 2) in the presence of a relatively high concentration of salt [17]. The acidic molten globule state of this protein shows a similar amount of secondary structure to the native form as judged from the far-UV CD spectrum. However, it lacks rigid tertiary structural packing as indicated by the near-UV CD spectrum. Accordingly, the Soret absorption spectrum of the heme moiety that reflects the spin state of iron, and thus the conformational state around the protein chromophore, shows intermediate properties between the native and the acid denatured states. In the native state of cytochrome c, the fluorescence signal from a single tryptophan residue at the position 59 is completely quenched by the heme group, indicating a spatially close proximity of these chromophores. In contrast, the Trp 59 becomes exposed to solvent upon denaturation of the protein so that strong fluorescence signal can be observed. The acid molten globule state of the protein shows almost complete quenching of the Trp fluorescence by the heme group, suggesting that the overall molecular size is compact, similar to the native state. Indeed, the small angle X-ray scattering measurements for several proteins in the molten globule states revealed only a ~20% increase in radius of gyration (R_g) with respect to their native forms [18].

Kinetic Folding Intermediates

The finding of the molten globule state led to the concept of the folding pathway; that is, a protein denatures *via* an intermediate state(s) similar to the molten globule state, and the unfolded polypeptide would refold *via* the same pathway in the reverse direction. Extensive kinetics studies on the protein folding reactions have been addressed to verify this assumption. Refolding reaction of a small globular protein typically finishes within a second, thus a stopped-flow mixing device is often used to monitor such a fast reaction with millisecond time resolution. If the reaction is two-state, the refolding kinetics should be described by a single exponential phase. In addition, kinetic traces monitored by different probes should provide the same rate constants under the same refolding conditions. In case of the refolding of a chemically denatured α-lactalbumin, the secondary structure formation monitored by the far-UV CD spectroscopy was so rapid that the reaction was completed within the dead time of the stopped-flow apparatus, while the formation of the tertiary structure, monitored by the near UV-CD was slower and traceable using the same device [19]. This indicates a temporal accumulation of an intermediate state within the dead time of the apparatus, which has the secondary structure but lacks the tertiary structure, a characteristic feature of the equilibrium molten globule. Moreover, the CD spectra of this kinetically detected intermediate state obtained by a series of single wavelength stopped-flow measurements at different wavelengths were quite similar to that of the equilibrium molten globule state. More detailed structural aspects of a folding intermediate with atomic-level resolution were reported for apo-myoglobin (Figure 2). Peter Wright and his colleagues developed the 2D NMR detected quenched-flow hydrogen exchange pulse labeling method, which can monitor the formation of backbone hydrogen bonds with millisecond time resolution, to elucidate the structure of early folding intermediates. They found the A-, B-, G- and H-helices, which had been known to be formed in the equilibrium molten globule state, were already formed in the refolding intermediate of apo-myoglobin [20].

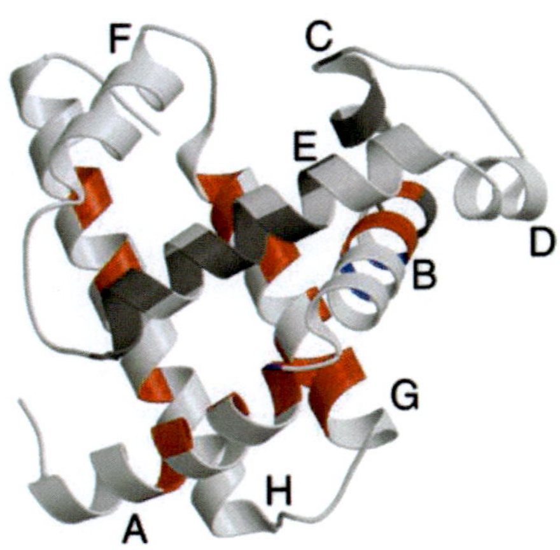

Figure 2. Kinetically detected "molten globule" state of apo-myoglobin. Residues structured in the kinetic intermediate state are colored on the three dimensional structure of myoglobin [160]. Red, fast folding residues within 6 ms; Blue, medium folding residues that are slightly structured; Grey, slow folding residues showing no protection against the pulsed HX. Data are taken from Jennings and Wright [20]. Drawn by Molscript [161] and Raster3D [162].

The simple two-state kinetics represented by a single exponential curve does not prove the absence of intermediates on the reaction pathway, and indeed many proteins have "hidden" intermediates showing apparent two-state kinetic behaviors, depending on relative stabilities of the denatured and intermediate states [21]. One of the strictest criteria for the two-state folding mechanism is obtained by collecting many kinetic traces under multiple refolding (and unfolding) conditions with systematically altered denaturing strengths. Dilution of a high concentration of denaturant to a particular concentration gives the rate a constant for refolding (k_f) at the intended denaturant concentration. Similarly, the rate constant for unfolding (k_u) at a particular denaturant concentration can be measured by a concentration jump of denaturant from zero to the intended concentration. For many proteins, it is found that logarithms of the refolding rate constants at low denaturant concentrations and those of the unfolding rate constants at high denaturant concentrations depend linearly on the final denaturant concentration. Thus, a plot of logarithm of the apparent rate constant ($k_{app} = k_f + k_u$) against the final denaturant concentration, often called a chevron plot, demonstrates a V-shaped curve if the reaction goes through a single transition between the native and denatured states (Figure 3). The downward deviation from the chevron plot (sometimes referred to as "rollover") implies the presence of a "hidden" intermediate(s) even in an apparent two-state kinetics with a single exponential time course.

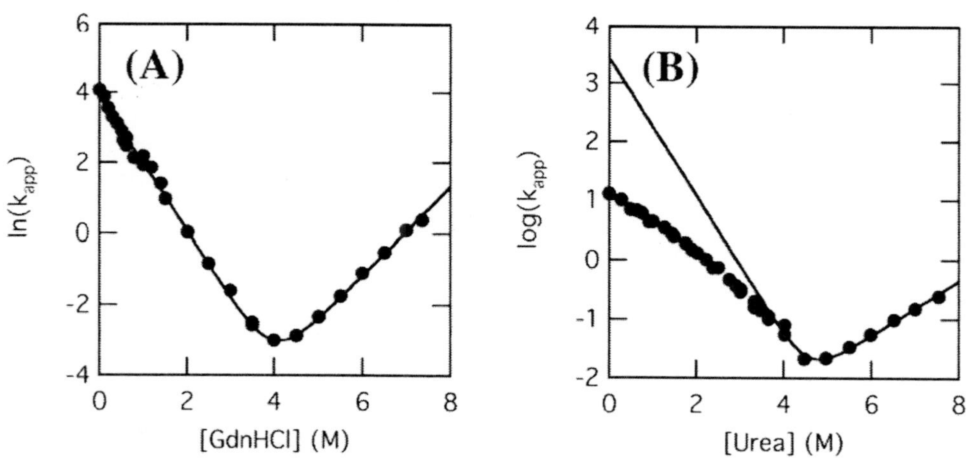

Figure 3. (A) Chevron plot of a two-state folding protein, chymotrypsin inhibitor 2. Characteristic "V-shape" demonstrates the lack of any kinetic intermediate in the refolding and unfolding reactions of this protein. Solid line is the theoretical curve on the assumption of two-state folding. (B) Chevron plot of barnase. Deviation from the theoretical curve is seen as "rollover" at low urea concentrations, indicating the presence of a "hidden" intermediate. Solid line is the theoretical curve on the assumption of two-state folding. Data are taken from Jackson and Fersht [163].

Folding Pathways

Observation of folding intermediates is ubiquitous. Many multi-domain proteins exhibit kinetic profiles with multiple exponential phases. Some small proteins show an apparent single phase refolding kinetics, while a rollover in the chevron plot reveals the presence of a "hidden" intermediate(s). It appears that these intermediate states are characteristic key points in the process of protein folding, and thus they would define the pathway of the folding reaction.

There are, in concept, two kinds of intermediates in the course of folding reaction. One is the on-pathway intermediate represented by,

$$[D]\underset{k_{ID}}{\overset{k_{DI}}{\rightleftarrows}}[I]\underset{k_{NI}}{\overset{k_{IN}}{\rightleftarrows}}[N] \qquad \text{(Scheme 1)}$$

and the other is the off-pathway intermediate given by,

$$[I]\underset{k_{ID}}{\overset{k_{DI}}{\rightleftarrows}}[D]\underset{k_{NI}}{\overset{k_{IN}}{\rightleftarrows}}[N] \qquad \text{(Scheme 2)}$$

A well-known nature of protein misfolding into aggregation suggests the presence of off-pathway intermediates. In principle, two apparent rate constants should be observable in each model, but practically, only one overall rate constant is measured due to too fast conversion between I and D that cannot be resolved by conventional stopped-flow methods. Thus, an apparent two-state process describes such a kinetic profile, and the accumulation of the intermediate is manifested by the discontinuity in kinetic trace at the starting data point. This, so-called burst phase amplitude, reflects the population of I that is accumulated within the dead time of measurement, which provides the equilibrium constant between D and I. While the rate constant of refolding is proportional to f_I, the fractional concentration of I, in the on-pathway model, whereas it is proportional to $(1 - f_I)$ in the off-pathway model. That is, accumulation of I has an opposite effect on the apparent folding rate, k_f, between the on-pathway model and off-pathway model. Even though the structural details of such an intermediate are unclear, increasing evidence suggests that the intermediate is more compact than the fully denatured state under the strongly denaturing conditions. Accordingly, increasing concentration of denaturant would stabilize D compared to I, which leads to a decreased population of I at the starting point on the refolding detection. Based on this assumption, we can judge whether the intermediate is on-pathway or off-pathway; the presence of rollover with a positive slope in chevron plot means an increase in folding rate at higher denaturant concentrations, that is accumulation of the off-pathway intermediate.

Another criterion to distinguish between the on-pathway and the off-pathway intermediates is given by a comparison between the conformational conversion rate from the intermediate to the native state and that from the intermediate to the denatured state; if the intermediate folds to the native state are faster than when it goes back to the unfolded state, then the intermediate should be kinetically on-pathway. Based on this criterion, the folding intermediate state of cytochrome c is confirmed to be kinetically on the folding pathway [22].

When the folding reaction involves an intermediate state, the whole reaction might be described by a trianglular kinetic scheme as below.

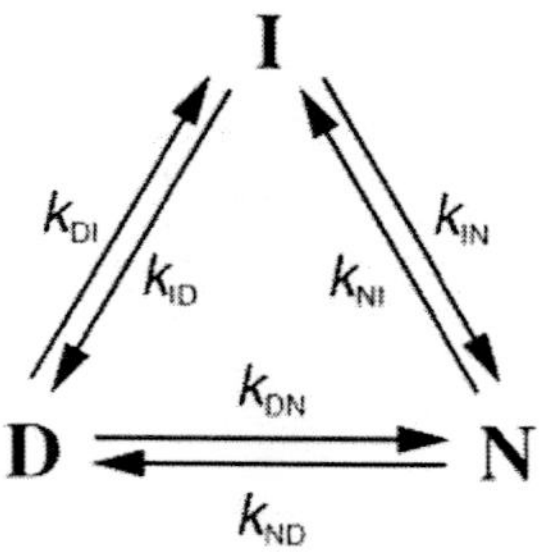

(Scheme 3)

In one example, apoflavodoxin shows a slow overall refolding kinetics, where the equilibrium between U and I is slow enough to separate the kinetic phases. Mathematical analyses of possible three-species kinetic models similar to those described above concluded that apoflavodoxin folds *via* a triangular, but virtually an off-pathway mechanism, in which microscopic rate constants for direct conversion between I and N is very small compared to the other rate constants [23].

It is, in practice, quite difficult to describe the folding pathway unambiguously, because all three possible kinetic pathways (schemes 1-3) would provide not more than two apparent kinetic rate constants, regardless of the number of microscopic rate constants involved. In addition, it is very difficult to simultaneously determine both the population of the intermediate(s) at a given time and signal amplitude of the transiently populated intermediate(s) so that fractional signal contribution of the intermediate state to the observed apparent amplitude cannot be resolved. To address this issue, Thomas Kiefhaber performed a double-jump kinetic experiment to analyze the folding kinetics of hen lysozyme in detail [24]. In this experiment, initially unfolded protein was diluted into the native conditions to start refolding. After a given time, the refolded protein (mixture of the native and intermediate states) was transferred back to denatured conditions. Due to the large energy barrier between the native state and others, the unfolding from the native states is slow (~20 sec), while partially folded intermediates unfold within a few milliseconds. Thus, the amplitude of the slow unfolding reaction as a function of refolding time estimates the accumulation of the native state, exclusive of any intermediate states. By analyzing the dependency of the folding rate constants on the denaturant concentrations, they concluded that a triangular kinetic model with alternative pathways best explains the experimental results. Thus, a rather complicated scenario emerged from the folding of lysozyme: while about 80% of initially denatured molecules fold *via* an intermediate state (slow track), the rest of the molecules fold directly to the native states. Such kinetic complexities must arise from heterogeneity of the unfolded state.

What is the determinant of the folding pathway? Comparisons of the folding kinetics between homologue proteins suggested that global fold is not a key determinant in defining the folding pathway. For example, refolding of a four-helix protein Im7 and that of its homologue Im9 show a three-state kinetics and a two state kinetics, respectively [25] Similarly, very different folding pathways were suggested between a β-clam fold protein, ileal lipid binding protein (ILBP) and its homologue, intestinal fatty acid binding protein (IFABP) [26]. It appears that relative stability of the intermediate form plays an important role in defining the folding kinetics. Indeed, stabilization of non-native interactions in Im9 by inducing mutations, even a single mutation, dramatically changed its refolding kinetics from two state to three state [27]. Remarkably, replacing the core residues between ILBP and IFABP swapped their folding pathways [28], highlighting the importance of the stable intermediate formation in defining the folding pathway.

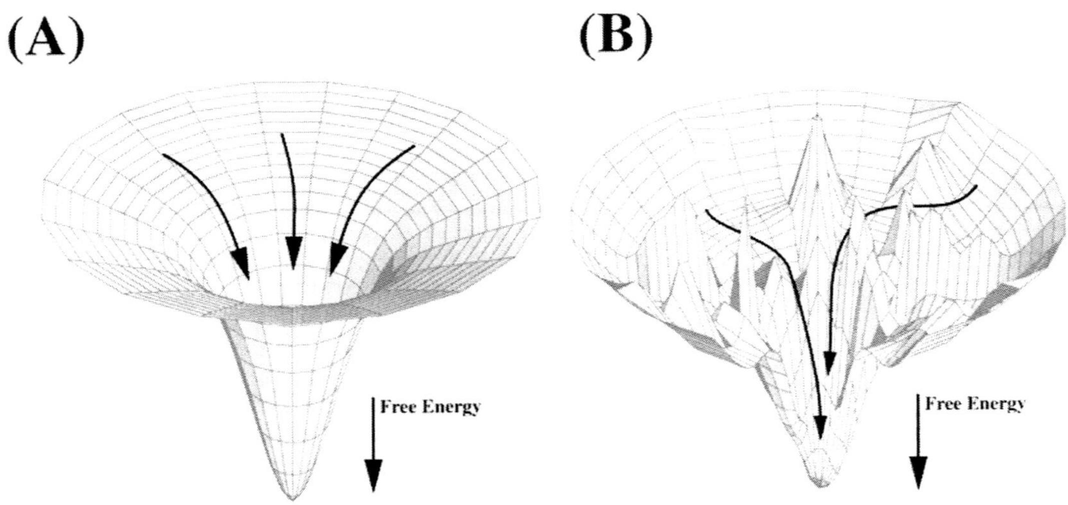

Figure 4. Schematic drawing of a free energy landscape for a hypothetical protein. The vertical axis represents energy level. The horizontal dimension represents conformational space. The bottom of the funnel typically corresponds to the native state. Arrows indicate possible pathways for folding.

Energy Landscape Theory

While a protein in the native state has the unique conformation, other states should be regarded as ensembles of a large number of conformations. If a polypeptide chain of 150-residue long performs a random conformational search in the whole conformational space that is theoretically accessible, it would take cosmological time to reach the native state. In reality, however, many proteins about this size fold into their native states in seconds or much less. These contradictory propositions by Cyrus Levinthal are known as the Levinthal's paradox [29], attracting people's interests towards protein folding problems. One of the attractive ideas to solve this problem is that a protein folds *via* a particular pathway with an obligate intermediate state(s), such as molten globule state, by which the conformational space to be searched becomes dramatically reduced. Since it was shown for many proteins that the kinetic intermediates with similar structural properties to that of the equilibrium molten globule state were populated in the process of folding, the molten globule hypothesis and the concept of the folding pathway have been widely accepted as the general solution for the Levinthal's paradox. In contrast, the "new view" for protein folding has emerged in the late 1990s based on the theoretical calculations using lattice simulations [30, 31]. In this theory, the energy landscape for protein folding can be represented as a smooth funnel-like shape, and the folding reaction towards the native structure can be viewed as a downhill conformational search on the energy surface. This theory precludes the concept of the pathway because each protein molecule can reach to the native conformation *via* an arbitrary "pathway". In the meantime, successive findings of very rapid folders without any populated intermediate state invoked an argument that the accumulation of intermediate(s), such as molten globule, may not be an obligated process, but a "trapped" state that retards the whole process of protein folding. These proteins are typically smaller than 10-15 KDa, and the energy landscape in this case would be described by a simplified smooth funnel (Figure 4A). On the other hand, folding behaviors of medium sized proteins, such as α-lactalbumin and apo-myoglobin described above, are well explained by the concept of a folding pathway; i.e., protein architecture is built up through a particular pathway with specific intermediate(s). Energy landscape theory can describe such a complicated mechanism with a more rugged surface as shown in Figure 4B.

While the landscape theory conceptually explains the protein folding reaction most successfully, drawing of the energy landscape with experimentally determined parameters is a very demanding challenge. In this respect, Shohei Koide and his colleagues have demonstrated a noteworthy approach to experimentally illustrate the energy landscape of a 28KDa protein, OspA [32]. OspA is a predominantly β-sheet protein consists of the N-terminal and C-terminal globular domains that are connected with a unique single-layer β-sheet (Figure 5). Its folding reaction involves multiple intermediate states [33], and, therefore, this protein is a good target for the ambitious attempt of sketching energy landscape. They employed a native-state hydrogen/deuterium exchange (HX) method, a powerful NMR technique that measures the HX rates of backbone amide protons in the native state upon rapid solvent replacement from a standard buffer to a deuterium buffer and vice versa [34] (see review such as Krishna et al. [35]). In general, the observed HX rate for each residue can be expressed as follows:

$$NH_{close} \underset{k_{cl}}{\overset{k_{op}}{\rightleftarrows}} NH_{open} \xrightarrow{k_{int}} ND \qquad [1]$$

$$k_{obs} = \frac{k_{op}k_{int}}{k_{op} + k_{cl} + k_{int}} \qquad [2]$$

where NH_{close} and NH_{open} denote the "close" and "open" sites that are exchange-protected or exchange-competent, respectively. k_{obs} is the observed HX rate, k_{op} and k_{cl} are the opening and closing rate, respectively, and k_{int} is intrinsic HX rate.

It is well known that k_{int} is highly dependent on pH and the value for each amino acid at pH of interest can be estimated from a dataset in literature [36]. When k_{cl} is considerably smaller than k_{int} ($k_{cl} << k_{int}$), which is referred to as the EX1 regime, k_{obs} is equal to k_{op}. In contrast, when k_{int} is considerably smaller than k_{cl} ($k_{int} << k_{cl}$), referred to as the EX2 regime, k_{obs} is proportional to the equilibrium constant between the closed and open forms, and therefore thermodynamic stability, ΔG_{HX}, can be obtained as follows.

$$\Delta G_{HX} = RT\, ln(k_{cl}/k_{op}) = RT\, ln(k_{int}/k_{obs}) \qquad [3]$$

Accordingly, comparison of the EX1 and EX2 data allows determination of k_{op} and k_{cl} for each residue. Yan et al., realized an approximately 100 fold dynamic range for k_{int} by changing pH from 5.5 to 7.5, as an increase of one pH unit boosts up k_{int} about 10 fold [32].

Thus, the authors obtained thermodynamic and kinetic parameters for OspA at residue-level resolution (i.e. ΔG_{HX}, $m(\Delta G_{HX})$, k_{cl}, $m(k_{cl})$, k_{op}, $m(k_{op})$, ΔG_{kin}, and m_{kin}, where m denotes so-called m-values). Careful analyses of these parameters revealed multiple cooperative folding units in OspA, and allowed them to illustrate a diagram of energy landscape of this protein (Figure 5). This work most successfully demonstrates the feasibility of experimentally drawing a complex energy landscape to date.

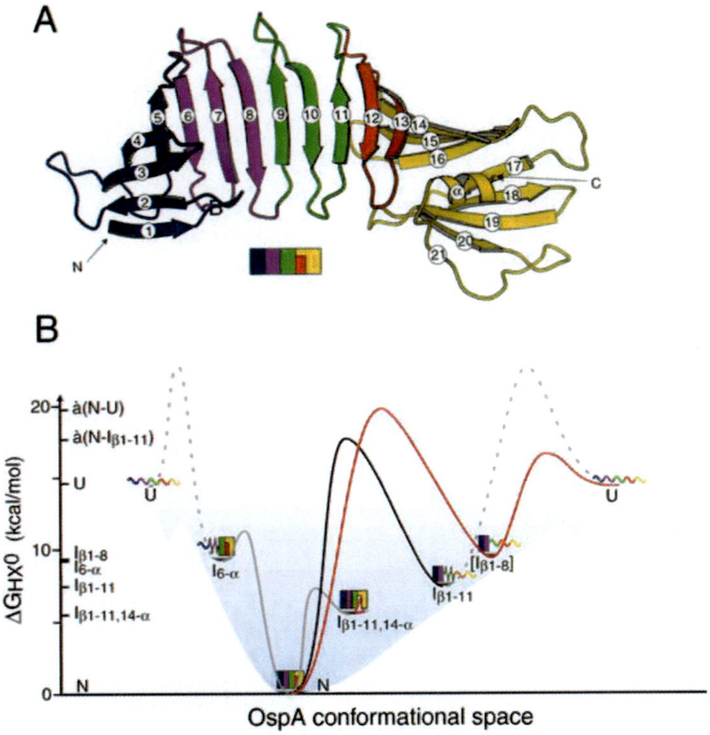

Figure 5. OspA energy landscape sketched by experimentally determined parameters. (A) Structure of OspA colored by groups of the HX rates and a rectangular model with the same color code. (B) Landscape with multiple thermodynamic states defined by kinetic barriers. Each rectangular model best describes the HX profile. Images are reprinted from *Journal of Molecular Biology*, 323, Yan, S., Kennedy, S. D., and Koide, S. Thermodynamic and kinetic exploration of the energy landscape of *Borrelia burgdorferi* OspA by native-state hydrogen exchange. 363-375 [32]. Copyright (2002) with permission from Elsevier.

The Native State, the Energy Minimum?

As represented by the energy landscape funnel, it is most widely accepted that the native state of a protein is at the global energy minimum. Nevertheless, there are several exceptions against this paradigm in protein folding. The extracellular bacterial protease, α-lytic protease (αLP) provides the best characterized counterexample. Fully denatured αLP in the presence of chemical denaturants refolds into a stable molten globule-like intermediate in the absence of the 166 amino acid pro region, and addition of this region leads to rapid conversion to the native state. Extensive studies on the kinetic and thermodynamic aspects of the folding properties of this protease revealed that the native state of αLP is less stable than both the intermediate state and the fully unfolded state [37-39]. The stability of this protein arises solely from the kinetic barrier that blocks its unfolding, and its folding is entirely dependent on the pro region, which catalyzes the folding reaction and stabilizes the native state. Similarly, metastable nature of the protein native state is reported for Streptomyces griseus protease B [40], serine protease inhibitor α1-antitrypsin [41], and Influenza membrane fusion protein hemagglutinin [42]. The peculiar metastable mechanism provides these proteins with an optimal solution, which prevents them from proteolysis. These observations emphasize subtle and profound strategies of nature for maintaining life, and suggest a possibility that some misfolded conformation may be stably present under certain conditions.

PROTEIN MISFOLDING AND INTERMEDIATES

Introduction

While the outbreak of bovine spongiform encephalopathy (BSE), also known as "mad cow disease", in Europe in 1980s caused a world-wide sensation of the "protein misfolding" issue, it has been long known that protein-containing insoluble deposits called amyloid plaques or amyloids, are commonly observed in a variety of diseases, including scrapies, kuru, Creutzfeldt-Jakob Disease, and Alzheimer's disease. An electron microscopic study in 1967 already suggested a common feature between the scrapie deposits and the amyloid plaques [43]. The infectivity of scrapies was resistant to ultraviolet radiation that breaks down nucleic acids [44], leading to a hypothesis that the prion diseases are caused by an infectious agent made solely of protein [45]. This idea was later developped by Nobel prize winner Stanley Prusiner to establish the well known "protein only hypothesis": a protein in a misfolded form could reproduce and propagate the abnormal conformation to be infectious [46]. This hypothesis was highly controversial at that time, since it contradicts the Anfinsen's dogma. However, increasing evidence supports this hypothesis at the molecular level, at least, and it has become widely accepted today. Particularly, the amyloid formation can be reproducable *in vitro* using isolated or chemically synthesized proteins and peptides, indicating that a group of proteins, at least, can spontaneously form amyloid fibrils.

Structural aspects of amyloids have been long known since the 1950-60s. In 1959, an electron microscopic study first observed fibrous morphology in the amyloid plaques [47], and in the late 1960s, two X-ray diffraction studies reported evidence for a regular structure rich in β-sheet [48, 49]. These observations suggest that amyloids are a fibrous assembly of polypeptide chains in a β-pleated manner. Later, a high-resolution X-ray diffraction study using synchrotron sources revealed that amyloid fibrils share a common substructure consisting of the "cross-β" motif regardless of the amino acid sequence [50]. Recently, a study using cryo-electron microscopy has presented high resolution images of protofibrils of insulin amyloid fibrils, which proposed a bundled cross-β filament model [51] (Figure 6). This higher order architecture in insoluble aggregates presents a good contrast to well-known behaviors of proteins forming amorphous aggregates and inclusion bodies.

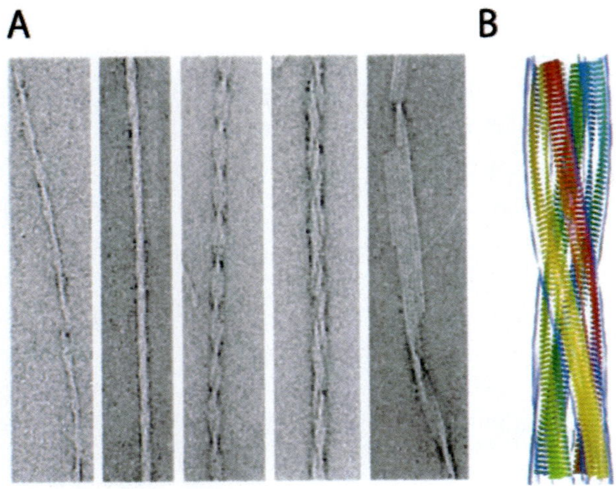

Figure 6. Cryo electron microscpic images (A) and a proposed structural model (B) of protofibrils of insulin Amyloid. Images are reprinted from *Proc Natl Acad Sci U.S.A,*, 99, Jimenez, J. L., Nettleton, E. J., Bouchard, M., Robinson, C. V., Dobson, C. M., and Saibil, H. R., The protofilament structure of insulin amyloid fibrils. 9196-9201 [51]. Copyright (2002) with permission from National Academy of Sciences, U.S.A.

Amorphous aggregates are typically caused by exposure of the hydrophobic interior of proteins upon denaturation. In some proteins, amorphous aggregates show considerable β-sheet content [52-54], however, systematic orientation of the secondary structure is usually absent. Perhaps, segments of unfolded polypeptides associate through backbone hydrogen bonds in a non-specific manner. The situation appears different in the case of inclusion bodies. Although little is known about molecular mechanisms of the inclusion body formation, studies using FTIR [55], CD and solid state NMR [56] suggest the existence of a native-like secondary structure with increased β-sheet content in the insoluble deposits. Nevertheless, it is something of a mystery that solubilized inclusion bodies with a high concentration of chemical denaturants usually do not refold easily, but precipitate again upon reduction of the denaturant concentration. Difficulty in forming disulfide bonds with the "right partners" is often discussed, but the formation of an inclusion body is not limited for proteins with intramolecular disulfide bonds, suggesting that the redox control is unlikely the critical factor in the mechanisms of inclusion body formation. Since inclusion body is formed in cell cytoplasm, it is possible that coexistence of minor fraction(s) of cytosolic molecules and/or a probable posttranslational modification prevent from complete folding into the native structure, which could lead to the *in situ* aggregation. In any case, low refolding efficiency of solubilized inclusion bodies suggests that the inclusion body cannot be described by a simple folding intermediate, and thus, the mechanisms of the inclusion body formation appear distinct from those of amyloid formation, as well as those of amorphous aggregation, both take place during dynamic processes of protein folding and unfolding [57, 58]. Hereafter, we focus on the mechanisms of amyloid formation in reference to canonical protein folding processes. First, we review studies on *in vitro* protein misfolding into amyloid fibrils for several well-characterized proteins.

Examples of Protein Misfolding into Amyloid Fibrils

Prions

Prion protein (PrP) in mammalian organisms has attracted keen interest because of its relation to a group of invariably fatal neurodegenerative diseases, i.e., the transmissible spongiform encephalopathies (TSEs), which include scrapie in sheep, BSE, Creutzfeldt–Jakob disease, and kuru in humans. The most important event in the origins of these diseases is thought that the normal cellular isoform of the prion protein, PrP^C converts into the abnormal pathological isoform, PrP^{Sc}. This conversion involves a substantial conformational change: PrP^C is an α-helical monomeric protein that is sensitive to proteinase K (PK) digestion, whereas PrP^{Sc} is an assembled multimer characterized by enhanced resistance to PK-digestion and a higher content of β-structure [59, 60]. Similar behavior of infectious conformational conversion has been reported for some proteins in yeast. They are referred to as yeast prions, although, not functionally or structurally related to mammalian prions. Sup35 and Ure2 are the best characterized yeast prions, and they have glutamine- and asparagine-rich regions in common. Several studies have pointed out the important role of this polar region on the formation of amyloid fibrils [61-63].

Mammalian prions in the native state (PrP^C) consist of an N-terminal flexible tail with about 100 residues and a C-terminal globular domain of about 110 residues. In contrast to the glutamine- and asparagine-rich tendency in the flexible tail of yeast prions, glycine is remarkably abundant in the flexible tail of the mammalian prion. Deletion of the N-terminal tail apparently reduces the ability of the conformational conversion from PrP^C to PrP^{Sc}, but the conversion cannot be totally inhibited [64]. The high resolution structure of the PrP^C C-terminal domain was first reported by Kurt Wüthrich and his coworkers through NMR methods on a recombinant mouse protein [65] (Figure 7). Subsequently, NMR structures of a series of mammalian prion C-terminal domains have been published; e.g. hamster [66], human [67], cattle [68], cats, dogs, pigs and sheep [69]. These prions essentially share the same structural feature: the flexible N-terminal tail about 100 residue long and the predominantly α-helical C-terminal domain with three α-helices and a short β-sheet.

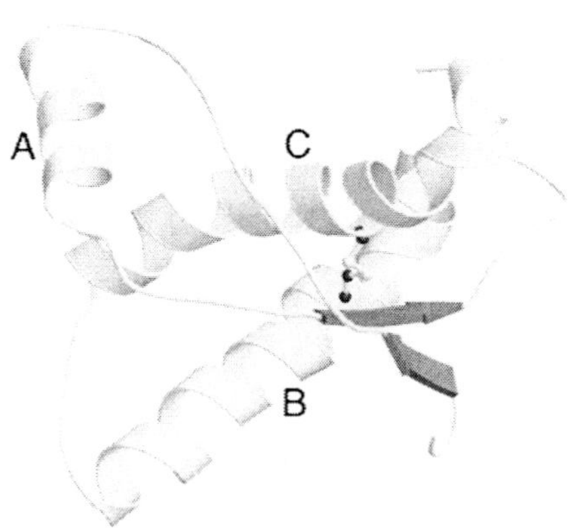

Figure 7. Three dimensional structure of the C-terminal fragment of the mouse prion protein in the PrP^C form determined by NMR [65]. Two cysteins forming an intramolecular disulfide bond are marked with ball-and-stick.

Main chain dynamics of the PrP^C structure has been studied in detail by the NMR spin relaxation techniques. The central portions of helices B and C form a relatively rigid core, but very fast dynamics motion with the picosecond-to-nanosecond time scale was detected in the remainder of the globular domain and helix A, suggesting that packing of the latter regions is less tight [70, 71]. The core region around helices B and C shows a slower fluctuation in the microsecond-to-millisecond time scale [72]. These results complementarily support their earlier results from a high-pressure NMR study on the PrP^C that local disorder in this core region was explicitly demonstrated [73]. These NMR results highlight a unique nature of the protein that the rigid core region around helix B and C is less robust than relatively flexible regions including helix A.

The PrP C-terminal globular domain reversibly unfolds in the presence of chemical denaturants. Kinetic studies on mouse PrP^C revealed unusually high folding and unfolding rates with no detectable folding intermediates at physiological pH [74]. While a NMR based HX study on human PrP^C could not detect accumulation of any partially unfolded intermediates in its conformational equilibrium [67], the authors found the existence of a residual structure in a small region around the disulfide bond between helix B and C in the fully unfolded state. This suggests that the residual structure in this region plays an important role in the conformational conversion from PrP^C to PrP^{Sc}. The authors concluded that the misfolding conversion unlikely occurred from a partially unfolded state, but rather from a largely unfolded state. This process appears distinct from those for other proteins, in which amyloid fibrils are presumably formed through a partially unfolded intermediate(s). It is possible that the core region implicated by the residual structure in the fully unfolded state might interact with some structural elements of the protein in the partially unfolded intermediate, which disfavors conformational conversion to PrP^{Sc}. The difference in the mechanisms for fibril formation is also suggested by a set of mutagenesis studies, where increased tendency for amyloid fibril formation upon mutation did not always accompany decrease in protein stability [75].

Although PrP unfolds *via* two-state mechanism at physiological pH, an alternative folding pathway was observed at acidic pH. Studies on recombinant human PrP [76] and mouse PrP [77] detected an equilibrium folding intermediate around pH 4.0 that shows a high content of β-sheet and a partial resistance to PK-digestion [78]. This monomeric intermediate reversibly associates into an oligomeric structure with a high content of β-strands (β-oligomer), but does not further associate into the amyloid fibrils. Therefore, it is unlikely that the β-olibomer is on the kinetic pathway to amyloid formation. As mentioned above, PrP^{Sc}, i.e. the abnormal form of PrP, was originally defined by resistance to PK-digestion in pathogenic diagnoses, and therefore this nomenclature does not represent detailed structural aspects of the protein. As a matter of fact, the structure of the β-oligomer is distinct from that of the amyloid fibrils, although the soluble oligomer shares some hallmarks of the amyloids [79]. In contrast to the high order assembly of polypeptides in the latter form, the β-oligomer is predominantly octameric, as evidenced by electron spray ionization mass spectrometry. Moreover, an antibody binding site of the β-oligomer shows a significant resistance to PK - digestion in the amyloid fibrils, suggesting that this region is buried in the latter form.

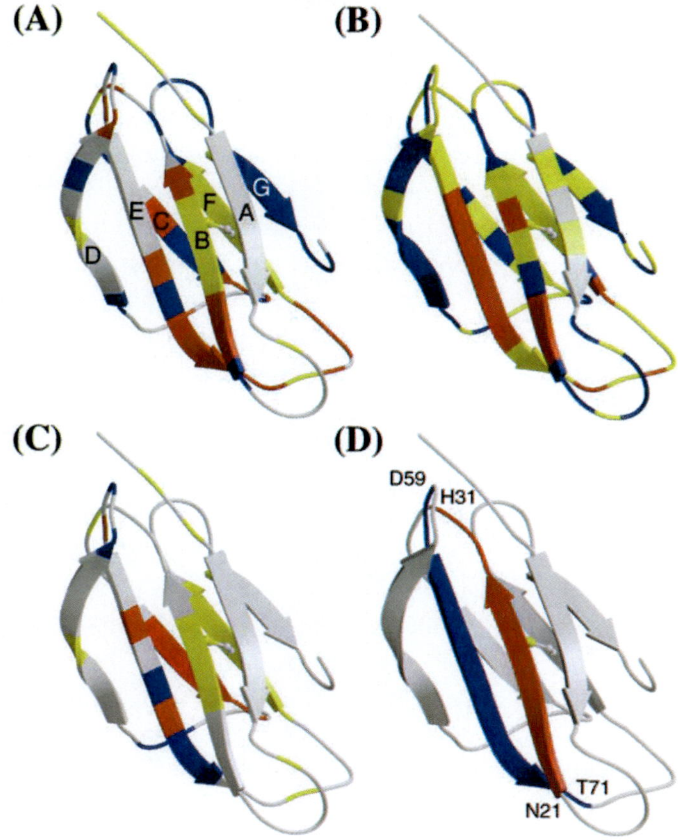

Figure 8. Comparison of the key residues for the amyloid fibril formation of β2m. (A) Core residues in thick, straight fibrils revealed by the DMSO-quenched-HX [88]. Residues with strong, medium and weak HX protection in the fibrilar state are indicated by red, blue and white, respectively. Residues of which HX profile was unavailable are indicated by yellow. (B) Structural properties in the amyloidogenic intermediate at pH 3.6 detected by a urea titration [89]. While the intermediate form shows severe overall line broadening due to intermediary dynamic motion, signals from residues in less stable regions become stronger upon the addition of urea due to increased chain dynamics. The pattern of increase in signal intensity with increased concentration of urea was classified into three groups; signals become detectable at high (red), modest (blue), and low (white) concentrations of urea. The requirement of high concentration of urea implies that the partially formed segments in the intermediate are stable. (C) Core residues in thin, curved filamentous structure detected by the DMSO-quenched-HX [90]. Color code is same as that in panel (A). (D) Minimal sequences for amyloid fibril formation of β2m. Two segments of peptide fragments known to form amyloid fibrils are marked in red and blue.

β2-microglobulin

β2-Microglobulin (β2m) is the light chain of the class I major histocompatibility (MHC) complex. It is a 12 kDa protein composed of 99 amino acids that forms a typical immunoglobulin domain fold, in which seven β-strands forms two β-sheets connected by a single disulfide bond between Cys25 and Cys80 (Figure 8). It is found as a major component of amyloid fibrils from patients of the dialysis-related amyloidosis, which is a common and serious complication in patients receiving long-term hemodialysis for more than 10 years [80,

81]. While the amyloid fibril formation of β2m *in vitro* occurs efficiently in a seed dependent manner at pH 2.5, the fibril formation is generally not observable at neutral pH. In addition, the fibrils formed at acidic pH easily depolymerize into monomers by increasing pH to neutral. Interestingly, low concentration of chemical agents such as trifluoroethanol, glycosaminoglycans and sodium dodecyl sulfate suppress the depolymerization at neutral pH, and the seeds prepared from these pH insensitive fibrils enhanced the fibril formation at neutral pH in the presence of these chemicals [82, 83]. This suggests that the fibril formation of β2m is potentially a reversible reaction with a high kinetic barrier, and that some chemical agents critically affect the kinetic barrier. Moreover, agitation remarkably enhances spontaneous fibril formation of β2m, and thus formed fibrils act as seeds for further fibril formation. These behaviors appear distinct from those observed in the process of amyloid fibril formation of other proteins, and therefore, involvement of other factors in the amyloid formation of β2m *in vivo* is discussed; e.g. truncation of N-terminal six residues [84], role of amyloid associated proteins, such as apolipoprotein E (apoE) [85], and specific Cu^{2+} ion binding to histidine residue [86]. In particular, a NMR spin relaxation study of β2m in the native form demonstrated an increased main chain dynamics upon Cu^{2+} binding, suggesting a possible role of copper in dialysis-related amyloids [87].

Yuji Goto and his coworkers mapped the β2m amyloid core region through a quenched hydrogen/deuterium exchange (HX) technique, where hydrogen exchanged amyloid fibrils were dissolved in a dimethyl sulfoxide (DMSO) solution, so that further HX reactions are quenched and the extent of HX is directly mapped on the monomeric protein [88]. This approach, referred to as DMSO-quenched HX method revealed that the amyloid core region consists of four strands B, E, C, G and flexible loop regions (Figure 8A). Sheena Radford and coworkers reported complementary results on a partially denatured form of β2m, in which the similar region to the core region identified by the Goto's group remained structured in the folding intermediate form [89] (Figure 8B). The remarkable consensus in the well-structured area around strands B and E, the modestly structured area around strands C and G, and the poorly structured area around strand A, between the amyloid fibrils and the monomeric folding intermediate, strongly suggests that this intermediate state can be regarded as a key turning point to the native form, or to the amyloid fibrils, which links two distinct schemes of protein folding and protein misfolding.

While various conditions are found to promote the amyloid fibril formation of β2m, the resulted fibrils are classified into at least two groups by morphology. One is a thick, straight, "needle-like" fibril with a diameter of ~10nm, and left-handed regular helical twists are visible on electron microscopy or atomic force microscopy [90] (Figure 9A). The other is a thin, curved, "noodle-like" filamentous structure with a diameter of ~5nm, which appears similar to protofibrils reported for other proteins that eventually grow into mature amyloid fibrils [90] (Figure 9B). However, these two types of fibrils are grown under different conditions and the conversion between them has never been observed.

Two different segments in the β2m polypeptide chain are known as a minimal region for the amyloid fibril formation. The 13 residue fragment from Asp59 to Thr71 corresponding to the strand E in the native form is capable of forming rigid straight fibrils similar to those formed by the whole protein [91]. This segment contains a consecutive aromatic and hydrophobic stretch (^{62}FYLLYY^{67}) that showed the highest HX protection in the partially denatured β2m in the presence of urea at pH 3.6 [89]. On the other hand, a proteolytic study on the amyloid fibrils of the full-length β2m identified that the 22-residue fragment from Ser20 to Lys41, corresponding to strands B and C in the native form has a remarkable tendency to form rigid "needle-like" fibrils [92]. The shorter version (Asn21-His31) of this peptide is also known to form rigid amyloid fibers [93]. These N-terminal fragments contain Cys25, which forms a disulfide bond with Cys80 in the native protein. The Cys25-Cys80 disulfide bond appears essential for the formation of rigid straight fibrils, as the reduced whole length polypeptide forms flexible and curved filaments [90]. However, formation of the rigid straight fibrils by the Ser20-Lys41 peptide is independent from the redox state of Cys25 [94]. The DMSO-quenched HX study revealed that most of the residues in the Ser20-Lys41 peptide form strong H-bonds in the rigid "needle-like" fibrils. Although information regarding the H-bond pattern in the curved filaments, formed by the reduced β2m is not available, the same HX approach on "noodle-like" β2m filaments formed at a high salt concentration detected that only a limited number of residues excluding those in the Asn21-His31 region form H-bonds [95]. In addition, NMR relaxation study of the acid denatured monomeric form of β2m, i.e., the precursors of the amyloid fibrils, revealed dramatically increased backbone dynamics in the Asn21-His31 and other regions upon cleavage of the Cys25-Cys80 disulfide bond [90]. Therefore, it is likely that cleavage of the single disulfide bond increases flexibility of the whole chain so that the core Asn21-His31 segment interacts with other regions of the polypeptide chain, causing a slight disorder upon tight molecular packing in the rigid fibrils.

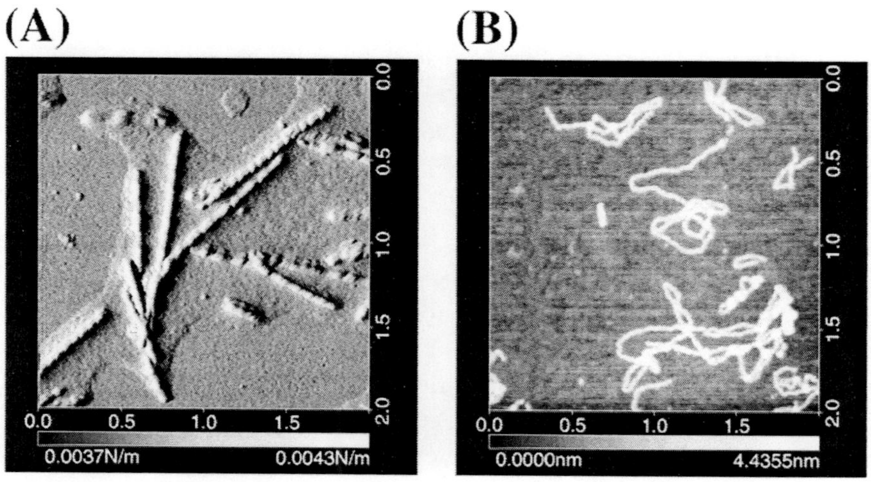

Figure 9. AFM images of amyloid fibrils of β2-microglobulin. (A) Thick, straight, "needle-like" rigid fibrils formed by the intact protein in the presence of 100 mM NaCl at pH 2.5 and 25C. (B) Thin, curved, "noodle-like" filamentous structure formed by a disulfide reduced protein under the same conditions as those used for the intact protein. Images are taken from *Protein Science*, 11, Katou, H., Kanno, T., Hoshino, M., Hagihara, Y., Tanaka, H., Kawai, T., Hasegawa, K., Naiki, H., and Goto, Y., The role of disulfide bond in the amyloidogenic state of beta(2)-microglobulin studied by heteronuclear NMR., 2218-2229. [90] Copyright (2002) with permission from Cold Spring Harbor Laboratory Press.

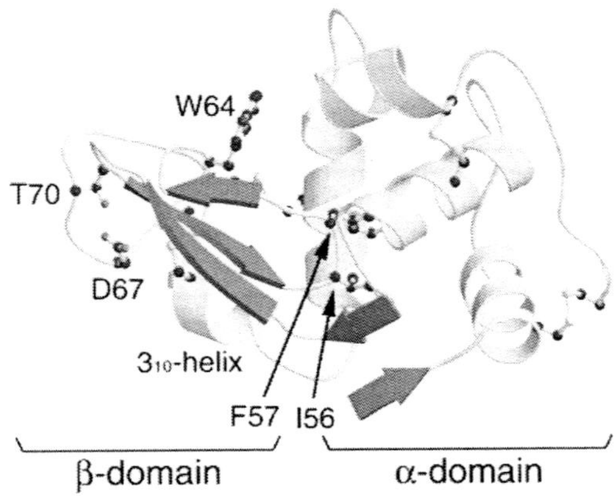

Figure 10. Three dimensional structure of human lysozyme. Mutation sites shown in amyloidgenic mutants (I56T, F57I, W64R, D67H), and that in non-amyloidgenic mutant (T70N) are marked with ball-and-stick.

Human Lysozyme

Human lysozyme is a 130 residue long α+β protein that consists of two domains (α and β domains). The α domain has a large hydrophobic core surrounded by four α-helices, and the β domain is mainly composed by a β-sheet (Figure 10). A few types of mutant human lysozymes, i.e., I56T, F57I, W64R, and D67H have been identified in patients of autosomal dominant hereditary amyloidoses that leads to death by the fifth decade [96-99]. The residues, 56 and 57 are located on the interface of the two domains, while the residues, 64 and 67 are located in the β domain. X-ray crystallography on I56T and D67H revealed that these amyloidogenic mutants share almost identical structure to the wild-type lysozyme except for minor deviations in the vicinity of the mutation sites [100, 101]. In contrast, thermodynamic and kinetic analyses found significantly decreased stability for the mutant lysozymes [100, 101], while the origin of the instability of these mutants appears different between the two variants; one case primarily destabilized by a reduction of the folding rate, while the other by an increased unfolding rate [102]. These results suggest that enhanced partial denaturation upon mutation is responsible for amyloid fibril formation. Subsequent studies on other amyloidogenic variants lead to the same conclusion [103-105]. The conclusion is further supported by direct observation of partial unfolding by HX study on the amyloidogenic variant D67H; this variant exhibits a significantly increased level of fluctuation in the β-domain, but not in the α-domain [106]. Similarly, a folding intermediate with a local disorder around the same β-domain region was detected in the refolding kinetics of another amyloidogenic mutant, I56T [107]. The key role of structural perturbation in the β-domain on the fibril formation is further supported by a protein engineering study, where insertion of the EAEA sequence in the β-domain resulted in a remarkably enhanced amyloidogenicity [108]. Moreover, peptide fragments derived from the corresponding β-sheet region in hen lysozyme exhibit a remarkable ability of amyloid fibril formation [109, 110]. These observations lead to the postulate that the β-sheet region likely plays a key role in the formation of amyloid fibrils, but that this region is secured for the misfolding reaction by interactions with other segments of the β-domain. A structural perturbation in the β-domain is necessary for the amyloid fibril formation of human lysozyme, probably because such unfavorable interactions to the misfolding need to be diminished.

The naturally occurring T70N variant is non-amyloidogenic, providing a good reference to the amyloidogenic variants [111]. Compared to the wild-type human lysozyme, this non-amyloidogenic mutant is less active, less stable and less protected in the hydrogen/deuterium exchange. However, residues in the 3_{10}-helix of this mutant show a significantly higher level of HX protection than those in the wild-type protein, suggesting that this region plays a key role on restricting further conformational fluctuation beyond a certain level to allow competitive formation of amyloid fibrils. These results suggest that destabilizing mutations do not always lead to amyloid fibril formation and that a particular intermediate structure is required for fibril formation.

α-synuclein

Parkinson's disease (PD) is a common neurodegenerative disease accompanied by movement disorder. Presence of deposits called Lewy bodies is one of the pathogenic hallmarks of PD, and α-synuclein is a major structural component of the spherical inclusion. This 140-residue neuronal protein is produced in the nerve cells involved in the dopamine pathway. In the normal cells, α-synuclein binds to another protein called ubiquitin, leading to its breakdown by the proteosome machinery. In the abnormal cells from the PD patients, on the other hand, α-synuclein fails to bind to ubiquitin, which results in accumulation of aggregated α-synuclein in Lewy bodies. The amino acid sequence of this protein shows unique features of low overall hydrophobicity and large net charge, and thereby its tertiary structure is not well defined so that this protein is recognized as one of so-called "natively unfolded proteins" [112]. The central region (around V63-V95) of this protein is relatively rich in hydrophobic residues, and mutational analyses have demonstrated that this hydrophobic region is important for the amyloid fibril formation of α-synuclein [113, 114].

The protein under near-physiological conditions contains a very little amount of regular secondary structures [115-117]. This state represents a conformational ensemble of monomeric, dynamic and expanded conformers, but the addition of 8M urea further expands the protein [118]. Increasing the temperature modestly, or changing pH to acidic leads to the accumulation of a relatively compact intermediate form that shows an increased level of α-helix content. Population of this intermediate conformer in the conformational equilibrium appears to correlate well with the rate of the conversion to amyloid fibrils, suggesting that this intermediate state plays a key role on the amyloid formation of α-synuclein.

Disease-Unrelated Proteins under Artificially Introduced Conditions

The aggregating nature of proteins has been long known, especially under the conditions where the proteins are more or less destabilized. Nevertheless, few people thought that not only the formation of amorphous aggregates, but also that of amyloid-like fibrils may be a common feature of proteins until the series of demonstrations by Christopher Dobson and his coworkers. They first demonstrated that the SH3 domain of the α-subunit of bovine phosphatidylinositol-3-kinase (PI3-SH3), which has no-relevance to amyloid disease, formed amyloid fibrils, not amorphous aggregates, under acidic conditions where this protein is partially denatured [119]. Subsequently, they reported amyloid fibril formations of other disease-unrelated proteins under artificially induced conditions: e.g. fragments from cold-shock protein B in the presence of a low polarity solvent [120], human muscle acylphosphatase in the presence of trifluoroethanol [121], hen lysozyme in the presence of an organic solvent at acidic pH [110], cytochrome c by substitutions of two Cys residues essential for the formation of the haem group [122] and apo-myoglobin incubated at a basic pH, 65°C [123]. These conditions are almost exclusively harsh to these proteins, inducing partially denatured intermediate forms. These proteins have a variety of secondary structure organization in their native states. While the SH3 domain and cold shock protein B have all β structure, hen lysozyme and acylphosphatase have an α+β fold. Remarkably, cytochrome c and myoglobin have all α structure. Thus, these demonstrations support the hypothesis that the potential for amyloid fibril formation may be a common property of all proteins [124, 125].

Common Features Found in Amyloid Fibril Formation

As suggested from the case studies above, it is quite unlikely that some specific sequence(s) and/or specific structural feature(s) in the native state are general key factors to the amyloid formation. Instead, partial denaturation, in all likelihood, must be an important factor. The most obvious feature of partial denaturation is loose packing of the polypeptide chain that makes the chain more dynamic, which must be necessary to induce a large conformational conversion of the folded polypeptide chain into a β-sheet rich conformation. Indeed, increased amyloidogenicity appears to correlate with the loss of conformational stability and increased dynamics for most of the proteins. Similarly, many short peptides that lack stable packing in monomeric states are able to form amyloid fibrils. However, importantly, these propositions are not *vice versa*; destabilization does not always lead to amyloid formation, which is most remarkably represented by the example of the naturally occurring T70N mutation in human lysozyme as mentioned previously [111]. Therefore, partial denaturation may be necessary to destabilize specific structure(s), which is commonly postulated to explain above-described observations in the case studies for prion, β2m, and lysozyme: PrP^{C} requires a large degree of unfolding for the conformational conversion to PrP^{Sc}; The core Asn21-His31 region of β2m is not well structured in the noodle-like filaments; The β-domain of amyloidogenic lysozymes is perturbed in the intermediate state despite the high amyloid forming tendency of β-strand segments in isolation.

If partial denaturation could be a prerequisite for amyloid formation, would stabilization of the natively unfolded protein prevent the conformational conversion? Anthony Fink and his colleagues examined the effect of trimethylamine N-oxide (TMAO), a well-known protein stabilizer, upon the fibrillization of a natively unfolded protein, α-synuclein [116]. As expected, a high concentration of TMAO (more than 3 M) suppressed the fibril formation, although lower concentration (less than 2M) rather accelerated the fibril formation. Perhaps, lower concentration of TMAO stabilizes only the (I) form and further addition of the osmolyte results in the formation of more tightly folded species, which likely inhibited the conversion to the amyloid fibrils. The situation is a little different in case of the fibril formation of the Aβ peptide. The addition of osmolytes accelerated the fibril formation depending on the osmolyte concentration, but the level of the acceleration reached to the plateau at high osmolyte concentrations, and the fibril formation was never suppressed even at the maximum concentration. Probably, any well-defined rigid structure of the Aβ peptide in monomeric form was stabilized by the addition of the osmolytes. In this context, strong stabilization of a protein may allow the protein to pass through the turning point to the non-native conformation. Indeed, Jeffery Kelly and his colleagues succeeded in preventing amyloid fibril formation of transthyretin by stabilizing the native form *via* mutagenesis [126] as well as through the binding of small compounds that increases kinetic stability of the native state [127]. These results suggest that amyloid fibril formation is branched out from a protein folding pathway *via* a key intermediate state, which is most evidently demonstrated in the case study of β2m as described above [88, 89].

It has been long known that proteins are susceptible to aggregation when exposed under (partially) denaturing conditions for a long period. Although there are not many studies reporting structural aspects of proteins in such aggregates, a few studies have reported a substantial β-sheet content in the precipitates or gels formed upon thermal denaturation of proteins at high concentration [52-54]. Interestingly, thermal denatured aggregations of an α + β protein, monelin and those of a β-barrel protein, acidic fibroblast growth factor nFGF-1, both exhibited hallmarks of amyloid fibrils [128, 129]. However, these cases are probably exceptional, because aggregates induced upon (partial) denaturation of proteins usually lack a high order regulation of specific structures despite their elevated levels of β-sheet content. Two distinct folding intermediates of immunoglobulin light chain (VL domain) identified in the process of acid denaturation [130] may provide a perspective in this direction. This protein forms an intermediate form at pH below 3, which leads to the formation of amyloid fibrils, while at pH around 4-6 it forms another intermediate form that leads to the formation of amorphous aggregates. These distinct behaviors suggest that amyloid fibril formation is driven by different mechanisms from those for amorphous aggregation *via* different turning points.

An approach using high pressure may offer a unique perspective in studying protein association including amyloid fibrils, amorphous aggregates and inclusion bodies. High pressure destabilizes protein native conformation by acting on volume and it shifts the conformational equilibrium in favor of a lower volume conformer. Accordingly, population of disordered conformers increases under high pressure, as they have a smaller volume than the native form by solvent inaccessible cavities. In contrast to the thermal denaturation mechanism that enhances hydrophobic interaction, high pressure denaturation is driven by disfavored hydrophobic and electrostatic interactions, and thereby affect on polypeptide chain packing by a novel mechanism. This approach has been applied to protein recovery from amorphous aggregates and inclusion bodies, resulting in significant yields of rhodanese [131], human growth hormone, lysozyme, β-lactamase [132] and tailspile protein [133, 134]. Similarly, high pressure induced dissociation of β-oligomers of an amyloid precursor [135] and those of amyloid protofibrils [136, 137] have been reported. Interestingly, the dissociation of the amyloid protofibrils was reversible, while the matured fibrils were insensitive to high pressure. These observations suggest that early stages of amyloid fibril formation are under kinetic control, while growths of the immature amyloid precursors are energetically downhill processes.

Another common feature of amyloid formation is a multi-step process that consists of a slow nucleation step, followed by a molecular assembly step [138, 139]. The reaction monitored by molecular dimension typically exhibits a sigmoidal time course with a long lag phase of the nucleation step, and seeding of pre-formed fibrils diminishes the lag phase. Thus, the fibril formation proceeds in a nucleation dependent manner, which is reminiscent of crystal growth. Indeed, polypeptides align regularly in the cross-β fibrils as evidenced by X-ray diffraction patterns. Most interestingly, a set of short polar peptides derived from the yeast prion protein Sup35 form microcrystals that share hallmarks of amyloid fibrils, from which David Eisenberg and his colleagues determined the atomic structure of the core cross-β spine [140]. The structure revealed a new feature that two parallel β-sheets pack through the "steric zipper" motif; complementarily shaped asparagine and glutamine side chains pack tightly by van der Waals forces so that water molecules are excluded on this interface. This structure explains how the assembly grows with recruiting additional peptides into extremely stable amyloid fibrils.

Kinetic Model of Amyloid Fibril Formation

Here, we attempt to understand the "infectious nature" of amyloid fibril formation through a model scheme controlled by a seed as follows. While the fibril formation is initiated by the addition a "seed" or "nucleus" into the solution of monomeric proteins, soluble monomeric form does not spontaneously form amyloid fibrils in observable timescale. The fibril growth from in the presence of seed can be described by a first order kinetic model [141] as:

$$[P]+[M] \underset{koff}{\overset{kon}{\rightleftarrows}} [P] \qquad [4]$$

where [P] is the number concentration of amyloid fibrils, [M] is the concentration of the monomeric proteins, and k_{on} and k_{off} are the rate constants for polymerization and depolymerization, respectively. From equation [4], the differential equation can be derived as:

$$-\frac{d[M]}{dt} = k_{on}[P][M] - k_{off}[P] \qquad [5]$$

The equation [5] can be solved as follows, assuming constant number concentration of fibrils during the reaction.

$$[M] = \frac{k_{off}}{k_{on}} + ([M]_0 - \frac{k_{off}}{k_{on}})\exp(-k_{on}[P]_0 t) \qquad [6]$$

Here, $[M]_0$ and $[P]_0$ are the initial concentrations of monomer and polymer, respectively. From the equation [4], the system will reach the equilibrium between polymerization and depolymerization at the end of reaction, where,

$$k_{on}[P][M] = k_{off}[P] \qquad [7]$$

and thus equation [6] can be rewritten as:

$$[M] = [M]_e + ([M]_0 - [M]_e)\exp(-k_{on}[P]_0 t) \qquad [6']$$

in which $[M]_e = k_{off}/k_{on}$ is the concentration of residual monomeric protein at equilibrium.

If t is small enough, the equation [6'] can be approximated by Taylor's expansion to:

$$\begin{aligned} [M] &= [M]_0 - k_{on}([M]_0 - [M]_e)[P]_0 t \\ &= [M]_0 - k_{on}[M]_0[P]_0 t \end{aligned} \qquad [6'']$$

where the last equality is obtained by assuming $[M]_0 >> [M]_e$.

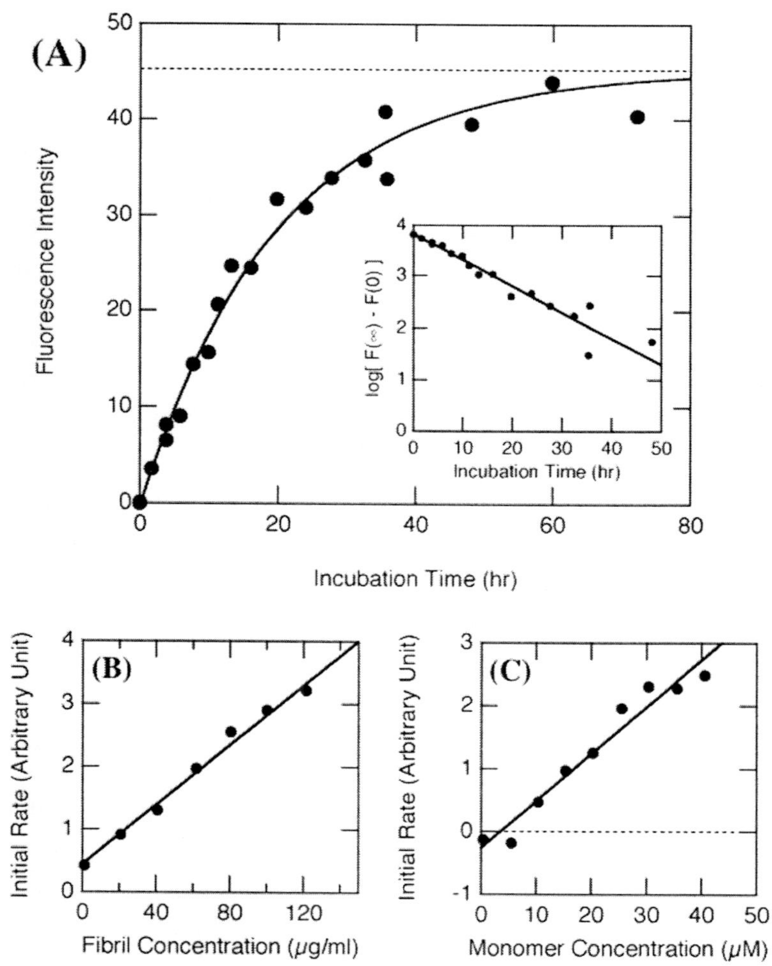

Figure 11. Amyloid fibril formation of immunoglobulin light chain analyzed by the first-order kinetic model. (A) Time course of the fibril formation monitored by the increase in fluorescence signal from thioflavin T, a dye that specifically binds to amyloid fibrils. The inset shows the linearity of the logarithm of fluorescence intensity against time. (B), (C) Linear dependence of initial rate constant for fibril formation on the initial seed concentration $[P]_0$ (B) and initial monomer concentration $[M]_0$ (C). Data are taken from Takahashi et al. [164].

Equation [6] can reproduce the experimental results in a good approximation at least for several amyloid fibrils. That is, the fibril growth can be approximated by a single exponential curve, and the initial rate of fibril formation is proportional to the concentrations of initial seed and monomer (Figure 11). However, deviation from this simple kinetic model is observed when fibril formation occurs spontaneously without seeds. Such a spontaneous fibril formation usually follows a long (typically days or weeks) lag period. This lag phase indicates a high energy barrier between monomeric form and amyloid form, and the seeds can be regarded as the catalysts that lower the high energy barrier. In the absence of preexisting fibrils, the rate-limiting step is most likely a formation of oligomers that act as a nucleolus for fibril growth. Rigorous agitation often dramatically enhances the rate of spontaneous fibril formation, suggesting that the increased probability of molecular association to form the oligomeric nucleoli.

Thus, the association of protein molecules into nucleus oligomers seems to be a critical step for the amyloid fibril formation. Although we do not know detailed structural aspects of the amyloid nuclei, they must share the fundamental architecture with the mature fibrils, which are considered as cross-β structure stabilized by regular H-bond networks. However, solvent exposed H-bonds are generally weak due to a large dielectric constant of the aqueous solvent, as well as a rapid exchange with surrounding water molecules. Therefore, additional mechanisms are likely involved in order to stabilize the nuclei. As described above, the steric zipper mechanism suggested from the crystal structure of the core cross-β of the amyloid forming peptides proposes a new mechanism [140]. The self-complementary interface of the polypeptide must be properly arranged to act as a nucleus, presenting a high energetic barrier between the amyloid fibrils and monomeric polypeptides. Once the fibrils are formed, on the other hand, the barrier to the reverse reaction, i.e., dissociation into the monomer, is even higher, resulting in extremely stable nature of amyloid fibrils.

CONCLUSION

We have highlighted the dynamic aspects of protein polypeptides that exist in conformational equilibrium between their native and unfolded states. Although we are still far from drawing a detailed picture of such a dynamic process, information from experimentally captured folding intermediates provides snapshots of the conformational ensemble. As reviewed in this chapter, for example, studying only the native states and/or the misfolded states cannot unveil the mechanisms of protein misfolding phenomena. Techniques used for studying folding intermediates, such as kinetic studies and hydrogen/deuterium exchange studies combined with site-directed mutagenesis, successfully collect information regarding intermediates in the protein misfolding reaction to propose reasonable mechanisms and models.

There is an increasing amount of evidence supporting that configuration space of a polypeptide chain in freedom is not astronomically vast, and unfolded polypeptides are not classical random coils [142-146]. Nevertheless, the nature of an unfolded polypeptide chain remains unclear. David Shortle and his colleagues proposed that a polypeptide can be viewed as a relatively stiff chain with structure encoded by local interactions between side chains and backbone [147-152]. It follows that the structural propensity of each amino acid and conformational restrictions imposed from adjacent residues encode a crude topology of the polypeptide in the unfolded states. In particular, local clustering of hydrophobic residues and charged pairs often induces residual structures [143, 153-155], which is likely relevant to recent reports that the intermediate states detected in early stages of protein folding exhibit relatively defined structures [156-158]. Although transient, residual structures in the unfolded states and encoded chain topology by the sequence must be key determinants in protein folding as well as in amyloid fibril formation.

ACKNOWLEDGEMENTS

We are grateful to Drs. Masamichi Ikeguchi and Kohei Tsumoto for helpful discussions, Dr. Shohei Koide for kindly providing Figure materials for Figure 5, and Dr. Satoshi Takahashi for advices and critical reading of the manuscript.

REFERENCES

[1] Anfinsen, C. B. (1973) Principles that govern the folding of protein chains. *Science 181*, 223-30.

[2] Benson, D. E., Conrad, D. W., de Lorimier, R. M., Trammell, S. A., and Hellinga, H. W. (2001) Design of bioelectronic interfaces by exploiting hinge-bending motions in proteins. *Science 293*, 1641-4.

[3] Bolon, D. N., and Mayo, S. L. (2001) Enzyme-like proteins by computational design. *Proc Natl Acad Sci U S A 98*, 14274-9.

[4] Dwyer, M. A., Looger, L. L., and Hellinga, H. W. (2004) Computational design of a biologically active enzyme. *Science 304*, 1967-71.

[5] Kortemme, T., Joachimiak, L. A., Bullock, A. N., Schuler, A. D., Stoddard, B. L., and Baker, D. (2004) Computational redesign of protein-protein interaction specificity. *Nat Struct Mol Biol 11*, 371-9.

[6] Looger, L. L., Dwyer, M. A., Smith, J. J., and Hellinga, H. W. (2003) Computational design of receptor and sensor proteins with novel functions. *Nature 423*, 185-90.

[7] Kuhlman, B., Dantas, G., Ireton, G. C., Varani, G., Stoddard, B. L., and Baker, D. (2003) Design of a novel globular protein fold with atomic-level accuracy. *Science 302*, 1364-8.

[8] Azuma, T., Hamaguchi, K., and Migita, S. (1972) Denaturation of Bence Jones proteins by guanidine hydrochloride. *J Biochem (Tokyo) 72*, 1457-67.

[9] Rief, M., Gautel, M., Oesterhelt, F., Fernandez, J. M., and Gaub, H. E. (1997) Reversible unfolding of individual titin immunoglobulin domains by AFM. *Science 276*, 1109-12.

[10] Edwin, F., and Jagannadham, M. V. (1998) Sequential unfolding of papain in molten globule state. *Biochem Biophys Res Commun 252*, 654-60.

[11] Konno, T., Kamatari, Y. O., Tanaka, N., Kamikubo, H., Dobson, C. M., and Nagayama, K. (2000) A partially unfolded structure of the alkaline-denatured state of

pepsin and its implication for stability of the zymogen-derived protein. *Biochemistry 39*, 4182-90.

[12] Pearce, M. C., Rubin, H., and Bottomley, S. P. (2000) Conformational change and intermediates in the unfolding of alpha 1-antichymotrypsin. *J Biol Chem 275*, 28513-8.

[13] Goto, Y., Calciano, L. J., and Fink, A. L. (1990) Acid-induced folding of proteins. *Proc Natl Acad Sci U S A 87*, 573-7.

[14] Griko, Y. V., Privalov, P. L., Venyaminov, S. Y., and Kutyshenko, V. P. (1988) Thermodynamic study of the apomyoglobin structure. *J Mol Biol 202*, 127-38.

[15] Hughson, F. M., Wright, P. E., and Baldwin, R. L. (1990) Structural characterization of a partly folded apomyoglobin intermediate. *Science 249*, 1544-8.

[16] Ikeguchi, M., Kuwajima, K., and Sugai, S. (1986) Ca2+-induced alteration in the unfolding behavior of alpha-lactalbumin. *J Biochem (Tokyo) 99*, 1191-201.

[17] Ohgushi, M., and Wada, A. (1983) 'Molten-globule state': a compact form of globular proteins with mobile side-chains. *FEBS Lett 164*, 21-4.

[18] Kataoka, M., Hagihara, Y., Mihara, K., and Goto, Y. (1993) Molten globule of cytochrome c studied by small angle X-ray scattering. *J Mol Biol 229*, 591-6.

[19] Kuwajima, K., Hiraoka, Y., Ikeguchi, M., and Sugai, S. (1985) Comparison of the transient folding intermediates in lysozyme and alpha-lactalbumin. *Biochemistry 24*, 874-81.

[20] Jennings, P. A., and Wright, P. E. (1993) Formation of a molten globule intermediate early in the kinetic folding pathway of apomyoglobin. *Science 262*, 892-6.

[21] Bai, Y. (2003) Hidden intermediates and levinthal paradox in the folding of small proteins. *Biochem Biophys Res Commun 305*, 785-8.

[22] Bai, Y. (2000) Kinetic evidence of an on-pathway intermediate in the folding of lysozyme. *Protein Sci 9*, 194-6.

[23] Fernandez-Recio, J., Genzor, C. G., and Sancho, J. (2001) Apoflavodoxin folding mechanism: an alpha/beta protein with an essentially off-pathway intermediate. *Biochemistry 40*, 15234-45.

[24] Kiefhaber, T. (1995) Kinetic traps in lysozyme folding. *Proc Natl Acad Sci U S A 92*, 9029-33.

[25] Friel, C. T., Capaldi, A. P., and Radford, S. E. (2003) Structural analysis of the rate-limiting transition states in the folding of Im7 and Im9: similarities and differences in the folding of homologous proteins. *J Mol Biol 326*, 293-305.

[26] Dalessio, P. M., and Ropson, I. J. (2000) Beta-sheet proteins with nearly identical structures have different folding intermediates. *Biochemistry 39*, 860-71.

[27] Friel, C. T., Beddard, G. S., and Radford, S. E. (2004) Switching two-state to three-state kinetics in the helical protein Im9 via the optimisation of stabilising non-native interactions by design. *J Mol Biol 342*, 261-73.

[28] Dalessio, P. M., Boyer, J. A., McGettigan, J. L., and Ropson, I. J. (2005) Swapping core residues in homologous proteins swaps folding mechanism. *Biochemistry 44*, 3082-90.

[29] Levinthal, C. (1968) Are there pathways for protein folding? *J. Chim. Phys. 65*, 44-45.

[30] Chan, H. S., and Dill, K. A. (1998) Protein folding in the landscape perspective: chevron plots and non-Arrhenius kinetics. *Proteins 30*, 2-33.

[31] Dill, K. A., and Chan, H. S. (1997) From Levinthal to pathways to funnels. *Nat Struct Biol 4*, 10-9.

[32] Yan, S., Kennedy, S. D., and Koide, S. (2002) Thermodynamic and kinetic exploration of the energy landscape of Borrelia burgdorferi OspA by native-state hydrogen exchange. *J Mol Biol 323*, 363-75.

[33] Koide, S., Bu, Z., Risal, D., Pham, T. N., Nakagawa, T., Tamura, A., and Engelman, D. M. (1999) Multistep denaturation of Borrelia burgdorferi OspA, a protein containing a single-layer beta-sheet. *Biochemistry 38*, 4757-67.

[34] Schmid, F. X., and Baldwin, R. L. (1979) Detection of an early intermediate in the folding of ribonuclease A by protection of amide protons against exchange. *J Mol Biol 135*, 199-215.

[35] Krishna, M. M., Hoang, L., Lin, Y., and Englander, S. W. (2004) Hydrogen exchange methods to study protein folding. *Methods 34*, 51-64.

[36] Bai, Y., and Englander, S. W. (1994) Hydrogen bond strength and beta-sheet propensities: the role of a side chain blocking effect. *Proteins 18*, 262-6.

[37] Baker, D., Sohl, J. L., and Agard, D. A. (1992) A protein-folding reaction under kinetic control. *Nature 356*, 263-5.

[38] Cunningham, E. L., Jaswal, S. S., Sohl, J. L., and Agard, D. A. (1999) Kinetic stability as a mechanism for protease longevity. *Proc Natl Acad Sci U S A 96*, 11008-14.

[39] Jaswal, S. S., Sohl, J. L., Davis, J. H., and Agard, D. A. (2002) Energetic landscape of alpha-lytic protease optimizes longevity through kinetic stability. *Nature 415*, 343-6.

[40] Truhlar, S. M., Cunningham, E. L., and Agard, D. A. (2004) The folding landscape of Streptomyces griseus protease B reveals the energetic costs and benefits associated with evolving kinetic stability. *Protein Sci 13*, 381-90.

[41] Lee, C., Park, S. H., Lee, M. Y., and Yu, M. H. (2000) Regulation of protein function by native metastability. *Proc Natl Acad Sci U S A 97*, 7727-31.

[42] Carr, C. M., Chaudhry, C., and Kim, P. S. (1997) Influenza hemagglutinin is spring-loaded by a metastable native conformation. *Proc Natl Acad Sci U S A 94*, 14306-13.

[43] Field, E. J., Raine, C. S., and Joyce, G. (1967) Scrapie in the rat: an electron-microscope study. I. Amyloid bodies and deposits. *Acta Neuropathol (Berl) 8*, 47-56.

[44] Alper, T., Cramp, W. A., Haig, D. A., and Clarke, M. C. (1967) Does the agent of scrapie replicate without nucleic acid? *Nature 214*, 764-6.

[45] Griffith, J. S. (1967) Self-replication and scrapie. *Nature 215*, 1043-4.

[46] Prusiner, S. B. (1982) Novel proteinaceous infectious particles cause scrapie. *Science 216*, 136-44.

[47] Cohen, A. S., and Calkins, E. (1959) Electron microscopic observations on a fibrous component in amyloid of diverse origins. *Nature 183*, 1202-3.

[48] Bonar, L., Cohen, A. S., and Skinner, M. M. (1969) Characterization of the amyloid fibril as a cross-beta protein. *Proc Soc Exp Biol Med 131*, 1373-5.

[49] Eanes, E. D., and Glenner, G. G. (1968) X-ray diffraction studies on amyloid filaments. *J Histochem Cytochem 16*, 673-7.

[50] Sunde, M., Serpell, L. C., Bartlam, M., Fraser, P. E., Pepys, M. B., and Blake, C. C. (1997) Common core structure of amyloid fibrils by synchrotron X-ray diffraction. *J Mol Biol 273*, 729-39.

[51] Jimenez, J. L., Nettleton, E. J., Bouchard, M., Robinson, C. V., Dobson, C. M., and Saibil, H. R. (2002) The protofilament structure of insulin amyloid fibrils. *Proc Natl Acad Sci U S A 99*, 9196-201.

[52] Clark, A. H., Saunderson, D. H., and Suggett, A. (1981) Infrared and laser-Raman spectroscopic studies of thermally-induced globular protein gels. *Int J Pept Protein Res 17*, 353-64.
[53] Ismail, A. A., Mantsch, H. H., and Wong, P. T. (1992) Aggregation of chymotrypsinogen: portrait by infrared spectroscopy. *Biochim Biophys Acta 1121*, 183-8.
[54] Kato, A., and Takagi, T. (1988) Formation of intermolecular beta-sheet structure during heat denaturation of ovalbumin. *J.Agric. Food Chem. 36*, 1156-1159.
[55] Oberg, K., Chrunyk, B. A., Wetzel, R., and Fink, A. L. (1994) Nativelike secondary structure in interleukin-1 beta inclusion bodies by attenuated total reflectance FTIR. *Biochemistry 33*, 2628-34.
[56] Umetsu, M., Tsumoto, K., Ashish, K., Nitta, S., Tanaka, Y., Adschiri, T., and Kumagai, I. (2004) Structural characteristics and refolding of in vivo aggregated hyperthermophilic archaeon proteins. *FEBS Lett 557*, 49-56.
[57] Fink, A. L. (1998) Protein aggregation: folding aggregates, inclusion bodies and amyloid. *Fold Des 3*, R9-23.
[58] Ohnishi, S., and Takano, K. (2004) Amyloid fibrils from the viewpoint of protein folding. *Cell Mol Life Sci 61*, 511-24.
[59] Caughey, B. W., Dong, A., Bhat, K. S., Ernst, D., Hayes, S. F., and Caughey, W. S. (1991) Secondary structure analysis of the scrapie-associated protein PrP 27-30 in water by infrared spectroscopy. *Biochemistry 30*, 7672-80.
[60] Pan, K. M., Baldwin, M., Nguyen, J., Gasset, M., Serban, A., Groth, D., Mehlhorn, I., Huang, Z., Fletterick, R. J., Cohen, F. E., and et al. (1993) Conversion of alpha-helices into beta-sheets features in the formation of the scrapie prion proteins. *Proc Natl Acad Sci U S A 90*, 10962-6.
[61] DePace, A. H., Santoso, A., Hillner, P., and Weissman, J. S. (1998) A critical role for amino-terminal glutamine/asparagine repeats in the formation and propagation of a yeast prion. *Cell 93*, 1241-52.
[62] Masison, D. C., and Wickner, R. B. (1995) Prion-inducing domain of yeast Ure2p and protease resistance of Ure2p in prion-containing cells. *Science 270*, 93-5.
[63] Michelitsch, M. D., and Weissman, J. S. (2000) A census of glutamine/asparagine-rich regions: implications for their conserved function and the prediction of novel prions. *Proc Natl Acad Sci U S A 97*, 11910-5.
[64] Lawson, V. A., Priola, S. A., Wehrly, K., and Chesebro, B. (2001) N-terminal truncation of prion protein affects both formation and conformation of abnormal protease-resistant prion protein generated in vitro. *J Biol Chem 276*, 35265-71.
[65] Riek, R., Hornemann, S., Wider, G., Billeter, M., Glockshuber, R., and Wuthrich, K. (1996) NMR structure of the mouse prion protein domain PrP(121-321). *Nature 382*, 180-2.
[66] James, T. L., Liu, H., Ulyanov, N. B., Farr-Jones, S., Zhang, H., Donne, D. G., Kaneko, K., Groth, D., Mehlhorn, I., Prusiner, S. B., and Cohen, F. E. (1997) Solution structure of a 142-residue recombinant prion protein corresponding to the infectious fragment of the scrapie isoform. *Proc Natl Acad Sci U S A 94*, 10086-91.
[67] Hosszu, L. L., Baxter, N. J., Jackson, G. S., Power, A., Clarke, A. R., Waltho, J. P., Craven, C. J., and Collinge, J. (1999) Structural mobility of the human prion protein probed by backbone hydrogen exchange. *Nat Struct Biol 6*, 740-3.

[68] Hornemann, S., Schorn, C., and Wuthrich, K. (2004) NMR structure of the bovine prion protein isolated from healthy calf brains. *EMBO Rep 5*, 1159-64.

[69] Lysek, D. A., Schorn, C., Nivon, L. G., Esteve-Moya, V., Christen, B., Calzolai, L., von Schroetter, C., Fiorito, F., Herrmann, T., Guntert, P., and Wuthrich, K. (2005) Prion protein NMR structures of cats, dogs, pigs, and sheep. *Proc Natl Acad Sci U S A 102*, 640-5.

[70] Liu, H., Farr-Jones, S., Ulyanov, N. B., Llinas, M., Marqusee, S., Groth, D., Cohen, F. E., Prusiner, S. B., and James, T. L. (1999) Solution structure of Syrian hamster prion protein rPrP(90-231). *Biochemistry 38*, 5362-77.

[71] Viles, J. H., Donne, D., Kroon, G., Prusiner, S. B., Cohen, F. E., Dyson, H. J., and Wright, P. E. (2001) Local structural plasticity of the prion protein. Analysis of NMR relaxation dynamics. *Biochemistry 40*, 2743-53.

[72] Kuwata, K., Kamatari, Y. O., Akasaka, K., and James, T. L. (2004) Slow conformational dynamics in the hamster prion protein. *Biochemistry 43*, 4439-46.

[73] Kuwata, K., Li, H., Yamada, H., Legname, G., Prusiner, S. B., Akasaka, K., and James, T. L. (2002) Locally disordered conformer of the hamster prion protein: a crucial intermediate to PrPSc? *Biochemistry 41*, 12277-83.

[74] Wildegger, G., Liemann, S., and Glockshuber, R. (1999) Extremely rapid folding of the C-terminal domain of the prion protein without kinetic intermediates. *Nat Struct Biol 6*, 550-3.

[75] Liemann, S., and Glockshuber, R. (1999) Influence of amino acid substitutions related to inherited human prion diseases on the thermodynamic stability of the cellular prion protein. *Biochemistry 38*, 3258-67.

[76] Swietnicki, W., Petersen, R., Gambetti, P., and Surewicz, W. K. (1997) pH-dependent stability and conformation of the recombinant human prion protein PrP(90-231). *J Biol Chem 272*, 27517-20.

[77] Hornemann, S., and Glockshuber, R. (1998) A scrapie-like unfolding intermediate of the prion protein domain PrP(121-231) induced by acidic pH. *Proc Natl Acad Sci U S A 95*, 6010-4.

[78] Jackson, G. S., Hill, A. F., Joseph, C., Hosszu, L., Power, A., Waltho, J. P., Clarke, A. R., and Collinge, J. (1999) Multiple folding pathways for heterologously expressed human prion protein. *Biochim Biophys Acta 1431*, 1-13.

[79] Baskakov, I. V., Legname, G., Baldwin, M. A., Prusiner, S. B., and Cohen, F. E. (2002) Pathway complexity of prion protein assembly into amyloid. *J Biol Chem 277*, 21140-8.

[80] Gejyo, F., and Arakawa, M. (1990) Dialysis amyloidosis: current disease concepts and new perspectives for its treatment. *Contrib Nephrol 78*, 47-59; discussion 59-60.

[81] Gejyo, F., Yamada, T., Odani, S., Nakagawa, Y., Arakawa, M., Kunitomo, T., Kataoka, H., Suzuki, M., Hirasawa, Y., Shirahama, T., and et al. (1985) A new form of amyloid protein associated with chronic hemodialysis was identified as beta 2-microglobulin. *Biochem Biophys Res Commun 129*, 701-6.

[82] Yamamoto, S., Hasegawa, K., Yamaguchi, I., Tsutsumi, S., Kardos, J., Goto, Y., Gejyo, F., and Naiki, H. (2004) Low concentrations of sodium dodecyl sulfate induce the extension of beta 2-microglobulin-related amyloid fibrils at a neutral pH. *Biochemistry 43*, 11075-82.

[83] Yamamoto, S., Yamaguchi, I., Hasegawa, K., Tsutsumi, S., Goto, Y., Gejyo, F., and Naiki, H. (2004) Glycosaminoglycans enhance the trifluoroethanol-induced extension of beta 2-microglobulin-related amyloid fibrils at a neutral pH. *J Am Soc Nephrol 15*, 126-33.

[84] Esposito, G., Michelutti, R., Verdone, G., Viglino, P., Hernandez, H., Robinson, C. V., Amoresano, A., Dal Piaz, F., Monti, M., Pucci, P., Mangione, P., Stoppini, M., Merlini, G., Ferri, G., and Bellotti, V. (2000) Removal of the N-terminal hexapeptide from human beta2-microglobulin facilitates protein aggregation and fibril formation. *Protein Sci 9*, 831-45.

[85] Yamada, T., Kakihara, T., Gejyo, F., and Okada, M. (1994) A monoclonal antibody recognizing apolipoprotein E peptides in systemic amyloid deposits. *Ann Clin Lab Sci 24*, 243-9.

[86] Morgan, C. J., Gelfand, M., Atreya, C., and Miranker, A. D. (2001) Kidney dialysis-associated amyloidosis: a molecular role for copper in fiber formation. *J Mol Biol 309*, 339-45.

[87] Villanueva, J., Hoshino, M., Katou, H., Kardos, J., Hasegawa, K., Naiki, H., and Goto, Y. (2004) Increase in the conformational flexibility of beta 2-microglobulin upon copper binding: a possible role for copper in dialysis-related amyloidosis. *Protein Sci 13*, 797-809.

[88] Hoshino, M., Katou, H., Hagihara, Y., Hasegawa, K., Naiki, H., and Goto, Y. (2002) Mapping the core of the beta(2)-microglobulin amyloid fibril by H/D exchange. *Nat Struct Biol 9*, 332-6.

[89] McParland, V. J., Kalverda, A. P., Homans, S. W., and Radford, S. E. (2002) Structural properties of an amyloid precursor of beta(2)-microglobulin. *Nat Struct Biol 9*, 326-31.

[90] Katou, H., Kanno, T., Hoshino, M., Hagihara, Y., Tanaka, H., Kawai, T., Hasegawa, K., Naiki, H., and Goto, Y. (2002) The role of disulfide bond in the amyloidogenic state of beta(2)-microglobulin studied by heteronuclear NMR. *Protein Sci 11*, 2218-29.

[91] Jones, S., Manning, J., Kad, N. M., and Radford, S. E. (2003) Amyloid-forming peptides from beta2-microglobulin-Insights into the mechanism of fibril formation in vitro. *J Mol Biol 325*, 249-57.

[92] Kozhukh, G. V., Hagihara, Y., Kawakami, T., Hasegawa, K., Naiki, H., and Goto, Y. (2002) Investigation of a peptide responsible for amyloid fibril formation of beta 2-microglobulin by achromobacter protease I. *J Biol Chem 277*, 1310-5.

[93] Hasegawa, K., Ohhashi, Y., Yamaguchi, I., Takahashi, N., Tsutsumi, S., Goto, Y., Gejyo, F., and Naiki, H. (2003) Amyloidogenic synthetic peptides of beta2-microglobulin-a role of the disulfide bond. *Biochem Biophys Res Commun 304*, 101-6.

[94] Ohhashi, Y., Hasegawa, K., Naiki, H., and Goto, Y. (2004) Optimum amyloid fibril formation of a peptide fragment suggests the amyloidogenic preference of beta2-microglobulin under physiological conditions. *J Biol Chem 279*, 10814-21.

[95] Yamaguchi, K., Katou, H., Hoshino, M., Hasegawa, K., Naiki, H., and Goto, Y. (2004) Core and heterogeneity of beta2-microglobulin amyloid fibrils as revealed by H/D exchange. *J Mol Biol 338*, 559-71.

[96] Gillmore, J. D., Booth, D. R., Madhoo, S., Pepys, M. B., and Hawkins, P. N. (1999) Hereditary renal amyloidosis associated with variant lysozyme in a large English family. *Nephrol Dial Transplant 14*, 2639-44.

[97] Pepys, M. B., Hawkins, P. N., Booth, D. R., Vigushin, D. M., Tennent, G. A., Soutar, A. K., Totty, N., Nguyen, O., Blake, C. C., Terry, C. J., and et al. (1993) Human lysozyme gene mutations cause hereditary systemic amyloidosis. *Nature 362*, 553-7.

[98] Valleix, S., Drunat, S., Philit, J. B., Adoue, D., Piette, J. C., Droz, D., MacGregor, B., Canet, D., Delpech, M., and Grateau, G. (2002) Hereditary renal amyloidosis caused by a new variant lysozyme W64R in a French family. *Kidney Int 61*, 907-12.

[99] Yazaki, M., Farrell, S. A., and Benson, M. D. (2003) A novel lysozyme mutation Phe57Ile associated with hereditary renal amyloidosis. *Kidney Int 63*, 1652-7.

[100] Booth, D. R., Sunde, M., Bellotti, V., Robinson, C. V., Hutchinson, W. L., Fraser, P. E., Hawkins, P. N., Dobson, C. M., Radford, S. E., Blake, C. C., and Pepys, M. B. (1997) Instability, unfolding and aggregation of human lysozyme variants underlying amyloid fibrillogenesis. *Nature 385*, 787-93.

[101] Funahashi, J., Takano, K., Ogasahara, K., Yamagata, Y., and Yutani, K. (1996) The structure, stability, and folding process of amyloidogenic mutant human lysozyme. *J Biochem (Tokyo) 120*, 1216-23.

[102] Canet, D., Sunde, M., Last, A. M., Miranker, A., Spencer, A., Robinson, C. V., and Dobson, C. M. (1999) Mechanistic studies of the folding of human lysozyme and the origin of amyloidogenic behavior in its disease-related variants. *Biochemistry 38*, 6419-27.

[103] Chamberlain, A. K., Receveur, V., Spencer, A., Redfield, C., and Dobson, C. M. (2001) Characterization of the structure and dynamics of amyloidogenic variants of human lysozyme by NMR spectroscopy. *Protein Sci 10*, 2525-30.

[104] Morozova-Roche, L. A., Zurdo, J., Spencer, A., Noppe, W., Receveur, V., Archer, D. B., Joniau, M., and Dobson, C. M. (2000) Amyloid fibril formation and seeding by wild-type human lysozyme and its disease-related mutational variants. *J Struct Biol 130*, 339-51.

[105] Takano, K., Funahashi, J., and Yutani, K. (2001) The stability and folding process of amyloidogenic mutant human lysozymes. *Eur J Biochem 268*, 155-9.

[106] Canet, D., Last, A. M., Tito, P., Sunde, M., Spencer, A., Archer, D. B., Redfield, C., Robinson, C. V., and Dobson, C. M. (2002) Local cooperativity in the unfolding of an amyloidogenic variant of human lysozyme. *Nat Struct Biol 9*, 308-15.

[107] Dumoulin, M., Canet, D., Last, A. M., Pardon, E., Archer, D. B., Muyldermans, S., Wyns, L., Matagne, A., Robinson, C. V., Redfield, C., and Dobson, C. M. (2005) Reduced global cooperativity is a common feature underlying the amyloidogenicity of pathogenic lysozyme mutations. *J Mol Biol 346*, 773-88.

[108] Goda, S., Takano, K., Yamagata, Y., Maki, S., Namba, K., and Yutani, K. (2002) Elongation in a beta-structure promotes amyloid-like fibril formation of human lysozyme. *J Biochem (Tokyo) 132*, 655-61.

[109] Frare, E., Polverino De Laureto, P., Zurdo, J., Dobson, C. M., and Fontana, A. (2004) A highly amyloidogenic region of hen lysozyme. *J Mol Biol 340*, 1153-65.

[110] Krebs, M. R., Wilkins, D. K., Chung, E. W., Pitkeathly, M. C., Chamberlain, A. K., Zurdo, J., Robinson, C. V., and Dobson, C. M. (2000) Formation and seeding of amyloid fibrils from wild-type hen lysozyme and a peptide fragment from the beta-domain. *J Mol Biol 300*, 541-9.

[111] Esposito, G., Garcia, J., Mangione, P., Giorgetti, S., Corazza, A., Viglino, P., Chiti, F., Andreola, A., Dumy, P., Booth, D., Hawkins, P. N., and Bellotti, V. (2003) Structural

and folding dynamic properties of the T70N variant of human lysozyme. *J Biol Chem 278*, 25910-8.

[112] Uversky, V. N., Gillespie, J. R., and Fink, A. L. (2000) Why are "natively unfolded" proteins unstructured under physiologic conditions? *Proteins 41*, 415-27.

[113] Giasson, B. I., Murray, I. V., Trojanowski, J. Q., and Lee, V. M. (2001) A hydrophobic stretch of 12 amino acid residues in the middle of alpha-synuclein is essential for filament assembly. *J Biol Chem 276*, 2380-6.

[114] Yoshimoto, M., Iwai, A., Kang, D., Otero, D. A., Xia, Y., and Saitoh, T. (1995) NACP, the precursor protein of the non-amyloid beta/A4 protein (A beta) component of Alzheimer disease amyloid, binds A beta and stimulates A beta aggregation. *Proc Natl Acad Sci U S A 92*, 9141-5.

[115] Eliezer, D., Kutluay, E., Bussell, R., Jr., and Browne, G. (2001) Conformational properties of alpha-synuclein in its free and lipid-associated states. *J Mol Biol 307*, 1061-73.

[116] Uversky, V. N., Li, J., and Fink, A. L. (2001) Trimethylamine-N-oxide-induced folding of alpha-synuclein. *FEBS Lett 509*, 31-5.

[117] Weinreb, P. H., Zhen, W., Poon, A. W., Conway, K. A., and Lansbury, P. T., Jr. (1996) NACP, a protein implicated in Alzheimer's disease and learning, is natively unfolded. *Biochemistry 35*, 13709-15.

[118] Uversky, V. N. (2002) What does it mean to be natively unfolded? *Eur J Biochem 269*, 2-12.

[119] Guijarro, J. I., Sunde, M., Jones, J. A., Campbell, I. D., and Dobson, C. M. (1998) Amyloid fibril formation by an SH3 domain. *Proc Natl Acad Sci U S A 95*, 4224-8.

[120] Gross, M., Wilkins, D. K., Pitkeathly, M. C., Chung, E. W., Higham, C., Clark, A., and Dobson, C. M. (1999) Formation of amyloid fibrils by peptides derived from the bacterial cold shock protein CspB. *Protein Sci 8*, 1350-7.

[121] Chiti, F., Webster, P., Taddei, N., Clark, A., Stefani, M., Ramponi, G., and Dobson, C. M. (1999) Designing conditions for in vitro formation of amyloid protofilaments and fibrils. *Proc Natl Acad Sci U S A 96*, 3590-4.

[122] Pertinhez, T. A., Bouchard, M., Tomlinson, E. J., Wain, R., Ferguson, S. J., Dobson, C. M., and Smith, L. J. (2001) Amyloid fibril formation by a helical cytochrome. *FEBS Lett 495*, 184-6.

[123] Fandrich, M., Fletcher, M. A., and Dobson, C. M. (2001) Amyloid fibrils from muscle myoglobin. *Nature 410*, 165-6.

[124] Dobson, C. M. (2004) Principles of protein folding, misfolding and aggregation. *Semin Cell Dev Biol 15*, 3-16.

[125] Dobson, C. M. (2001) The structural basis of protein folding and its links with human disease. *Philos Trans R Soc Lond B Biol Sci 356*, 133-45.

[126] Hammarstrom, P., Schneider, F., and Kelly, J. W. (2001) Trans-suppression of misfolding in an amyloid disease. *Science 293*, 2459-62.

[127] Hammarstrom, P., Wiseman, R. L., Powers, E. T., and Kelly, J. W. (2003) Prevention of transthyretin amyloid disease by changing protein misfolding energetics. *Science 299*, 713-6.

[128] Konno, T., Murata, K., and Nagayama, K. (1999) Amyloid-like aggregates of a plant protein: a case of a sweet-tasting protein, monellin. *FEBS Lett 454*, 122-6.

[129] Srisailam, S., Wang, H. M., Kumar, T. K., Rajalingam, D., Sivaraja, V., Sheu, H. S., Chang, Y. C., and Yu, C. (2002) Amyloid-like fibril formation in an all beta-barrel protein involves the formation of partially structured intermediate(s). *J Biol Chem 277*, 19027-36.

[130] Khurana, R., Gillespie, J. R., Talapatra, A., Minert, L. J., Ionescu-Zanetti, C., Millett, I., and Fink, A. L. (2001) Partially folded intermediates as critical precursors of light chain amyloid fibrils and amorphous aggregates. *Biochemistry 40*, 3525-35.

[131] Gorovits, B. M., and Horowitz, P. M. (1998) High hydrostatic pressure can reverse aggregation of protein folding intermediates and facilitate acquisition of native structure. *Biochemistry 37*, 6132-5.

[132] St John, R. J., Carpenter, J. F., and Randolph, T. W. (1999) High pressure fosters protein refolding from aggregates at high concentrations. *Proc Natl Acad Sci U S A 96*, 13029-33.

[133] Foguel, D., Robinson, C. R., de Sousa, P. C., Jr., Silva, J. L., and Robinson, A. S. (1999) Hydrostatic pressure rescues native protein from aggregates. *Biotechnol Bioeng 63*, 552-8.

[134] Lefebvre, B. G., and Robinson, A. S. (2003) Pressure treatment of tailspike aggregates rapidly produces on-pathway folding intermediates. *Biotechnol Bioeng 82*, 595-604.

[135] Niraula, T. N., Konno, T., Li, H., Yamada, H., Akasaka, K., and Tachibana, H. (2004) Pressure-dissociable reversible assembly of intrinsically denatured lysozyme is a precursor for amyloid fibrils. *Proc Natl Acad Sci U S A 101*, 4089-93.

[136] Dirix, C., Meersman, F., MacPhee, C. E., Dobson, C. M., and Heremans, K. (2005) High hydrostatic pressure dissociates early aggregates of TTR105-115, but not the mature amyloid fibrils. *J Mol Biol 347*, 903-9.

[137] Kamatari, Y. O., Yokoyama, S., Tachibana, H., and Akasaka, K. (2005) Pressure-jump NMR study of dissociation and association of amyloid protofibrils. *J Mol Biol 349*, 916-21.

[138] Lomakin, A., Chung, D. S., Benedek, G. B., Kirschner, D. A., and Teplow, D. B. (1996) On the nucleation and growth of amyloid beta-protein fibrils: detection of nuclei and quantitation of rate constants. *Proc Natl Acad Sci U S A 93*, 1125-9.

[139] Lomakin, A., Teplow, D. B., Kirschner, D. A., and Benedek, G. B. (1997) Kinetic theory of fibrillogenesis of amyloid beta-protein. *Proc Natl Acad Sci U S A 94*, 7942-7.

[140] Nelson, R., Sawaya, M. R., Balbirnie, M., Madsen, A. O., Riekel, C., Grothe, R., and Eisenberg, D. (2005) Structure of the cross-beta spine of amyloid-like fibrils. *Nature 435*, 773-8.

[141] Naiki, H., and Gejyo, F. (1999) Kinetic analysis of amyloid fibril formation. *Methods Enzymol 309*, 305-18.

[142] Fitzkee, N. C., and Rose, G. D. (2004) Reassessing random-coil statistics in unfolded proteins. *Proc Natl Acad Sci U S A 101*, 12497-502.

[143] Klein-Seetharaman, J., Oikawa, M., Grimshaw, S. B., Wirmer, J., Duchardt, E., Ueda, T., Imoto, T., Smith, L. J., Dobson, C. M., and Schwalbe, H. (2002) Long-range interactions within a nonnative protein. *Science 295*, 1719-22.

[144] Pappu, R. V., Srinivasan, R., and Rose, G. D. (2000) The Flory isolated-pair hypothesis is not valid for polypeptide chains: implications for protein folding. *Proc Natl Acad Sci U S A 97*, 12565-70.

[145] Wong, K. B., Clarke, J., Bond, C. J., Neira, J. L., Freund, S. M., Fersht, A. R., and Daggett, V. (2000) Towards a complete description of the structural and dynamic properties of the denatured state of barnase and the role of residual structure in folding. *J Mol Biol 296*, 1257-82.

[146] Zagrovic, B., Snow, C. D., Khaliq, S., Shirts, M. R., and Pande, V. S. (2002) Native-like mean structure in the unfolded ensemble of small proteins. *J Mol Biol 323*, 153-64.

[147] Ackerman, M. S., and Shortle, D. (2002) Robustness of the long-range structure in denatured staphylococcal nuclease to changes in amino acid sequence. *Biochemistry 41*, 13791-7.

[148] Gillespie, J. R., and Shortle, D. (1997) Characterization of long-range structure in the denatured state of staphylococcal nuclease. II. Distance restraints from paramagnetic relaxation and calculation of an ensemble of structures. *J Mol Biol 268*, 170-84.

[149] Ohnishi, S., Lee, A. L., Edgell, M. H., and Shortle, D. (2004) Direct demonstration of structural similarity between native and denatured eglin C. *Biochemistry 43*, 4064-70.

[150] Ohnishi, S., and Shortle, D. (2003) Effects of denaturants and substitutions of hydrophobic residues on backbone dynamics of denatured staphylococcal nuclease. *Protein Sci 12*, 1530-7.

[151] Ohnishi, S., and Shortle, D. (2003) Observation of residual dipolar couplings in short peptides. *Proteins 50*, 546-51.

[152] Shortle, D., and Ackerman, M. S. (2001) Persistence of native-like topology in a denatured protein in 8 M urea. *Science 293*, 487-9.

[153] Crowhurst, K. A., Tollinger, M., and Forman-Kay, J. D. (2002) Cooperative interactions and a non-native buried Trp in the unfolded state of an SH3 domain. *J Mol Biol 322*, 163-78.

[154] Neira, J. L., and Fersht, A. R. (1996) An NMR study on the beta-hairpin region of barnase. *Fold Des 1*, 231-41.

[155] Neri, D., Billeter, M., Wider, G., and Wuthrich, K. (1992) NMR determination of residual structure in a urea-denatured protein, the 434-repressor. *Science 257*, 1559-63.

[156] Ferguson, N., and Fersht, A. R. (2003) Early events in protein folding. *Curr Opin Struct Biol 13*, 75-81.

[157] Kimura, T., Akiyama, S., Uzawa, T., Ishimori, K., Morishima, I., Fujisawa, T., and Takahashi, S. (2005) Specifically collapsed intermediate in the early stage of the folding of ribonuclease A. *J Mol Biol 350*, 349-62.

[158] Maki, K., Cheng, H., Dolgikh, D. A., Shastry, M. C., and Roder, H. (2004) Early events during folding of wild-type staphylococcal nuclease and a single-tryptophan variant studied by ultrarapid mixing. *J Mol Biol 338*, 383-400.

[159] Nolting, B. (2003) *Methods in Modern Biophysics*, Springer-Verlag New York, LLC.

[160] Phillips, S. E. (1980) Structure and refinement of oxymyoglobin at 1.6 A resolution. *J Mol Biol 142*, 531-54.

[161] Kraulis, P. J. (1991) MOLSCRIPT: A Program to Produce Both Detailed and Schematic Plots of Protein Structures. *J. Appl. Cryst. 24*, 946-950.

[162] Merritt, E. A., and Murphy, M. E. (1994) Raster3D Version 2.0. A program for photorealistic molecular graphics. *Acta Crystallogr D Biol Crystallogr 50*, 869-73.

[163] Jackson, S. E., and Fersht, A. R. (1991) Folding of chymotrypsin inhibitor 2. 1. Evidence for a two-state transition. *Biochemistry 30*, 10428-35.

[164] Takahashi, N., Hasegawa, K., Yamaguchi, I., Okada, H., Ueda, T., Gejyo, F., and Naiki, H. (2002) Establishment of a first-order kinetic model of light chain-associated amyloid fibril extension in vitro. *Biochim Biophys Acta 1601*, 110-20.

In: Protein Folding: New Research
Editor: Tony R. Obalinsky, pp. 89-171
ISBN 1-59454-835-8

Chapter 3

MECHANISM OF THE CHAPERONE-LIKE ACTIVITY

K. A. Markossian[1*], B. I. Kurganov[1], D. I. Levitsky[1], H. A. Khanova[1], N. A. Chebotareva[1], A. M. Samoilov[1], T. B. Eronina[1], N. V. Fedurkina[1], L. G. Mitskevich[1], A. V. Merem'yanin[1], S. Yu. Kleymenov[1], V. F. Makeeva [1], V. I. Muronetz[2,3], I. N. Naletova[2], I. N. Shalova[2,3], R. A. Asryants[2], E. V. Schmalhausen[2], L. Saso[4], Yu. V. Panyukov[3], E. N. Dobrov[2], I. K. Yudin[5], A. C. Timofeeva[2], K. O. Muranov[6] and M. A.Ostrovsky[6]

[1]Bach Institute of Biochemistry, Moscow, Russia;
[2]A.N. Belozersky Institute of Physico-Chemical Biology, Moscow State University, Moscow, Russia;
[3]Faculty of Bioengineering and Bioinformatics, Moscow State University, Russia
[4]University of Rome "La Sapienza", Rome, Italy;
[5]Oil and Gas Research Institute, Moscow, Russia
[6]Emanuel Institute of Biochemical Physics, Moscow, Russsia

ABSTRACT

Mechanism of thermal aggregation of protein substrates (bovine lens β_L-crystallin; yeast alcohol dehydrogenase; rabbit skeletal muscles glycogen phosphorylase *b* and glyceraldehydes 3-phosphate dehydrogenase; coat protein of tobacco mosaic virus) has been studied by dynamic light scattering. The stage of denaturation of the proteins under study was characterized using differential scanning calorimetry. It has been established that the aggregation process involves a latent stage, its duration (t_0) being determined by the point in time at which the initial increase in the light scattering intensity is observed. The initial parts of the dependences of the light scattering intensity on the hydrodynamic

* Corresponding author: fax: (7-095) 954-2732, E-mail: markossian@inbi.ras.ru

radius (R_h) are linear and the length on the abscissa axis cut off by the straight line allows the size of the start aggregates formed over the latent stage to be estimated ($R_{h,0}$ refers to the hydrodynamic radius of the start aggregates). The calculations of the $R_{h,0}$ value for different proteins show that the start aggregates may contain hundreds or even thousands of molecules of denatured monomers. The dependences of the R_h value on time t are described by the power function: $R_h = R_{h,0}[1 + K_1(t - t_0)]^{1/d_f}$ (K_1 is the constant; d_f is the fractal dimension of aggregates, i. e., exponent at the particle radius in the equation connecting the molecular mass M and the radius of the particle R: $M \sim R^{d_f}$). For the kinetics of protein aggregation parameter d_f is close to 1.8; that is, after the formation of the start aggregates the aggregation process proceeds in the kinetic regime wherein the rate of interaction of the particles is limited by diffusion («diffusion-limited aggregation»). The sticking probability at the collision of particles is equal to unity. In the presence of α-crystallin (a protein possessing the chaperone-like activity) the decrease in the size of the start aggregates (the decrease in the $R_{h,0}$ value) and the increase in the duration of the latent stage (the increase in the t_0 value) have been observed. The dependences of R_h on t in the presence of α-crystallin obey the exponential law: $R_h = R_{h,0}\exp[K_2(t - t_0)]$ (K_2 is the constant); that is, the aggregation process switches to the kinetic regime wherein the sticking probability at the collision of particles becomes less than unity («reaction-limited aggregation»). The conclusion has been made that the protective action of chaperones is connected with formation of the protein aggregates of lesser size.

Key words: protein aggregation; start aggregates; chaperone-like activity; α-crystallin; dynamic light scattering; differential scanning calorimetry

Introduction

Protein Aggregation

Native, functionally active proteins form by folding of newly synthesized polypeptide chains, which results in information transfer from the linear chains of amino acids to a three dimensional structure [Anfinsen, 1973]. Protein folding in native structure is a spontaneous process. However, as a result of misfolding in response to mutations, posttranslational modifications or changes of local conditions such as pH and temperature proteins can aggregate. Protein aggregation occurs on "incorrect" interactions of completely or partially unfolded protein molecules, leading to the formation of agglomerates of random shape [Jaenicke, 1995]. Protein aggregates are produced when folded or unfolded intermediates interact mainly through contact of their hydrophobic surfaces, turning into large, stable complexes [Haase-Pettingell and King, 1988; Wetzel, 1994; Jaenicke, 1998]. Structured or amorphous aggregates produced [Kopito, 2000; Markossian and Kurganov, 2004] are defined by poor solubility in water or detergents and by non-native secondary structure [Fink, 1998].

The basic models of protein aggregation have been discussed by Speed et al. [Speed et al., 1997]. These models include (1) sequential particle-cluster aggregation, in which monomeric units add individually to a growing aggregate; (2) multimeric cluster-cluster aggregation, in which multimers of any size associate rather than sequential addition of monomeric units to a growing aggregate; or (3) nucleation-dependent aggregation, characterized by the relatively slow formation of nucleus followed by rapid growth of the aggregate. According to Kurganov [Kurganov, 1998; 2002], the mechanism of protein aggregation together with unfolding of a protein molecule involves the stage of the aggregate seed formation (nucleation stage), and the stage of aggregate growth. Active centers of the chain reaction at protein aggregation are the growth points of the aggregate. It follows from comparison of the protein aggregation process with chemical chain reactions that aggregation (at the stage of aggregate growth) may be considered as an unramified chain reaction, and the chaperones, blocking the aggregation of the protein substrate, as inhibitors of the chain reaction at protein aggregation [Kurganov, 2002]. On the basis of investigation of the tobacco mosaic virus coat protein and firefly luciferase new concepts of aggregation kinetics have been formulated [Kurganov, 2002; Kurganov et al., 2002; Wang and Kurganov, 2003]. Concepts about two kinetic regimes of protein aggregation have been introduced. At rather low protein concentrations a kinetic regime is realized, when rate-limiting stage is the stage of aggregate growth on nuclei, formed in the nucleation stage. At rather high protein concentrations a kinetic regime is realized, when rate-limiting stage is the stage of complete or partial protein molecule unfolding.

Under normal, physiological conditions, protein aggregates do not accumulate despite their continued production in cells, due in part to the existence of cellular "quality control" machinery, which involves a joint effect of chaperones and proteinases [Hammond and Helenius, 1995; Brodsky and McCracken, 1999]. Under conditions of disturbed proteolysis in cells, aggregated proteins can accumulate and form aggregates or discrete depositions termed inclusion bodies [Perutz, 1997]. Recombinant proteins, obtained biotechnologically, also aggregate frequently and form inclusion bodies [Wetzel, 1994; Kopito, 2000; Carrio and Villaverde, 2002]. Inclusion bodies consist of compact packed protein molecules, partially possessing a secondary structure [Kane and Hartley, 1991]. In today's view, inclusion body formation in procaryotic and eucaryotic cells proceeds by different mechanisms. In procaryotic cells, aggregation is seeded at a single or limited number of sites, and inclusion bodies form due to the assembly of nonnative monomers into growing polymers [Speed, 1996]. Because the addition of monomers to existing aggregate favors the thermodynamic stability of the aggregate, initially arisen aggregates will tend to dominate. In this connection, the number of aggregation foci or inclusion bodies in the cell will be limited. According to this model, inclusion bodies in procaryotic cells are giant aggregates, formed by monomer diffusion to the site of inclusion body formation. In eucaryotic cells, an inclusion body is a structured complex of aggregates [Kopito, 2000]. Such inclusion bodies arise from the coalescence of individual aggregates into a single or limited number of foci. Cytoplasmic inclusion bodies in animal cells often result from the expression of mutant or heterologous proteins, and in the course of a number of various diseases. In mammalian cells, formation of cytoplasmic inclusion bodies has been shown to be associated with retrograde transport of misfolded protein on microtubules, which participate in the growth of protein aggregates within the cytoplasm [Johnston et al., 1998]. Such microtubule dependent cytoplasmic inclusion bodies have been proposed to be called "aggresomes". Aggresomes are pericentrosomal structures of 6080 nm, containing misfolded, aggregated, ubiquitinated proteins.

Because protein misfolding and aggregation into insoluble intracellular complexes underlie pathogenesis of a considerable part of human degenerative and neurodegenerative diseases [Fink, 1998; Hurtley and Helenius, 1989; Dobson, 1999; Wood et al., 2003; Bloemendal et al., 2004], special attention has been given in recent years to the investigation of protein misfolding and aggregation. Such disorders as Alzheimer's and Parkinson's diseases [Carrell and Lomas, 1997], Huntington's disease [Busch et al., 2003], Machado-Joseph's disease (spinocerebellar ataxia) [Goti et al., 2004], prion encephalopathies [Prusiner and Hsiao, 1994; Gu et al., 2003], Charcot's disease (amyotrophic lateral sclerosis) [Johnston et al., 2000; Julien, 2001], systemic amyloidosis [Perutz, 1999], cystic fibrosis [Johnston et al., 1998], and cataract [Bloemendal et al., 2004] are part of a growing list of inherited diseases known as «conformational diseases» [Carrell and Lomas, 1997] that arise when proteins undergo structural rearrangement promoting their aggregation. A distinctive feature of these diseases is alteration of protein conformation that results in the formation of protein aggregates with various supramolecular organization [Merlini et al., 2001].

Formation of protein aggregates in cells is proceeded by different molecular mechanisms, and understanding of these processes opens up new prospects for investigation and treatment of conformational diseases.

Functions of Molecular Chaperones

In cells, heat shock proteins (Hsps) synthesized under the stress conditions, including heat shock, serve as molecular chaperones that interact with unfolded polypeptide chains, prevent their irreversible aggregation and assist folding and assembly of proteins [Hendrick and Hartl, 1993; Becker and Craig, 1994; Fink, 1999; Frydman, 2001; Soti et al., 2005; Borges and Ramos, 2005]. Numerous studies have investigated the structural and functional characteristics of molecular chaperones, classifying them into six main families on the basis of their molecular mass and structure: Hsp100 (ClpA/B/X, HslU), Hsp90 (HtpG), Hsp70 (DnaK), Hsp60 (GroEL), Hsp40 and the small Hsps (sHsps) (shown in parentheses are *Escherichia coli* chaperones of corresponding classes). In mammalian cells, Hsp60, Hsp70 and Hsp90 are the most abundant and most studied Hsps [Bukau and Horwich, 1998; Wegele et al., 2004; Mayer and Bukau, 2005]. Hsp90 chaperones are an essential component of the eukaryotic cytosol [Smith et al., 1998], where they stabilize misfolded proteins and regulate the activity of various signaling proteins, including steroid hormone receptors, tyrosine kinases, nitric oxide synthase and calcineurin [Young and Hartl, 2002]. Such chaperones as Hsp70 and Hsp60 interact transiently with unfolded or partially folded intermediates, prevent their hydrophobic surfaces from "incorrect" intermolecular and intramolecular interactions, and favor folding of polypeptide chains [Hartl, 1996; Bukau and Horwich, 1998]. Hsp70 chaperones (with Hsp40s co-chaperones) assist in the stabilization and folding of protein substrates and are found in most cellular compartments [Bukau and Horwich, 1998] All Hsp70 proteins have a conserved amino-terminal ATPase domain that binds and hydrolyses ATP, and a carboxy (C)-terminal substrate-binding domain [Hartl, 1996; Minami et al., 1996]. Hsp60 (GroEL) chaperones are heptameric complexes of identical subunits stacked back to back in a double-ring structure that contains a large central cavity in which unfolded polypeptides undergo productive folding [Bukau and Horwich, 1998]. The three-dimensional structure of GroEL reveals that the GroEL molecule has two substrate-binding sites on each end of the double ring [Braig et al., 1994]. GroEL binds to a large number of polypeptides, prevents their self-association, and mediates appropriate folding in a GroES and ATP-dependent manner [Hartl and Hayer-Hartl, 2002].

Small Heat Shock Proteins

Among Hsp families, small heat shock proteins (sHsps) of 15-40 kDa are expressed practically in all organisms and involved in stabilization of other proteins under conditions of stress [Haslbeck, 2002]. Although most of sHsps do not participate significantly in refolding of the substrate proteins, they are also included in the superfamily of molecular chaperones. Similar to Hsp90 chaperones, sHsps transiently interact with and stabilize unfolding proteins, until the Hsp70/Hsp40 system can refold them [Horwitz, 1992; Smith et al., 1998; Clark and Muchowski, 2000]. A unique property of many sHsps including α-crystallin is their ability to form soluble complexes with denatured proteins, thereby preventing their precipitation. This is known as the chaperone-like activity. All sHsps contain a conserved, C-terminal α-crystallin domain of about 100 residues, form dynamic oligomeric structures of 300-800 kDa ranging from 9 to 50 subunits most of uncertain quaternary structure, and oligomerization is prerequisite to their function as molecular chaperones [MacRae, 2000; Clark and Muchowski, 2000; Giese and Vierling, 2002; Stromer et al., 2003].

α-Crystallin: Structure, Properties and Chaperone-Like Function

The crystallins are the major structural proteins of the mammal eye lens that account for up to 90% of total soluble proteins. There are three distinct families of crystallins denoted as α, β and γ. α-Crystallin, being a member of the sHsps family, acts as a molecular chaperone [Horwitz, 1992;. Augusteyn and Stevens, 1998; Treweek et al., 2003], whereas β- and γ-crystallins are structural proteins [Delaye and Tardieu, 1983; Bloemendal et al., 2004]. In the lens, α-crystallin through the chaperone-like activity protects β- and γ-crystallins against non-specific aggregation [Boyle and Takemoto, 1994;. Rao et al., 1995]. Loss of the chaperone-like activity of α-crystallin may be accompanied by aggregation of β- and γ-crystallins and development of cataract [Groenen et al., 1994]. Since no protein turnover occurs in the center of the lens [Horwitz, 2000], a knowledge of the role of α-crystallin in maintaining lens transparency is of great importance for understanding cataract formation and developing strategies for the treatment or prevention of cataracts [van den Ijssel et al., 1996].

The lenticular α-crystallin consists of two 20 kDa subunits, αA and αB, that share about 60% sequence homology. Although α-crystallin is highly soluble, the subunits easily self-aggregate and form roughly spherical oligomeric complexes that contain 30–50 subunits. As a result of subunit exchange between individual oligomers [van den Oetelaar, 1990; Bova et al., 1997] α-crystallin has a dynamic quaternary structure that depends on external conditions such as pH, temperature, ionic strength and concentration [Siezen et al., 1980; Vanhoudt et al., 1997]. It has been shown [Vanhoudt et al., 2000] that the average molecular weight of α-crystallin in a dilute solution at 37°C is about 550 kDa, while in the native state it is estimated to be 700 kDa. Several models have been proposed for the structure of the oligomers based on various structural observations. Open micellar [Bhat and Nagineni, 1989] and a pitted-flexible models [Smulders et al., 1998] are more popular. A variable quaternary structure of αB-crystallin with a central cavity was revealed by cryo-electron microscopy [Halye et al., 1998]. However, it should take into account that these data have been obtained for dilute solution (1-2 mg/ml) of α-crystallin, whereas protein concentration in the lens is about 300-500 mg/ml. Study of α-crystallin in solution at a concentration of 100-190 mg/ml with laser light scattering, found the molecular diameter of protein about 35 nm [Mach et al., 1990], whereas in dilute solution of α-crystallin diameter was equal to 16 nm [Krivandin et al., 2004a]. Native α-crystallin has been shown to undergo heat induced conformational changes and at 60°C undergoes a thermal transition. That results in partial unfolding of the protein, which then doubles in molecular weight and increases in size [Raman and Rao, 1994; Surewicz and Olesen, 1995; Das et al., 1997; Burgio et al., 2000a; Putilina et al., 2003; Regini and Grossman, 2003], but does not aggregate further [Burgio et al., 2000b]. Quaternary structure changes have been observed using FPLC [Das et al., 1997], quasi-elastic light scattering [Thurston et al., 1998], transmission electron microscopy [Koretz et al., 1999], and non-denaturing gel electrophoresis [Burgio et al., 2000b].

Under elevated temperature conditions α-crystallin due to chaperone-like activity suppresses aggregation of a wide range of proteins [Horwitz, 1992; Wang and Spector, 1994; Raman and Rao, 1994; Raman et al., 1995; Saso et al., 2000; Abgar et al., 2001; Krivandin et al., 2004a; 2004b]. However, the mechanism of chaperoning of substrate proteins by α-crystallin is not well understood. It has been reported that the ability of α-crystallin to suppress heat-induced aggregation of proteins is a result of hydrophobic interactions with denatured proteins and that this ability increases when α-crystallin is heated [Wang and Spector, 1994; Surewicz and Olesen, 1995]. Tests of chaperone-like activity of α-crystallin at 37 and 66°C indicated that the protein can act to prevent the superaggregation of partially denatured proteins, but both α-crystallin aggregate size and shape are significantly altered with increasing temperature [Burgio et al., 2000]. Characterization of these changes showed that secondary, tertiary, and quaternary structure were modified, with the latter effect especially striking above 50°C. Furthermore, these changes appear to be irreversible when the temperature is returned to 25 or 37°C. Functionally, the protein is effective in chaperone-like activity at all temperatures, but exhibits a somewhat increased capability after a cycle of heating and cooling. The results indicate the heat-induced formation of high-molecular-weight aggregates of α-crystallin is a slow progressive process. The increased activity of these aggregates suggests that chaperone-like activity depends in part on the packing parameters of the aggregate and on conformation of the subunit within the aggregate.

The increase of α-crystallin in size at elevated temperatures is accompanied by the changes in environments around tryptophan and cysteine residues [Putilina et al., 2003]. The hydrophobic tryptophan residues move to the surface of the protein and thereby increase external hydrophobic interactions [Mandal et al., 2000]. However, the data on the importance of quaternary structure of α-crystallin for chaperone-like activity and the location of substrate-binding site(s) are contradictory. In analogy with Hsp60 it was suggested that the active form of α-crystallin is multimeric, and it binds substrate in the central cavity [Boyle et al., 1993]. Other results suggest that oligomeric structure is not important. Thus, α-crystallin binds insulin B-chains in equimolar ratio per subunit [Farahbakhsh et al., 1995]. It was shown that subunit exchange is not required for α-crystallin's chaperone function. Bovine α-crystallin crosslinked with glutaraldehyde under conditions designed to minimize intermolecular reactions was able to inhibit the thermally-induced precipitation of β_L-crystallin and appeared to be more effective than the native protein under the same conditions [Augusteyn, 2004]. Horwitz et al. [Horwitz et al., 2004] have shown that native oligomeric state of α-crystallin may not be essential for its ability to suppress non-specific aggregation, since prepared tetramers of α-crystallin had the same chaperone-like activity as the native oligomeric α-crystallin. Moreover, it has been shown that synthetic peptides, provided hydrophobic interaction of α-crystallin, have chaperone-like characteristics similar to those of αA-crystallin in *in vitro* thermal aggregation assay [Sharma et al., 2000]. However, data obtained by surface plasmon resonance study showed that subunits of α-crystallin, in contrast to α-crystallin oligomers, do not bind unfolded protein [Avilov et al., 2004]. These data indicate that quaternary structure of α-crystallin is necessary for its chaperone-like activity.

It is of interest that α-crystallin has the ability to specifically inhibit nucleation-dependent aggregation of proteins [Devlin et al., 2003]. This ability has been demonstrated by selective suppression of the nucleation-dependent aggregation of α_1-antichymotrypsin at 50°C. On the contrary, the nucleation-independent aggregation of α_1-antitrypsin was unaffected.

The goal of the present work was to study the mechanisms of heat-induced denaturation and aggregation of bovine lens β_L-crystallin, yeast alcohol dehydrogenase, rabbit skeletal muscles glyceraldehydes 3-phosphate dehydrogenase and glycogen phosphorylase, tobacco mosaic virus coat protein as well as mechanisms of suppression of protein aggregation by α-crystallin. Besides, self-association of phosphorylase kinase from rabbit skeletal muscles and the ability of α-crystallin to counteract the enhancement of the protein self-association under molecular crowding conditions was investigated.

EXPERIMENTAL PROCEDURES

Proteins

Isolation and Purification of Crystallins

Purification of α- and β_L-crystallins from freshly excised lenses of 2-year-old steers was performed according to the procedure described earlier [Chiou et al., 1979]. The lenses were obtained from a local slaughterhouse and stored frozen at –20°C. The decapsulated lens cortex was homogenized at 0°C in 40 mM sodium phosphate, pH 6.8, containing 100 mM NaCl, 1 mM EDTA, and 3 mM NaN_3. The homogenate was centrifuged at 27000g for 1 h at 4°C, and supernatant containing the soluble crystallins was fractionated by gel filtration using TSK-gel HW-55 (Sigma) column. The fraction containing α-crystallin was eluted in the void volume. The peak corresponded to β_L-crystallin was collected by measuring absorbance at 280 nm. Further purification of α-and β_L-crystallins was achieved by rechromatography of the crystallin-containing fractions using TSK-gel HW-55 and Sephacryl S200 (Sigma) columns, respectively. Finally, peaks corresponded to α- or β_L-crystallins were collected and concentrated by ultrafiltration (Millipore PTTK disk membrane (Sigma), NMWL 30000).

Crystallin concentrations were determined spectrophotometrically at 280 nm, using $A^{1\%}$ of 8.5 for α-crystallin and 23 for β_L-crystallin [Putilina et al., 2003].

Isolation and Purification of GroEL

GroEL was expressed in *Esherichia coli* strain W3110 transfected with the plasmid pOF39. The expression product was purified as described by Corrales and Fersht [1996] with some modifications. The cells were grown at 37°C in LB medium in the presence of ampicillin (100 μg/ml). The cell suspension was centrifuged (15000 g, 20 min). The pellets (10 g) were resuspended in buffer A (10 mM Tris/HCl, pH 8.1, containing 10 mM DTT, 0.1 mM EDTA, and 0.2 mg/ml phenylmethylsulfonyl fluoride (PMSF), and the cells were destructed by sonication (5 runs for 45 s at 22 kHz). The resulting suspension was centrifuged (20000 g, 30 min). The supernatant was fractionated with ammonium sulfate, collecting the fraction 30-80%. The pellet was dissolved in 5-7 ml of buffer B (50 mM Tris, pH 7.2, containing 2 mM dithiotreitol and 0.1 mM EDTA), and dialyzed against 3 l of buffer B. The dialyzate was loaded onto a DEAE-Sephacel Fast Flow column (3 x 8 cm) equilibrated in buffer B, and the column was washed with 100 ml of the same buffer. GroEL was eluted with 300 ml of 0-500 mM NaCl gradient in buffer B at 2 ml/min. The fractions containing GroEL (analyzed by SDS-PAGE) were pooled, dialyzed against 3 l of buffer B, and chromatographed again. The fractions containing admixtures were incubated at 58°C for 10 min, and the precipitated proteins were removed by centrifugation. The resulting preparation was concentrated to 4 mg/ml using YM-10 Centriprep centrifugal filter units, and dialyzedagainst 10 mM potassium phosphate buffer, pH 7.5. The solution of GroEL was stored at -70°C. GroEL concentration was determined spectrophotometrically at 280 nm, using $A^{1\%}$ of 2 [Sparrer et al., 1996].

Alcohol Dehydrogenase I (ADH) from Saccharomyces Cerevisiae

Alcohol Dehydrogenase I (ADH) from *Saccharomyces cerevisiae* was purchased from Sigma-Aldrich. ADH concentration was determined spectrophotometrically at 280 nm, using $A^{1\%}$ of 12.6 [Ganzhorn and Plapp, 1988]. Enzyme activity of ADH was determined in pyrophosphate buffer, pH 9.2, at 25°C by the method of Hayes and Velick [1954], in which the rate of absorbance at 340 nm resulting from reduction of NAD was measured. One unit reduces one micromole of NAD per minute at 25°C under the specified conditions and activity, v, was expressed as moles of NAD produced per second per mole of ADH.

Isolation and Purification of Glyceraldehyde-3-Phosphate Dehydrogenase (GAPDH)

GAPDH was isolated from rabbit muscles as described by Scopes and Stoter [1982] following with gel-filtration on a G-100 Sephadex column equilibrated with 10 mM potassium phosphate, pH 7.5, containing 1 mM EDTA, and 0.1 M ammonium sulfate. Concentration of GAPDH was determined spectrophotometrically at 280 nm, using the absorption coefficient $A^{1\%}$ of 10.6 [Kirschenbaum, 1972].

Isolation and Purification of Phosphorylase b (Phb)

Ph*b* was prepared from rabbit skeletal muscle according to the method described by Fisher and Krebs [1962] using dithiotreitol instead of cysteine. Preparations of the enzyme recrystallized four times and freed of AMP were used in the experiments. Ph*b* preparations were stored at -20°C in β-glycerophosphate-NaOH-buffer, pH 6,8, containing 50% glycerol and 30 mM β-mercaptoethanol. Ph*b* concentration was determined spectrophotometrically at 280 nm, using $A^{1\%}$ of 13.2 [Kastenschmidt et al., 1968].

Tobacco Mosaic Virus (TMV) Purification and Coat Protein (CP) Preparation

Wild-type (strain U1) TMV was obtained as described elsewhere (Dobrov, 1997), and its coat protein was isolated by the acetic acid method (Fraenkel-Conrat, 1957). The CP preparations were stored at concentrations of 4.5 to 6 mg/ml in 5 mM sodium phosphate buffer, pH 8.0, at +4 or –20°C. The TMV CP concentrations were determined spectrophotometrically at 280 nm, using $A^{1\%}$ of 13 (Dobrov et al., 1977).

Isolation and Purification of Phosphorylase Kinase (PhK)

PhK was isolated from rabbit skeletal muscle according to Cohen [1973], using ion-exchange chromatography on DEAE-Toyopearl at the final step of purification [Morozov et al., 1989]. The preparations of PhK in 25 mM Na-glycerol 2-phosphate buffer, pH 7.05, containing 1 mM EDTA, 0.5 mM β-mercaptoetanol, and 50% glycerol stored for 3 weeks at –20°C. Before the experiment PhK was dialyzed against 40 mM Hepes buffer, pH 6.8. The concentration of PhK was determined spectrophotometrically at 280 nm, using $A^{1\%}$ of 12.4 [Cohen, 1973]. When preparing the solutions containing osmolyte, the initial pH value of osmolyte solution in 40 mM Hepes buffer was adjusted so that the final pH value was 6.8.

The relative viscosity of the solutions containing osmolytes (TMAO and proline) were measured using Anton PAAR viscosimeter at 25°C, refractive indexes of proline solutions were measured using refractometer (IRF–22, Russia).

Methods

Gel Electrophoresis

Purity of the studied proteins was analyzed by SDS-PAAG electrophoresis performed according to Laemmli [1970] with discontinuous buffer system (25 mM Tris, 250 mM glycine, 0.1% SDS, pH 8.3) on 1 mm thick gels in a mini gel apparatus (Sigma-Aldrich, USA). Samples were solubilized in 50mM Tris-HCl buffer, pH 6.8, 100 mM dithiothreitol, 2% SDS, and boiled for 5 min prior to electrophoresis. Gels were stained with Coomassie brilliant blue R. Apparent molecular masses of proteins were estimated using a standard protein set (Sigma-Aldrich).

Calorimetric Studies

Thermal denaturation of proteins was studied by differential scanning calorimetry (DSC). DSC experiments were performed on a DASM-4M differential scanning microcalorimeter (Institute for Biological Instrumentation, Pushchino, Russia). Protein solutions (1.0–1.5 mg/ml) were heated with constant rate of 1°C /min from 5 to 90°C at the constant pressure 2.2 atmosphere. The reversibility of the thermal transitions was tested by checking the reproducibility of the calorimetric trace in a second heating of the protein sample immediately after cooling. The thermal denaturation of most proteins studied was fully irreversible while the denaturation of α-crystallin was reversible. Calorimetric traces of irreversibly denaturing proteins were corrected for instrumental background and for possible aggregation artifacts by subtracting the scans obtained from the second heating of the samples. The temperature dependence of the excess heat capacity was further analyzed and plotted using Origin software (MicroCal Inc.).

Study of Heat-Induced Aggregation of Proteins by Fluorescence Spectrophotometer

Light scattering measurements were performed on Cary Eclipse fluorescence spectrophotometer (Varian) equipped with temperature controller and thermoprobes under the same conditions and at the same heating rate (1°C/min) as the DSC experiments. The light scattering at 350 nm was measured with excitation and emission slits equal to 2.5 and 1.5 nm, respectively.

DLS Studies

DLS is commonly used to determine the size of nanoparticles in a suspension by measuring the dynamics of the light-scattering intensity fluctuations. Colloidal particles or macromolecules suspended in fluid undergo Brownian motion. This motion causes fluctuations in the local concentration of the particles resulting in local inhomogeneities of the refractive index. This in turn leads to the so-called Rayleigh light scattering. The time-dependent autocorrelation function $G(\tau)$ of the scattered light is a function of the delay time τ and for a single-exponential decay can be represented by

$$G(\tau) = b[1 + \varepsilon \exp(-\tau/\tau_c)], \qquad (1)$$

where the baseline ("accidental") correlation level b is proportional to the total intensity I. The coefficient ε depends on the amount of stray light and on the aperture, but this coefficient is always less than unity. The diffusion coefficient D of the particles is directly related to the decay rate τ_c of the time-dependent correlation function:

$$D = \frac{1}{2\tau_c k^2}, \qquad (2)$$

where k is the wave number of the scattered light, $k = \frac{2\pi n}{\lambda} \sin\frac{\theta}{2}$, n is the refractive index of the solvent, λ is the wavelength of the incident light in vacuum, and θ is the scattering angle. Eq. (2) follows from a Fourier representation of the common diffusion equation that describes diffusion of a particle at the scale of $2\pi/k$ [*Photon Correlation and Light Beating Spectroscopy*, 1974].

The mean hydrodynamic radius of the particles, R, then can be calculated by using the Stokes–Einstein equation:

$$D = \frac{k_B T}{6\pi\eta R_h}, \qquad (3)$$

where k_B is Boltzmann's constant, T is the absolute temperature, and η is the shear viscosity of the solvent. The size calculated from Eq. (3) is called the hydrodynamic radius. It may be larger than the radius of the bare particles because of possible layers of solvent, surfactant molecules, or (for charged particles) adsorbed ions. In most cases these layers add a negligible correction to the size except for the smallest sizes measurable. Equations (1) and (2) are valid for noninteracting spherical particles. If the particles are involved in an aggregation process, they certainly interact. However, these equations are still applicable to monitor the change of the apparent ("effective") particle size if the characteristic time of aggregation kinetics is much larger than the time of the measurements.

Features of the PhotoCor Complex DLS setup (Photocor Instruments Inc., USA; http://www.photocor.com) are typical in multipurpose installations for studying both static (intensity) and dynamic (time-dependent correlation function) light scattering [Yudin et al., 1997]. The optical bench and precision goniometer are based on a massive base. A He-Ne laser (Coherent, USA, Model 31-2082, 632.8 nm, 10 mW) and the focusing system are fixed on the bench. The thermostat and the cell holder are coaxial with the goniometer axis. The temperature is controlled by the PID temperature controller PhotoCor-TC to within ± 0.1°C. The receiving system (photon counting system PhotoCor-PC3) is located on the rotating goniometer arm. The photon counting system consists of a set of pinholes for selection of aperture, a low-noise photomultiplier tube (PMT), and an amplifier-discriminator. To avoid the after pulsing distortions the quasi-crosscorrelation scheme with two PMTs is used. The output signal produced by the photon counting system occurs as a sequence of standard pulses corresponding to escaped photoelectrons. The raw signal from the photon counting system is analyzed by a single-board correlator PhotoCor-FC, which is plugged into a personal computer. The correlator is a multichannel device that performs real-time data processing and accumulation of the correlation function of the light scattering fluctuations. The correlator PhotoCor-FC has two time-scale modes of operation, i.e., a linear mode with equidistant points of the measured correlation function and a so called multiple-tau mode with the logarithmic order of the correlation points in time. Operation of the correlator in multiple-tau mode needs no tuning of time-scale and is suitable for measurements of multi-peak particle distributions. The linear scale of the correlator enables one to achieve maximum accuracy for measurements of a monomodal narrow distribution. These crosscorrelation system and fast correlator allow the particle size in a very wide range of 1 nm to 5 μm to be measured. The personal computer performs data analysis and instrument control. Polydispersity analysis is performed using DynaLS software (Alango, Israel).

Origin 7.0 software (OriginLab Corporation, USA) was used for the calculations and construction of 3D plots.

DLS Studies of the Kinetics of Thermal Aggregation or Association of Proteins

All the solutions for DLS experiments were prepared using deionized water obtained with Easy-Pure II RF system (Barnstead). The buffer, in which protein studied was dissolved, was placed in a cylindrical cell and preincubated for 10 min at appropriate temperature. Cells with stopper were used for incubation at high temperature to avoid evaporation. The aggregation process was initiated by the addition of an aliquot of a protein to the final volume. When studying the kinetics of the protein aggregation, the scattering light was collected at 90° scattering angle. To study the effect of α-crystallin or GroEL on aggregation of different proteins aliquots of both proteins (protein substrate and chaperone) were added into the cell simultaneously.

Analytical Ultracentrifugation

Sedimentation velocity experiments were carried out in Model E analytical ultracentrifuge (Beckman), equipped with a photoelectric scanner, a monochromator, and computer on line; 12 mm double sector cells were used. Sedimentation profiles were recorded by measuring the absorbance of the enzyme at 280 nm. The time interval between scans was 4 min. The sedimentation coefficients were estimated from a differential sedimentation-coefficient distribution [$c(s)$ versus s], which was determined using SEDFIT program [Schuck, 2000; Schuck et al., 2002]. The $c(s)$ analysis was performed with regularization at a confidence level of 0.68 and a floating frictional ratio. The sedimentation coefficients were corrected to solvent density and viscosity (20°C, water) in the standard way.

RESULTS

Thermal Denaturation and Aggregation of Calf Lens β_L-Crystallin

β-Crystallins are major protein constituents of the mammalian lens, where their stability and association into higher order complexes are critical for lens clarity and refraction. The β-crystallin family comprises four acidic (βA1, βA2, βA3, βA4) and three basic (βB1, βB2, βB3) polypeptides [Wistow and Piatigorsky, 1988], which associate to form homo- and hetero-oligomers in a range of sizes [Slingsby and Bateman, 1990]. Monomers of β-crystallin consist of two similar domains connected by a short linker. Each domain is composed of two similar Greek key motifs of ~40 amino acids folded into a wedge-shaped β-sheet sandwich with approximate twofold symmetry [Sergeev et al., 2004]. All β-crystallins are in fast reversible monomer-dimer equilibria over the temperature range (5-35°C) and form tighter dimers at higher temperatures [Berbers et al., 1984]. β-crystallin association into dimers is energetically highly favored, but rapidly reversible under physiological conditions [Berbers et al., 1982].

The different β-crystallin polypeptides from adult human and bovine lenses can be separated by gel-permeation chromatography in three size fractions: β1, also called βH (hexamers/octomers), approximately of 160 kDa, β2 (βL_1) (dimers), about of 80 kDa, and β3 (βL_2) of 40 kDa [Zigler et al., 1980; Bindels et al. 1981; Berbers et al., 1982; Ajaz et al., 1997]. Intact βB1 is present only in the largest aggregate, βH. In bovine lenses, both βB3 and βA3 are major components, whereas in humans βB3 is produced only in fetal and newborn lenses, and βA3 is a very minor component [Slingsby and Bateman, 1990]. Furthermore, the βA3 that is present in adult lenses is truncated at the N terminus [Lampi et al., 1997]. The size of the β-crystallin aggregate correlates with the length of the N-terminal extension of βB1, indicating that the flexible N terminus of βB1 is critical to the formation of higher molecular weight aggregates [Feng et al., 2000]. Separation of the components by ion exchange chromatography under non-denaturing conditions shows that βB2 occurs as homo-dimers and homo-tetramers as well as contributing to hetero-oligomers. Other β-crystallins are present only as hetero-oligomers. It has been shown that hetero-dimerization is an important determinant of β-crystallin stability [Bateman et al., 2003].

According to the early reports, βB2-crystallin did not precipitate even when heated to 100°C. A reversible order-disorder transition was noted at about 58°C [Maiti et al., 1988]. Analysis of β-crystallins by HPLC and mass spectrometry before and after heating revealed large differences in the relative solubilities of the β-crystallins [Feng et al., 2000]. When β-crystallins were heated, much of the βA1/A3, βB1, and βA4 were precipitated, while only about 20% of the βB2 was precipitated [Lampi et al., 1997; Ma et al., 1998].

It has been demonstrated that β_L-crystallin starts to unfold around 60°C [Putilina et al., 2003]. Numerous studies have shown that α-crystallin is able to associate with a partially unfolded β_L-crystallin, thus preventing its aggregation and precipitation [Horwitz, 1992; Wang and Spector, 1994; Das et al., 1999; Putilina et al., 2003]. A high temperature stress, inducing a partial unfolding of β_L-crystallin and an irreversible structural transition in α-crystallin, results in the formation of a new dynamic structure. In this conformation, α-crystallin can form stable soluble complexes with denatured β_L-crystallin via multiple interactive surfaces over a wide range of protein concentrations [Putilina et al., 2003]. Thus, α-crystallin temperature-induced modifications were found necessary to allow for the association with denatured β_L-crystallin.

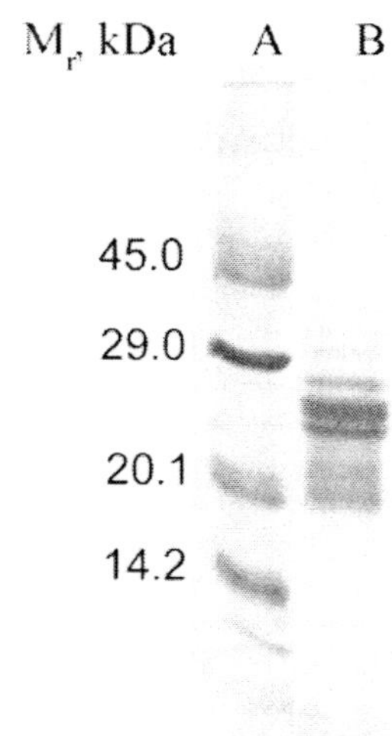

Figure 1. SDS-PAAG electrophoretic patterns of β_L-crystallin after Sephacryl S200 column. (A) Marker proteins: α-lactalbumin (14.2 kDa), trypsin inhibitor (20.1 kDa), carbonic anhydrase (29 kDa), egg albumin (45 kDa). (B) β_L-Crystallin polypeptides.

SDS-PAAGE of β_L-Crystallin Preparations

Data of electrophoresis have shown that β_L-crystallin used contained four main and three minor polypeptides (Figure 1). Number and molecular weights of main polypeptides agree with early data of Henbrink et al. [Henbrink et al., 1975]. We suppose that minor polypeptides are modified polypeptides of β_L-crystallin. According to Zigler et al. [Zigler et al., 1978], gel electrophoretic patterns of β_L-crystallin may depend on such factors as posttranslation modification, glycosylation, limited proteolysis.

Sedimentation Velocity Analysis of β_L-Crystallin Preparations

The differential sedimentation-coefficient distributions *c*(*s*) for native β_L -crystallin at 52000 rpm and 17°C are shown in Figure 2A. The sedimentation coefficient of the major peak was 4.62 S. The observed *s*-value was transformed to standard conditions ($s_{20,w}$ = 5.12 S). As the distribution *c*(*s*) shows a single major peak, it can be transformed to a molar mass distribution *c*(*M*) (Figure 2B) with major peak value 60.7 kDa that corresponds probably to a dimer. The minor peaks may be oligomeric forms of β_L-crystallin.

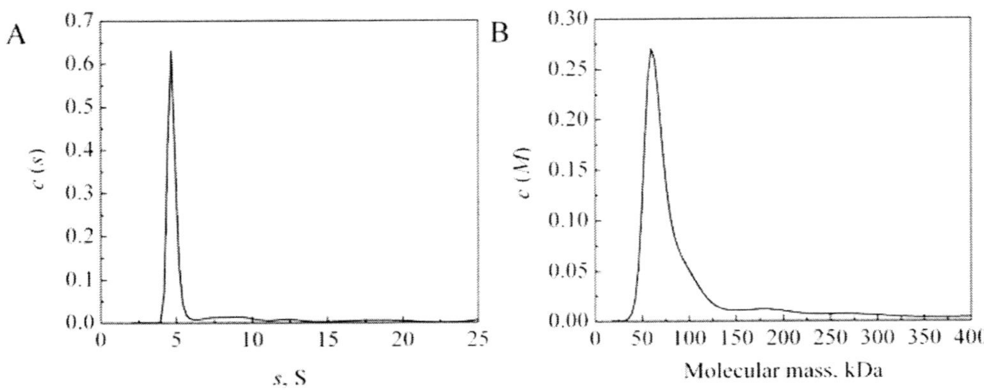

Figure 2. Sedimentation velocity analysis of native β_L-crystallin (0.3 mg/ml) at 17°C. The differential sedimentation-coefficient *c*(*s*) distribution (A) and a molar mass *c*(*M*) distribution (B) for β-crystallin.

Thermal Denaturation of β_L-Crystallin in the Absence or in the Presence of α-Crystallin

Differential scanning calorimetry (DSC) was used to analyze thermal denaturation of β_L-crystallin, α-crystallin, and their complexes. The thermal denaturation of β_L-crystallin was fully irreversible. We found that the heat sorption curve for isolated β_L-crystallin was represented by the main thermal transition at 62.5°C with a small shoulder at ~68°C (Figure 3, curve 1). Isolated α-crystallin demonstrated small thermal transition with maximum at 59°C (Figure 3, curve 2). If the mixture of β_L-crystallin and α-crystallin was subjected to DSC analysis, the thermal transition of β_L-crystallin remained at the same position (62.5°C) (Figure 3, curve 3). These results mean that the addition of α-crystallin has no appreciable influence on thermal denaturation of β_L-crystallin.

Heat-Induced Aggregation of β_L-Crystallin as Studied by Measuring Light Scattering by Fluorescence Spectrophotometer. Effect of α-Crystallin

The measuring of the dependence of light scattering by the aggregates of β_L-crystallin on temperature demonstrated that the curve of the aggregation was biphasic. In the absence of α-crystallin, the first phase was observed as a very small peak with maximum at about 56°C, whereas the second phase was much more pronounced and observed within the temperature range from 63 to 70°C (Figure 4, curve 1). The addition of α-crystallin strongly affected aggregation of β_L-crystallin by shifting the first phase of aggregation to higher temperature and making it much more pronounced. Protecting effect of α-crystallin on heat-induced aggregation of β_L-crystallin was concentration dependent (Figure 4). Increase in the α-crystallin concentration was accompanied by significant increase in the amplitude of the first phase of aggregation and by the shift of both phases of aggregation towards higher temperature (Figure 4). In the presence of relatively high concentrations of α-crystallin, the first phase of aggregation of β_L-crystallin became predominant, whereas the second phase was observed as a shoulder at ~80–87°C (Figure 4, curves 3 and 4). It is worthwhile to mention that after achieving maximum the light scattering started to decrease. This decrease seems to be due to the formation of very large protein aggregates that rapidly precipitate.

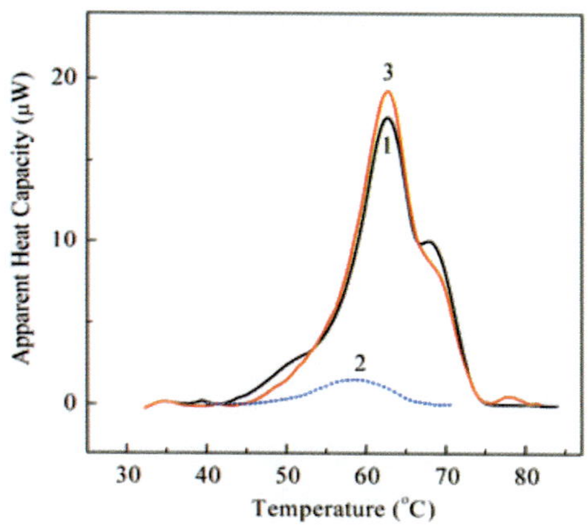

Figure 3. DSC profiles for isolated β_L-crystallin (1.5 mg/ml) (curve 1) and α-crystallin (1.2 mg/ml) (curve 2), and their mixture (curve 3). The conditions of the experiments: 40 mM Na-phosphate buffer, pH 6.8, 100 mM NaCl, 1 mM EDTA, and 3 mM NaN_3. The heating rate was 1°C/min.

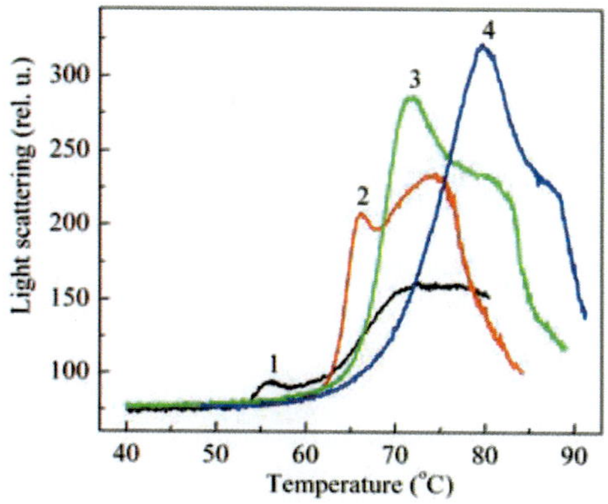

Figure 4. Concentration dependent effect of α-crystallin on heat-induced aggregation of β_L-crystallin. β_L-Crystallin (0.5 mg/ml) was heated with the constant rate of 1°C/min in the absence (curve 1) or in the presence (curves 2–4) of α-crystallin, and aggregation was followed by light scattering at 350 nm. Concentration of α-crystallin was equal to 0.1, 0.2, and 0.4 mg/ml for the curves 2, 3, and 4, respectively.

Thus, α-crystallin drastically altered the character of the thermally induced aggregation of β_L-crystallin, although it had no appreciable influence on thermal denaturation of β_L-crystallin. We propose the following explanation of the effects of α-crystallin on aggregation of denatured β_L-crystallin. β_L-Crystallin is represented by at least two isoforms, which denature and aggregate independently from each other. One of these isoforms unfolds with maximum at 62.5°C (Figure 3) and its denaturation is responsible for the first phase of aggregation (Figure 4). Thermal unfolding of the other isoform is expressed as a shoulder at ~68°C on the heat sorption curve (Figure 3, curve 1) , and it is responsible for the second phase of aggregation (Figure 3, curve 1). It seems very likely that the thermal unfolding of the less thermostable isoform of β_L-crystallin results in fast formation of large protein aggregates that rapidly precipitate. This can explain why the first phase of aggregation of β_L-crystallin is only expressed in a rather small peak. We propose that α-crystallin, when it interacts with denatured β_L-crystallin, prevents formation of very large aggregates, thus preventing rapid precipitation of denatured β_L-crystallin. As a result, in the presence of α-crystallin, the first phase of aggregation occurs at much higher temperature and with significantly increased amplitude, thus allowing clear recording of this phase (Figure 4). α-Crystallin also prevents aggregation of the other isoform of β_L-crystallin (the second phase of aggregation) by shifting this phase to a higher temperature by 7–20°C depending on the concentration of α-crystallin.

The Kinetics of Thermal Aggregation of β_L-crystallin as Studied by DLS

We have used DLS to characterize the size of particles formed in the course of thermal aggregation of β_L-crystallin. Figure 5 shows the typical autocorrelation functions measured at various times of incubation of β_L-crystallin (0.4 mg/ml) at 60°C. The distribution of protein aggregates by their size calculated by DynaLS software is represented in Figure 6. It is worth noting that the distribution function remains unimodal in the course of aggregation.

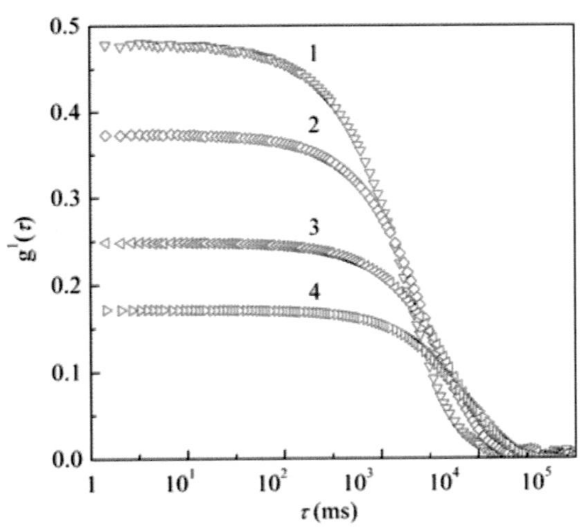

Figure 5. Autocorrelation function measured at various times of thermal aggregation of β_L-crystallin (0.4 mg/ml; 40 mM Na-phosphate buffer, pH 6.8, containing 100 mM NaCl, 1 mM EDTA, and 3 mM NaN_3) at 60°C: (1) 15, (2) 20, (3) 30, and (4) 50 min. All curves were measured at scattering angle of 90°.

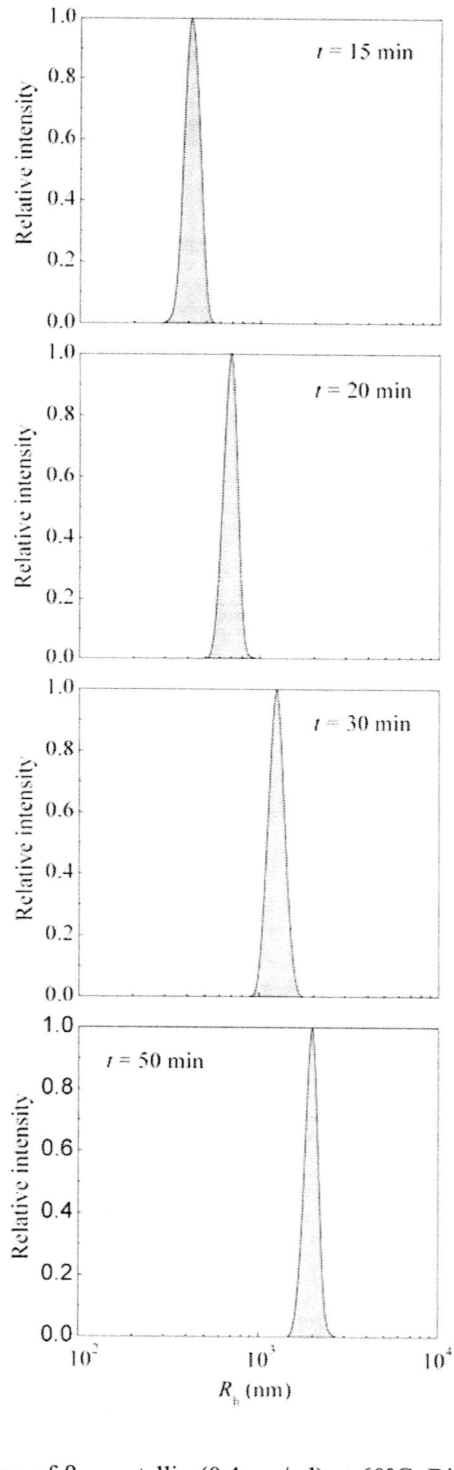

Figure 6. Thermal aggregation of β_L-crystallin (0.4 mg/ml) at 60°C. Distribution of the particles with their size registered at various times of incubation.

The dependences of the light scattering intensity (I) on time (Figure 7A) and the dependences of the hydrodynamic radius (R_h) on time (Figure 7B) were obtained at 60°C in the interval of β_L-crystallin concentrations from 0.025 to 0.4 mg/ml. The higher the concentration of the enzyme, the higher the increment of the intensity light scattering (Figure 7A). The increase in the R_h value with time (Figure 7B) became more pronounced with increasing of β_L-crystallin concentration.

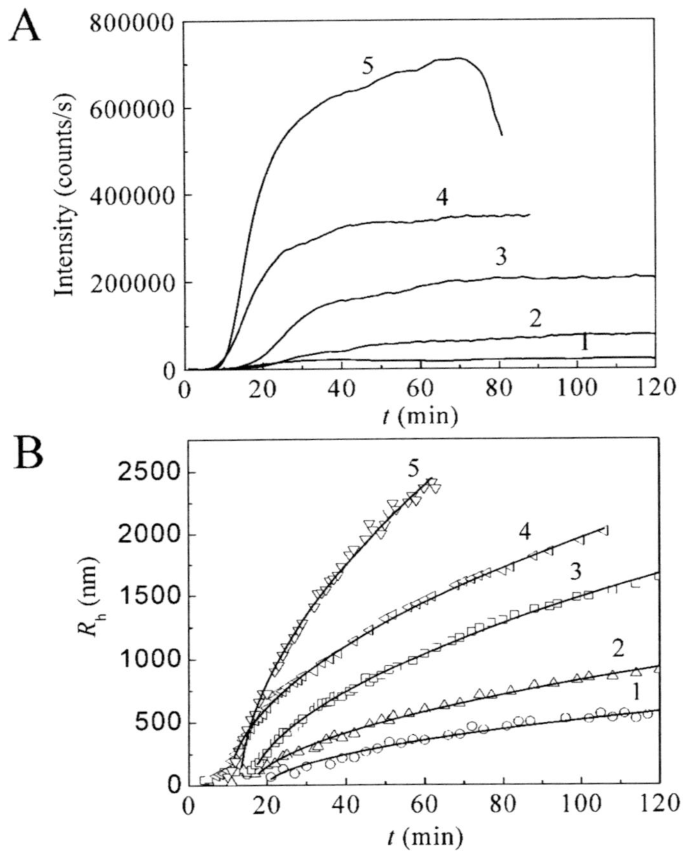

Figure 7. The kinetics of thermal aggregation of β_L-crystallin at 60°C. (A) The dependences of the light scattering intensity on time. (B) The dependences of the hydrodynamic radius (R_h) of aggregates on time. The concentrations of β_L-crystallin were: (1) 0.025, (2) 0.05, (3) 0.1, (4) 0.2, and (5) 0.4 mg/ml. The solid curves were calculated from Eq. (7).

It was of special interest to analyze the character of the dependence of the light scattering intensity on R_h. Such dependences were obtained at concentrations of β_L-crystallin varied in the interval from 0.025 to 0.4 mg/ml (Figure 8). As can be seen from this Figure, the dependences of I on R_h are linear (strictly speaking, for selected range of the R_h values). The length on the R_h-axis cut off by the straight line corresponds to the size of the start aggregates detected at the instant an initial increase in the light scattering intensity is observed. The hydrodynamic radius of the start aggregates was denoted by us as $R_{h,0}$. All dependences of I on R_h obtained at various concentrations of β_L-crystallin cut off the same length on the abscissa axis (Figure 8A). This means that the $R_{h,0}$ value is independent of the β_L-crystallin concentration. The average value of $R_{h,0}$ is equal to 84 ± 4 nm.

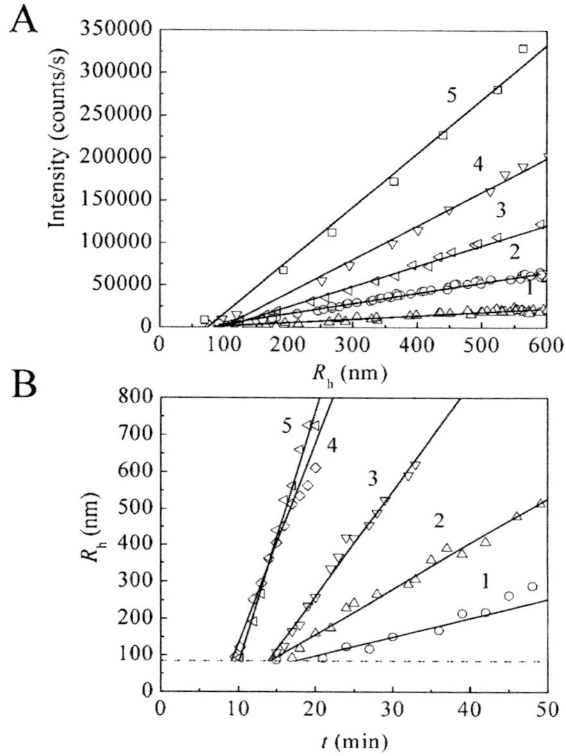

Figure 8. The characteristics of the latent stage for thermal aggregation of β_L-crystallin. The dependences of the light scattering intensity on the hydrodynamic radius (A) and the dependences of the hydrodynamic radius on time (B) obtained at various concentrations of β_L-crystallin: (1) 0.025, (2) 0.05, (3) 0.1, (4) 0.2, and (5) 0.4 mg/ml. The dotted line in Figure B corresponds to the value of R_h for the start aggregates ($R_{h,0}$ = 84 nm).

To determine the duration of the latent stage leading to the formation of the start aggregates, we used the R_h versus time plots (Figure 8B). First, we draw a horizontal line corresponding to the level $R_h = R_{h,0}$ (84 nm). In the interval of the selected values of time the dependences of R_h on time were linear. The length on the above-mentioned horizontal line cut off by the straight line in these coordinates corresponded to the duration of the latent stage (t_0). As can be seen from Figure 8B, the t_0 value increased from 10 to 16 min, when the concentration of β_L-crystallin decreased from 0.4 to 0.025 mg/ml.

The construction of the light scattering intensity versus the hydrodynamic radius plots has allowed us to conclude that the process of β_L-crystallin aggregation includes a latent stage. Over this stage the formation of aggregates is not detected by DLS because of their low concentration. The point of time at which the light scattering intensity was beginning to increase characterized the completion of the latent stage and onset of aggregation. We have designated the initial aggregates whose size may be characterized quantitatively as «start aggregates». The hydrodynamic radius of the start aggregates ($R_{h,0}$) was estimated simply as a length on the R_h-axis cut off by the linear dependence of the light scattering intensity on R_h.

The appearance of a lag period on the kinetic curves of β_L-crystallin aggregation registered by the increase in the absorbance at 360 nm was also observed by other authors [Horwitz, 1992; Wang and Spector, 1994; Putilina et al., 2003; Krivandin et al., 2004b]. In the experiments described in the cited works the temperature of aggregation was selected in the interval from 55 to 72°C. As has been proposed by Kurganov [Kurganov, 2002; Kurganov et al., 2002], the following equation can be used for the estimation of the duration of the lag period (t_0) for the kinetic curves of aggregation:

$$A = A_{\lim}\{1 - \exp[-k_I(t - t_0)]\}, \quad (4)$$

where A is the absorbance, $A_{\lim}$ is the A value at $t \to \infty$, and k_I is the rate constant of the first order. For thermal aggregation of β_L-crystallin the t_0 values fall in the range from 1.2 to 19.3 min; the main factor responsible for the decrease in the t_0 value is the elevation of temperature [Kurganov, 2002]. The duration of the lag period decreases with increasing of α-crystallin concentration [Horwitz, 2000].

To make a rough estimate of the number of polypeptide chains of β_L-crystallin forming the start aggregate, we can use an empiric relationship between the molecular mass (M_r, kDa) and the hydrodynamic radius (R_h, nm) of the protein (Creighton, 1993):

$$M_r = (1.68R_h)^{2.3398} \quad (5)$$

(this equation is valid only for the stages of aggregation preceding the formation of the start aggregates or involving the formation of the start aggregates by themselves). If we take into account that molecular mass of polypeptide chain of β_L-crystallin is 22-28 kDa [Berbers, 1984], the start aggregate with $R_{h,0}$ = 84 nm should contain approximately 3800-4900 monomers of β_L-crystallin.

We assume that formation of the primary aggregates (the start aggregates) from isolated denatured molecules of β_L-crystallin may be considered as a process of cooperative association proceeding in accordance with the principle "all-or-nothing". In other words, the concentration of intermediates (low-sized aggregates) was believed to be relatively small to be registered by DLS. The increment of the light scattering intensity registered in the aggregation experiments was predominantly due to the start aggregate sticking together.

For the diffusion-limited regime of aggregation the dependence of the R_h on time obeys the power law [Lin, et al., 1989]:

$$R_h = R_{h,0}(1 + K_1 t)^{1/d_f}, \quad (6)$$

where $R_{h,0}$ is the hydrodynamic radius of a seed particle, d_f is the fractal dimension, and K_1 is a constant. The fractal dimension is a structural characteristic of aggregates which are formed as a result of unordered interactions (random aggregation). The mass of an aggregate formed in such a way (M) is connected with its effective radius (R) by the following relationship: $M \sim R^{d_f}$. Since the process of aggregation of β_L-crystallin includes the nucleation stage, to demonstrate the validity of the power low for the dependence of R_h on time, we used the modified form of Eq. (6):

$$R_h = R_{h,0}\{1 + K_1(t - t_0)^{1/d_f}\}, \tag{7}$$

where t_0 is the duration of lag period and K_1 is a constant. As can be seen from Figure 7, the dependence of R_h on time for aggregation of β_L-crystallin (0.4 mg/ml) is described satisfactorily by Eq. (7) at $t > 15$ min. The solid curves in Figure 7 were calculated from Eq. (7) at the parameter values given in the Table 1. The parameter of d_f was found to be close to 1.8.

Table 1. The Parameters of Eq. (7) Used for Description of the Dependences of R_h on Time for the Aggregation of β_L-Crystallin (Na-phosphate buffer, pH 6.8, 60°C)

Concentration of β_L-crystallin, mg/ml	t^*, min	K, min^{-1}	t_0, min	d_f
0.025	21	0.37 ± 0.08	22,7 ± 0.9	1.86 ± 0.12
0.05	18	0.75 ± 0.10	17.5 ± 0.5	1.81 ± 0.06
0.1	17	2.03 ± 0.13	16.4 ± 0.2	1.79 ± 0.02
0.2	11	4.52 ± 0.28	10.4 ± 0.15	1.90 ± 0.02
0.4	15	8.23 ± 1.65	13.3 ± 0.4	1.78 ± 0.06

Eq. (7) is fulfilled at $t \geq t^*$.

For aggregation proceeding in the diffusion-limited regime a universal fractal dimension of 1.8 is observed [Lin et al., 1989; Weitz and Lin, 1986]. Thus, one can assume that aggregation of β_L-crystallin registered by DLS is a process involving the interaction of the start aggregates and this process proceeds as a diffusion-limited aggregation. This means that each collision of the particles results in their sticking. In other words, sticking probability is equal to unity. It should be noted that if the growth of the aggregate proceeds by an attachment of the denatured protein molecule to the initial nucleus, the R_h would approach a limiting value at rather high values of time as the denatured protein is depleted [Speed et al., 1997].

Effect of α–Crystallin on the Kinetics of β_L-Crystallin Aggregation

Figure 9 shows the autocorrelation functions measured at various times of incubation of β_L-crystallin (0.4 mg/ml) at 60°C in the presence of α-crystallin (0.05 mg/ml). The distribution of protein aggregates by their size is represented in Figure 10. As is evident from this Figure, the distribution function remained unimodal during the first 25 minutes of the aggregation process, and then it becomes bimodal. Figure 11 shows the kinetics of β_L-crystallin (0.4 mg/ml) aggregation in the presence of α-crystallin. The concentration of α-crystallin was varied in the interval from 0.025 to 0.15 mg/ml. The higher the concentration of α-crystallin, the more marked the suppression of the increment of the light scattering intensity in the course of aggregation (Figure 11A-D).

The dynamics of the change in the R_h value for the protein aggregates with time in the presence of α-crystallin was complicated. At a rather low concentration of α-crystallin (0.025 mg/ml; Figure 11E) the distribution of the protein aggregates by their size remained unimodal with time, and the R_h value increased slower than that for the control curve. At higher concentration of α-crystallin (0.05 mg/ml; Figure 11F) the distribution of the protein aggregates was unimodal ranging up to 25 min. When $t > 25$ min two types of aggregates were registered. Apart from the basic aggregates (curve 1), the large-sized aggregates appeared (curve 2). The point of time at which the function of distribution of the protein aggregates by their size became bimodal was designated by t_{crit}. The hydrodynamic radius of the basic aggregates at $t = t_{crit}$ was denoted by $R_{h,crit}$. When the concentration of α-crystallin was equal to 0.05 mg/ml, $R_{h,crit} \approx 250$ nm.

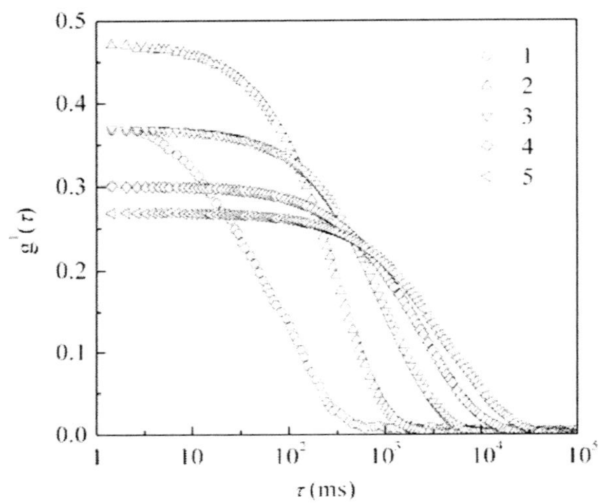

Figure 9. Autocorrelation function measured at various times of thermal aggregation of β_L-crystallin (0.4 mg/ml) at 60°C in the presence of α-crystallin (0.05 mg/ml): (1) 25, (2) 33, (3) 40, (4) 50, and (5) 70 min. All curves were measured at scattering angle of 90°.

Table 2. The Effect of α-Crystallin on the Parameters of the Latent Stage for the Thermal Aggregation of β_L-Crystallin (0.4 mg/ml) at 60°C

Concentration of α-crystallin, mg/ml	t_{crit}, min	$R_{h,crit}$, nm	$R_{h,0}$, nm	t_0, min
0	-	-	77 ± 4	10.1 ± 0.1
0.025	-	-	31 ± 3	17.0 ± 0.3
0.05	~25	~250	31 ± 2	16.3 ± 0.3
0.1	~65	~250	25 ± 1	15.7 ± 0.5
0.15	~80	~35	21 ± 1	23 ± 3

Bimodal distribution of protein aggregates by their size was also observed at concentrations of α-crystallin equal to 0.1 mg/ml (Figure 11G) and 0.15 mg/ml (Figure 11H). The increase in the α-crystallin concentration resulted in increasing the t_{crit} value ($t_{crit} \approx 65$

and 80 min at the α-crystallin concentration equal to 0.1 and 0.15 mg/ml, respectively). The $R_{h,crit}$ values were found to be ~250 and 35 nm, respectively (see Table 2). Superaggregates appeared at $t > t_{crit}$.

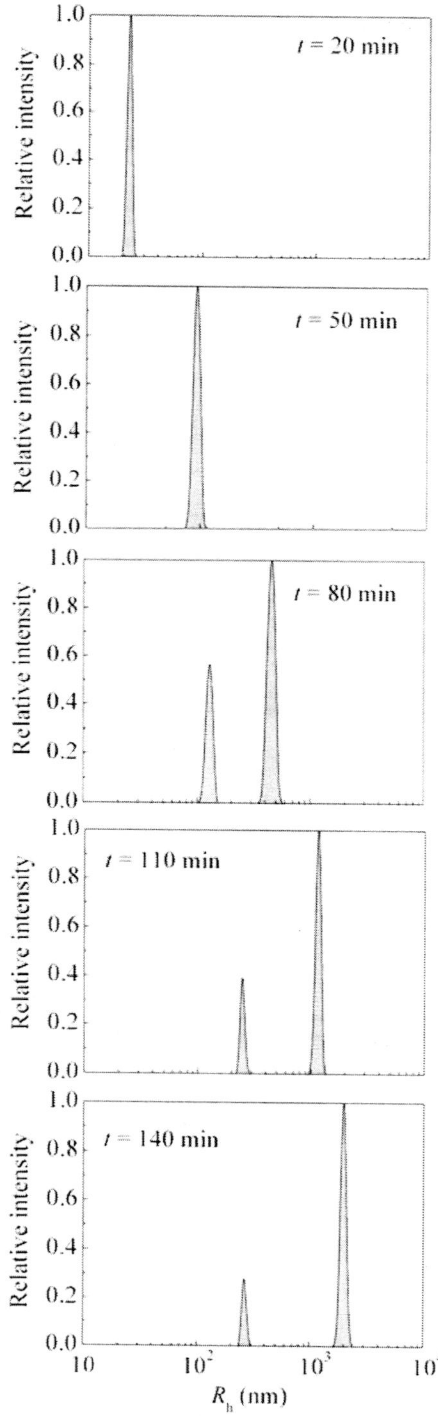

Figure 10. Thermal aggregation of β_L-crystallin (0.4 mg/ml) at 60°C in the presence of α-crystallin (0.05 mg/ml). Distribution of particles by their size registered at various times of incubation.

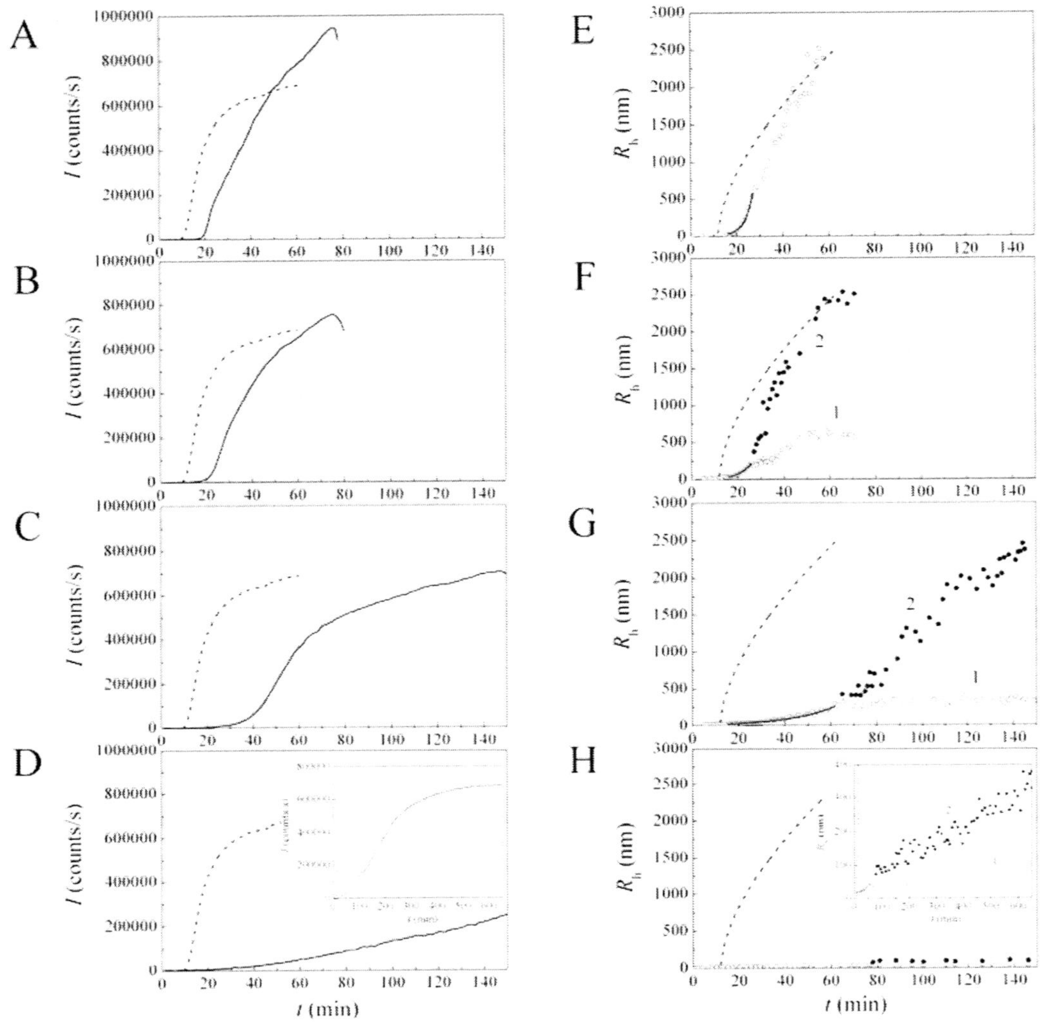

Figure 11. Effect of α-crystallin on kinetics of thermal aggregation of β_L-crystallin (0.4 mg/ml) at 60°C. The dependences of the intensity of light scattering (I) on time (Figures A-D) and the dependences of the hydrodynamic radius (R_h) on time (Figures E-H) obtained at various concentrations of α-crystallin: A and E, 0.025 mg/ml; B and F, 0.05 mg/ml; C and G, 0.1 mg/ml; D and H, 0.15 mg/ml. The dotted lines in Figures A-H correspond to the control (aggregation of β_L-crystallin in the absence of α-crystallin). Inset in Figure H shows the dependence of R_h on t with the expanded ordinate axis. Curves 1 and 2 in Figures F-H refer to the basic aggregates and superaggregates, respectively. Inset in Figure D shows the dependence of the light scattering intensity on time in a larger time interval. The solid curves in Figures E-H were drawn in accordance with Eq. (9).

To elucidate the character of influence of α-crystallin on the initial stage of β_L-crystallin aggregation, we have analyzed the initial parts of the kinetic curve of aggregation. The 3D plot in Figure 12 shows the initial part of the kinetic curve of β_L-crystallin (0.4 mg/ml) aggregation obtained at the concentration of α-crystallin equal to 0.1 mg/ml. The fact that the initial value of the light scattering intensity exceeded zero was connected with the presence of α-crystallin in the system. The DLS experiments were performed to determine the size of the α-crystallin oligomer. At 60°C the R_h of α-crystallin was found to be 10.5 ± 0.2 nm. The analysis of the dependence of the intensity of light scattering on the R_h value (the XZ projection in the 3D plot) shows that the increase in the I value becomes marked at $R_h \geq 25$ nm. Thus, the hydrodynamic radius of the start aggregates is equal to 25 nm. As can be seen from the XY projection, the R_h value increased monotonously with time. The R_h value reached the level $R_h = 25$ nm at $t = 15.7$ min. This value of time characterizes the duration of the latent stage (t_0 = 15.7 min). The break point in the dependence of the light scattering intensity on time (XZ projection) was also observed at $t = 15.7$ min.

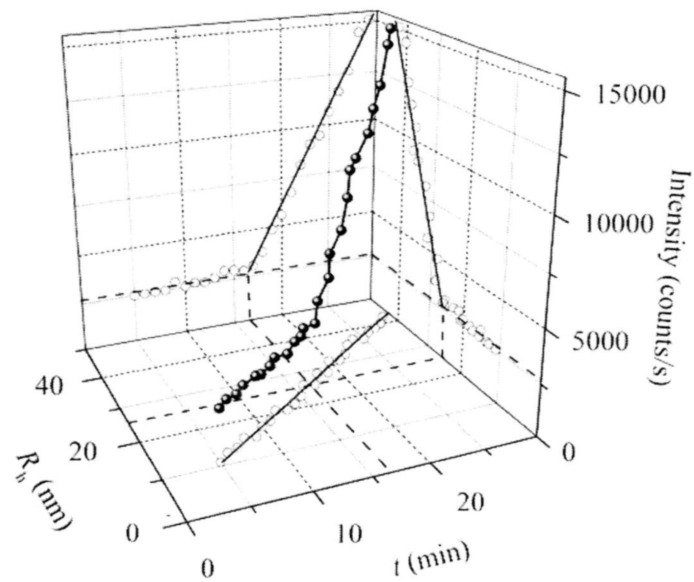

Figure 12. The 3D plot demonstrating the time-course of the light scattering intensity and hydrodynamic radius (R_h) for thermal aggregation of β_L-crystallin (0.4 mg/ml) at 60°C in the presence of α-crystallin (0.1 mg/ml). The dotted line on the XY projection corresponds to the value of R_h of the start aggregates ($R_{h,0}$ = 25 nm).

The size of the start aggregates (the $R_{h,0}$ value) and duration of the latent stage (the t_0 value) for thermal aggregation of β_L-crystallin studied at various concentrations of α-crystallin are given in Table 2. The enhancement of the α-crystallin concentration resulted in the decrease in the $R_{h,0}$ value and simultaneous increase in the t_0 value.

Figure 11 demonstrates the preventing effect of α-crystallin on thermal aggregation of β_L-crystallin (0.4 mg/ml). The main result of the DLS study was that α-crystallin at all concentrations used (0.025-0.15 mg/ml) was incorporated in the growing aggregates. Free α-crystallin was not found in the system. The decrease in the size of the start aggregates indicated that α-crystallin was incorporated in aggregates already on the nucleation stage. The start aggregates modified in this way stick together with a lesser rate. Deceleration of β_L-crystallin aggregation in the presence of α-crystallin is connected with the transition of the aggregation process from the regime of diffusion-limited aggregation into the regime of reaction-limited aggregation (the sticking probability becomes less than unity). If the reaction-limited regime is operative, the time-course of the hydrodynamic radius obeys the exponential law [Weitz, et al., 1985]:

$$R_{\mathrm{h}} = R_{\mathrm{h},0}\exp(K_2 t), \quad (8)$$

where K_2 is a constant. If the aggregation process involves the nucleation stage, Eq. (7) is modified as follows:

$$R_{\mathrm{h}} = R_{\mathrm{h},0}\exp[K_2(t - t_0)]. \quad (9)$$

The initial parts of the dependences of the R_{h} on time in the range of the time values from $t = t_0$ to $t = t_{\mathrm{crit}}$ are described by Eq. (9) (solid curves in Figure 11F, G and H). When the concentration of α-crystallin is equal to 0.025 mg/ml, Eq. (8) is fulfilled in the time range from $t = t_0$ to 28 min. Parameter K_2 in Eq. (9) characterizes the rate of aggregation. The K_2 value decreased with increasing α-crystallin concentration and was found to be 0.283 ± 0.004, 0.208 ± 0.003, 0.051 ± 0.001, and 0.020 ± 0.001 min^{-1} at α-crystallin concentrations 0.025, 0.05, 0.10, and 0.15 mg/ml, respectively.

The appearance of two types of protein aggregates differing in size in the course of aggregation was registered by DLS in the case of thermal aggregation of bovine serum albumin at 58°C (Militello, et al., 2004) and aggregation of dithiothreitol-denatured α-lactalbumin [Bettelheim, et al., 1999]. Krivandin et al. [Krivandin et al., 2004a; 2004b] observed the appearance of two types of aggregates at rather high times of incubation of the mixture of β_{L}-crystallin and α-crystallin at 60°C.

To explain the splitting of the aggregate population into two components at $t > t_{\mathrm{crit}}$, direct our attention to the nucleation stage. The start aggregates formed in the initial stage of the aggregation process have sticky regions participating in the interaction of the aggregating particles. Such sticky sites may be named the aggregation sites. Let us designate the start aggregates as A_1. The basic stage of the aggregation process is the interaction of the particles A_i (the particle, containing i "units" A_1) and A_j (the particle, containing j "units" A_1):

$$A_i + A_j \rightarrow A_{i+j} \quad (10)$$

This model of protein aggregation is identical to the model of the multimeric aggregation discussed by Speed et al. [Speed et al., 1997] provided that the «monomer» is the start aggregate A_1. Thus, the model proposed by us for thermal aggregation of β_{L}-crystallin involves the stage of formation of the start aggregate A_1 followed by aggregation of the multimers. It should be noted that aggregation of β_{L}-crystallin proceeds under the conditions where the denatured protein appears in the system. One can expect that the molecules of the denatured protein will add to the aggregates with increasing the size of the latter.

Sticking together of the A_i and A_j particles resulted in the steric screening of part of the aggregation sites. In the absence of a chaperone such a screening of the aggregation sites in the particles could not prevent the formation of the large-sized aggregates prone to precipitation. However, in the presence of chaperone, which is incorporated in the start aggregates with the simultaneous decrease in the number of the aggregation sites, the steric screening of the sticky sites in the course of aggregation becomes significant. Such a situation brings into existence of the population of aggregates, in which the number of the aggregation sites is reduced as a result of steric screening and becomes equal to zero with time. For this population of aggregates ("the conservative aggregates") the R_h value becomes constant in time. It should be noted that blocking the aggregation sites in the aggregating particles may be due to the attachment of the free denatured protein molecule. Apart from the «conservative aggregates», the system always contains the population of aggregates, in which the aggregation sites are retained even at high values of time. The aggregates of such a kind continued to stick together to the point of precipitation.

On the basis of the study of the chaperone-like activity of α-crystallin we can conclude that the suppression of aggregation of a protein substrate by a chaperone is due to the incorporation of the latter into the start aggregates with simultaneous decrease in the number of the aggregation sites. The reduction in the concentration of the aggregation sites resulted in the transition of the aggregation process from the kinetic regime of diffusion-limited aggregation to the kinetic regime of the reaction-limited aggregation. In the presence of α-crystallin the population of the β_L-crystallin aggregates was split into two components: the stable aggregates, which were not involved in further aggregation, and the aggregates whose growth continued to the point of precipitation.

Thermal Denaturation and Aggregation of Yeast Alcohol Dehydrogenase. Effect of α-Crystallin

Alcohol dehydrogenase (ADH) I from *Saccharomyces cerevisiae* (alcohol:NAD^+ oxidoreductase, EC 1.1.1.1) is a tetrameric enzyme (150 kDa), consisting of four identical subunits, that contains two zinc ions per subunit, one in the active site (catalytic zinc) [Veillon and Sitkowsky, 1975] and one in a loop (conformational zinc, stabilizing the tertiary structure of the enzyme) [Magonet et al., 1992].

ADH is destabilized and aggregates at elevated temperatures. Changes in the CD spectra of ADH heated at 60°C indicate that the secondary structure of the enzyme molecule is slightly dependent on temperature [He et al., 1997]. The unfolding courses of ADH during thermal denaturation followed by changes in the UV difference absorbance and intrinsic fluorescence have demonstrated that ADH unfolding during denaturation at 52°C and at 56°C is a biphasic kinetic process, which consists of two first-order reactions.

Heat-induced aggregation of yeast ADH has been commonly used to assay the chaperone activity of sHsps [Carver et al., 1994a; Clark and Huang, 1996; Reddy et al., 2000; Sharma et al., 2000; Panasenko et al., 2002]. Study of an effect of α-crystallin on ADH heat-induced aggregation has demonstrated that ADH aggregates at 48°C, whereas α-crystallin retains significant native structure under these conditions. [Carver et al., 1994b]. In the presence of α-crystallin, ADH forms a complex with the chaperone and the reaction mixture remains transparent.

Thermal Denaturation and Aggregation of Alcohol Dehydrogenase. Effect of α-Crystallin

First of all, we analyzed the thermal denaturation of ADH by DSC to examine a possibility of using ADH as a target protein for the subsequent DSC and light scattering experiments on the effects of α-crystallin. The thermal unfolding of ADH was fully irreversible, and the heat sorption curve was represented by the main thermal transition at 63°C with a broad low-temperature shoulder at 40–55°C (Figure 13, curve 1). Because of the presence of such a shoulder, this ADH preparation is not quite suitable as a target protein for detailed studies of the chaperone effects of α-crystallin. We have eliminated the broad low-temperature shoulder by using the following procedure. The protein was heated in the calorimeter cell up to 52°C and cooled. The thermally unstable part of the protein was irreversibly denatured during this heating. As a result, in the second heating of the same protein sample we observed a sharp thermal transition with maximum at 63°C (Figure 13, curve 2). This transition is well described by a two-state model:

$$N \xrightarrow{k} D, \tag{11}$$

where N is the native protein, D is the denatured state, and k is the first-order rate constant.

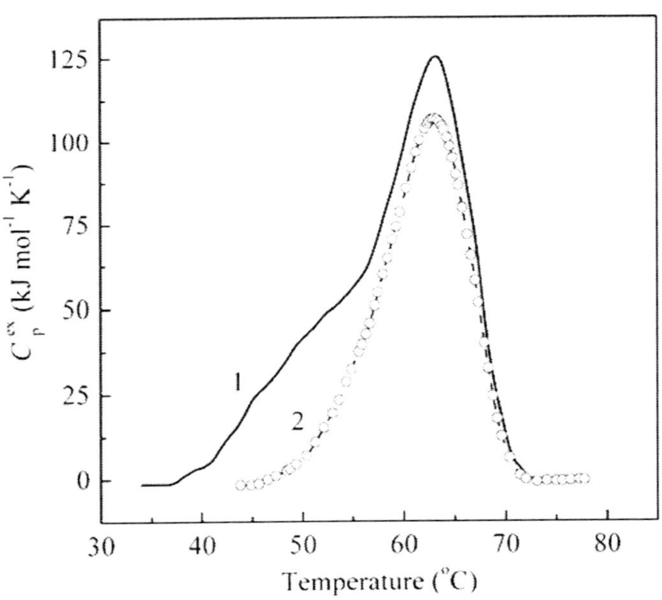

Figure 13. Temperature dependences of excess heat capacity (C_p^{ex}) of the original ADH preparation (curve 1) and ADH after heating in the calorimeter cell up to 52°C and subsequent cooling (curve 2; points are the experimental values; solid curve is calculated from Eq. (12)). Concentration of ADH was 1.5 mg/ml. Other conditions: 50 mM Na-phosphate buffer, pH 7.4, 100 mM NaCl. The arrow indicates the temperature (52°C) to which the protein was preheated to obtain the curve 2 during reheating. The heating rate was 1°C/min.

For the quantitative treatment of the dependence of excess heat capacity C_p^{ex} on temperature the following equation system may be used:

$$\begin{cases} \dfrac{d\gamma_N}{dT} = -\dfrac{k\gamma_N}{v} \\ C_p^{ex} = Q_t \dfrac{k\gamma_N}{v} \end{cases} \quad (12)$$

where γ_N is the mole fraction of the native state, T is an absolute temperature, v is the temperature scanning rate; Q_t is the heat absorbed through the denaturation process (calorimetric enthalpy), and k is the first-order rate constant. It is assumed that the temperature dependence of the k value follows the Arrhenius equation:

$$k = \exp\{E_a(1/T^* - 1/T)/R\}, \quad (13)$$

where E_a is the energy of activation, R is the gas constant, and T^* is the temperature at which the rate constant equals 1 min^{-1}. The following values of parameters were obtained using the SCIENTIST (MicroMath, USA) software for thermal denaturation of preheated ADH: Q_t = 1450 ± 1 kJ/mol, E_a = 204.8 ± 0.2 kJ/mol, and T^* = 339.83 ± 0.01 K.

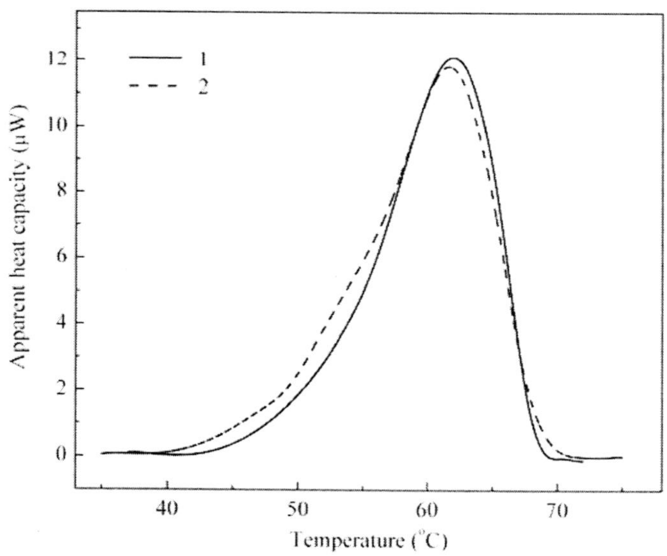

Figure 14. DSC profiles for ADH (1.5 mg/ml) in the absence (curve 1) and in the presence of α-crystallin (0.65 mg/ml; curve 2). Other conditions were identical to those in Figure 13. Before the experiments ADH preparation was preheated for 13 min at 52°C.

In further experiments on the thermal aggregation of ADH the enzyme preparations preheated at 52°C for 13 min were used. The excess heat capacity versus temperature profile for ADH prepared in this way was identical to curve 2 in Figure 13. Determination of the enzyme activity of preheated ADH showed that preliminary heating of ADH preparations does not affect the specific enzyme activity. The specific activities of the original and preheated preparations were 153 and160 micromole NAD/min/mg of protein, respectively.

The DSC profiles obtained for so treated ADH in the absence and in the presence of α-crystallin were essentially the same (Figure 14). This means that α-crystallin had no appreciable influence on the thermal denaturation of ADH.

Heat-Induced Aggregation of Alcohol Dehydrogenase as Studied by Measuring Light Scattering by Fluorescence Spectrophotometer

Figure 15 (curve 1) shows the increase of the light scattering intensity at 350 nm of preheated ADH (0.15 mg/ml; 50 mM sodium phosphate buffer, pH 7.4, 100 mM NaCl) in the course of thermal aggregation of the protein caused by temperature elevation with the constant rate (1°C/min). The addition of α-crystallin (0.065 mg/ml) results in the marked suppression of ADH aggregation. The suppression was revealed as a pronounced shift of the intensity versus temperature profile towards the higher temperature (curve 2). Thus, α-crystallin does not affect the thermal unfolding of ADH, but effectively prevents aggregation of thermally denatured ADH.

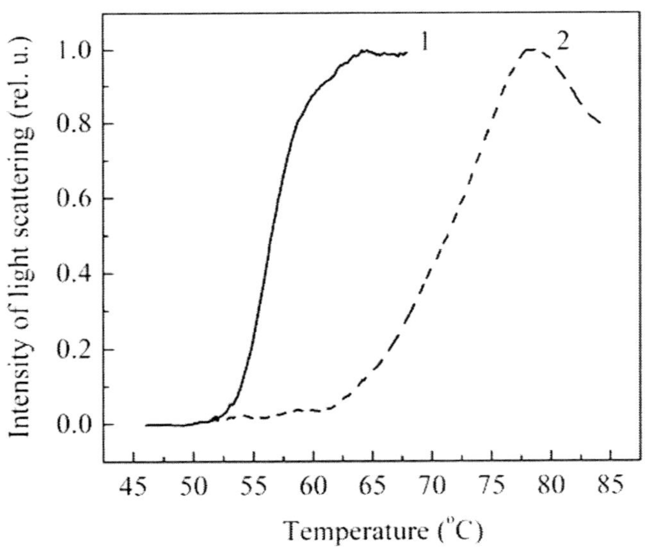

Figure 15. Effect of α-crystallin on thermal aggregation of preheated ADH. ADH (0.15 mg/ml) was heated with the constant rate of 1°C/min in the absence (curve 1) or in the presence of α-crystallin (0.065 mg/ml; curve 2), and aggregation was followed by light scattering at 350 nm.

The Kinetics of Thermal Aggregation of Alcohol Dehydrogenase as Studied by DLS

The kinetics of thermal aggregation of preheated ADH were studied at 56°C (50 mM sodium phosphate buffer, pH 7.4, 100 mM NaCl) by DLS. Figure 16 gives an idea of the rate of the protein unfolding under these conditions. Using parameters of Eq. (12) determined from the DSC data (E_a = 204.8 kJ/mol, and T^* = 339.83 K) we calculated the rate constant of the denaturation process: k = 0.096 min^{-1}. The time of half-conversion ($t_{1/2} = \ln 2/k$) was equal to 7.2 min. The dependence of the portion of the denatured protein (γ_D) on time (Figure 16) was calculated from equation:

$$\gamma_D = 1 - \exp(-kt). \tag{14}$$

At t = 50 min the portion of the denatured protein was equal to 0.99.

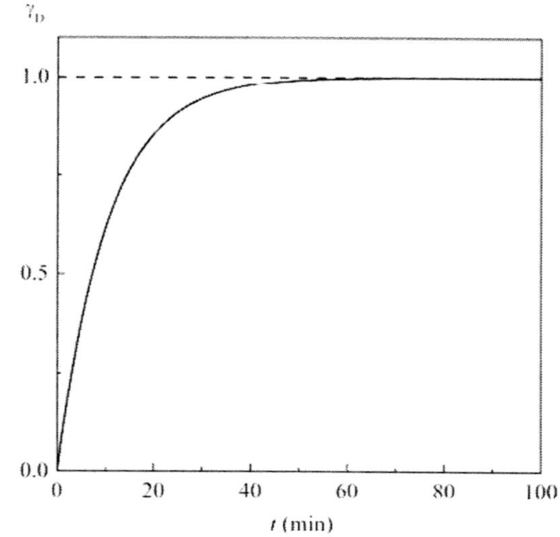

Figure 16. The dependence of the portion of denatured ADH (γ_D) on time at 56°C calculated from Eq. (14) at k = 0.096 min^{-1}.

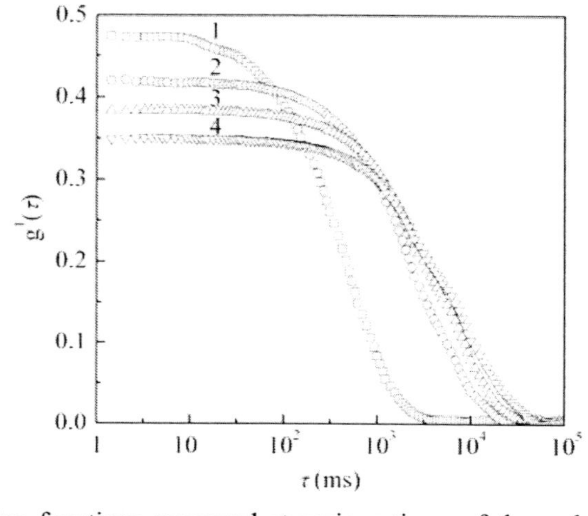

Figure 17. Autocorrelation functions measured at various times of thermal aggregation of preheated ADH (0.2 mg/ml; 50 mM Na-phosphate buffer, pH 7.4; 100 mM NaCl) at 56 °C: (1) 20, (2) 35, (3) 45, and (4) 60 min. All curves were measured at scattering angle of 90°.

Figures 17 and 18 show the autocorrelation functions and distribution of aggregates, respectively, by their size obtained at various times of incubation of ADH at 56°C (50 mM sodium phosphate buffer, pH 7.4, 100 mM NaCl). As can be seen from Figure 18, the distribution of aggregates by their size was unimodal at the initial stages of incubation. However, the splitting of the aggregate population into two components occurred in the course of aggregation.

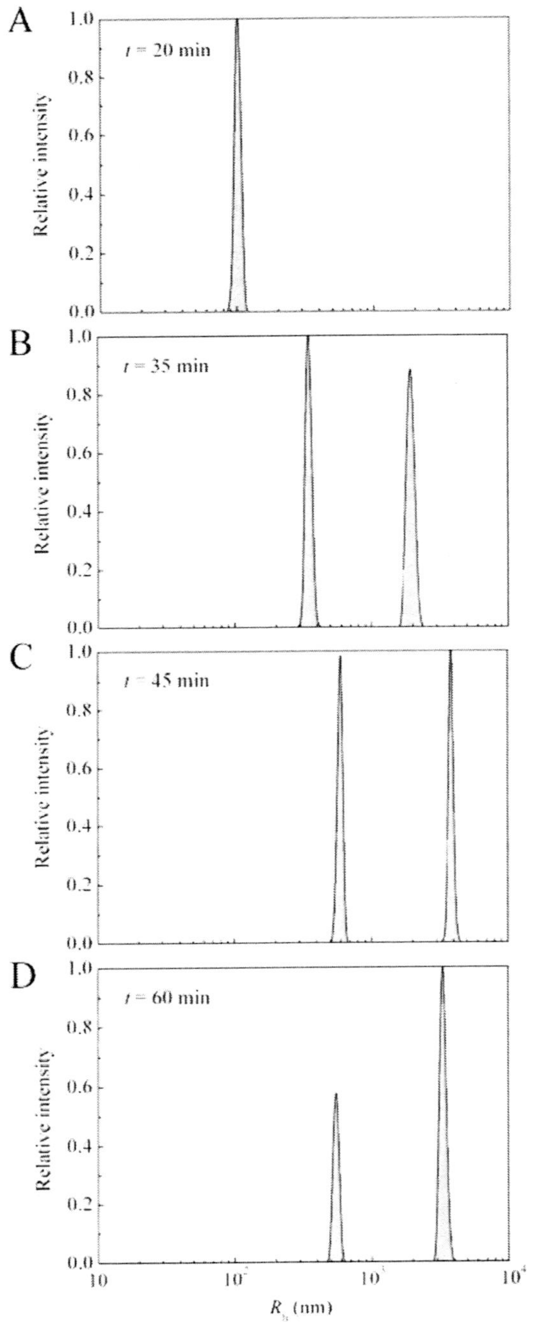

Figure 18. Thermal aggregation of preheated ADH (0.2 mg/ml) at 56°C. The distribution of the particles by their size registered at various times of incubation: (A) 20, (B) 35, (C) 45, and (D) 60 min.

Figures 19 and 20 present the dependences of the light scattering intensity and hydrodynamic radius (R_h) on time obtained at various times of incubation. Both dependences show well-defined lag periods. As in the case of aggregation of β_L-crystallin, the dependences of light scattering intensity on R_h were linear. The length cut off by straight lines on the abscissa axis gives the value of R_h of the start aggregates ($R_{h,0}$). The $R_{h,0}$ was independent of the ADH concentration and the average value of $R_{h,0}$ was found to be 24 ± 1 nm. The start aggregates of such a size contain approximately 167 ± 10 of denatured monomers; this estimation was made using Eq. (5).

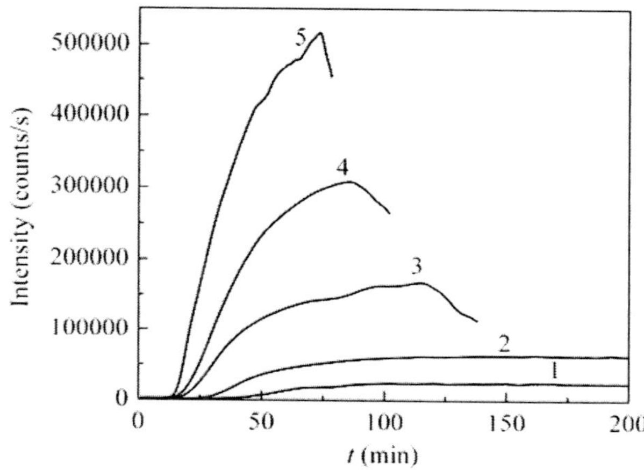

Figure 19. Kinetics of thermal aggregation of preheated ADH at 56°C. The dependences of the light scattering intensity on time at various concentrations of ADH: (1) 0.025, (2) 0.05, (3) 0.1, (4) 0.2, and (5) 0.3 mg/ml.

Thermal aggregation of ADH is characterized by transition from the unimodal distribution of the aggregates with their size to bimodal distribution in the course of aggregation. The value of time at which splitting of the aggregate population into two components occurred (t_{crit}) decreased with increasing the ADH concentration (Figure 21). The initial parts of the dependences of R_h on time obey the exponential law described by Eq. (7). Parameter K_2, which may be considered as a measure of the aggregation rate, increases with increasing the protein concentration $[P]_0$:

$[P]_0$, mg/ml	0.025	0.05	0.1	0.2	0.3
K_2, min^{-1}	0.027 ± 0.002	0.099 ± 0.002	0.140 ± 0.018	0.226 ± 0.007	0.307 ± 0.013

The satisfiability of the exponential law indicates that aggregation of ADH proceeds in the kinetic regime that corresponds to the reaction-limited aggregation (the sticking probability of colliding particles is less than unity).

Thus, the kinetics of thermal aggregation of ADH closely resemble those of thermal aggregation of β_L-crystallin in the presence of α-crystallin. In both cases the initial parts of the dependences of R_h on time follow the exponential law, and unimodal distribution of

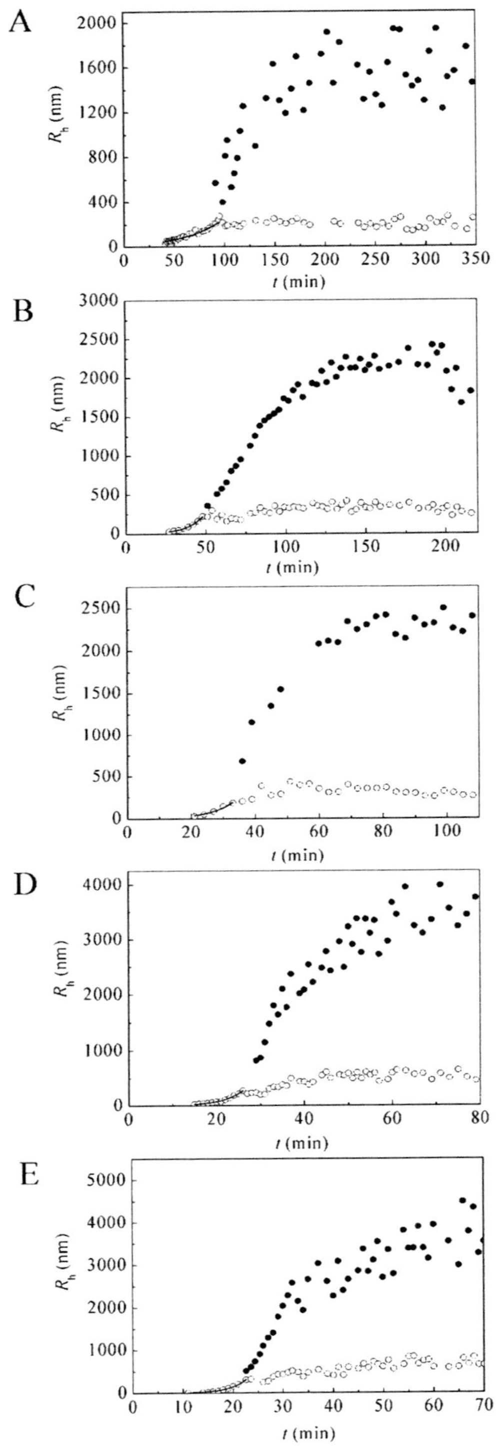

Figure 20. Kinetics of thermal aggregation of preheated ADH at 56°C. The dependences of the hydrodynamic radius (R_h) of aggregates on time obtained at various concentrations of ADH: (A) 0.025, (B) 0.05, (C) 0.1, (D) 0.2, and (E) 0.3 mg/ml. The solid curves for the initial parts of the dependences of R_h on time were drawn using Eq. (9).

aggregates with their size is changed in the course of aggregation to bimodal distribution. One can assume that the unfolded molecules of ADH may act as chaperones blocking protein aggregation.

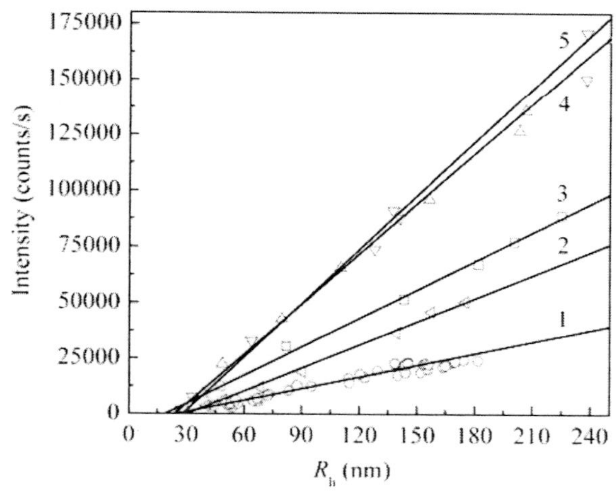

Figure 21. The dependences of the light scattering intensity on the hydrodynamic radius (R_h) obtained at various concentrations of ADH: (1) 0.025, (2) 0.05, (3) 0.1, (4) 0.2, and (5) 0.3 mg/ml.

The addition of α-crystallin suppresses thermal aggregation of ADH. This is evident from Figure 22, which demonstrates the decrease in the increment of the light scattering intensity in the presence of α-crystallin. It is important that α-crystallin blocks precipitation of large-sized aggregates formed at high values of incubation time.

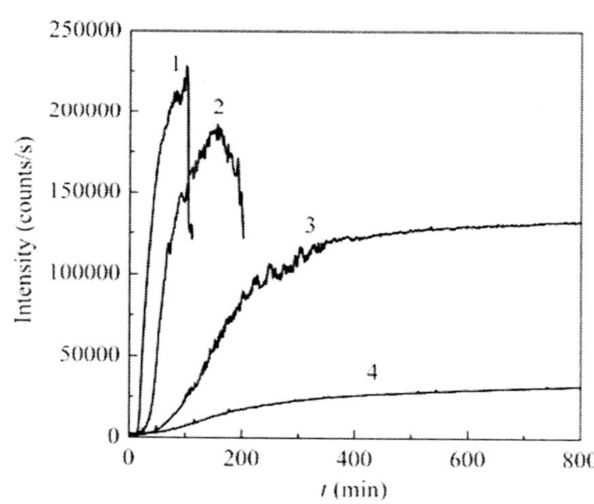

Figure 22. The effect of α-crystallin on kinetics of thermal aggregation of preheated ADH (0.2 mg/ml; 50 mM Na-phosphate buffer, pH 7.4; 100 mM NaCl) at 56°C. The dependences of the intensity of light scattering on time in the presence of various concentrations of α-crystallin: (1) in the absence of α-crystallin; in the presence of (2) 0.015, (3) 0.03, and (4) 0.045 mg/ml α-crystallin.

As can be seen from Figure 23, aggregates of lesser size are formed in the presence of α-crystallin. The exponential law described by Eq. (9) for the initial parts of the dependences of R_h on time is retained (Figure 23B and C). The value of time, at which splitting of the aggregate population into two components occurs, increases with increasing the α-crystallin concentration from 30 min for the control to 200 min for aggregation in the presence of α-crystallin (0.03 mg/ml). At a rather high concentration of α-crystallin (0.045 mg/ml) splitting of the aggregate population is lacking (Figure 23D).

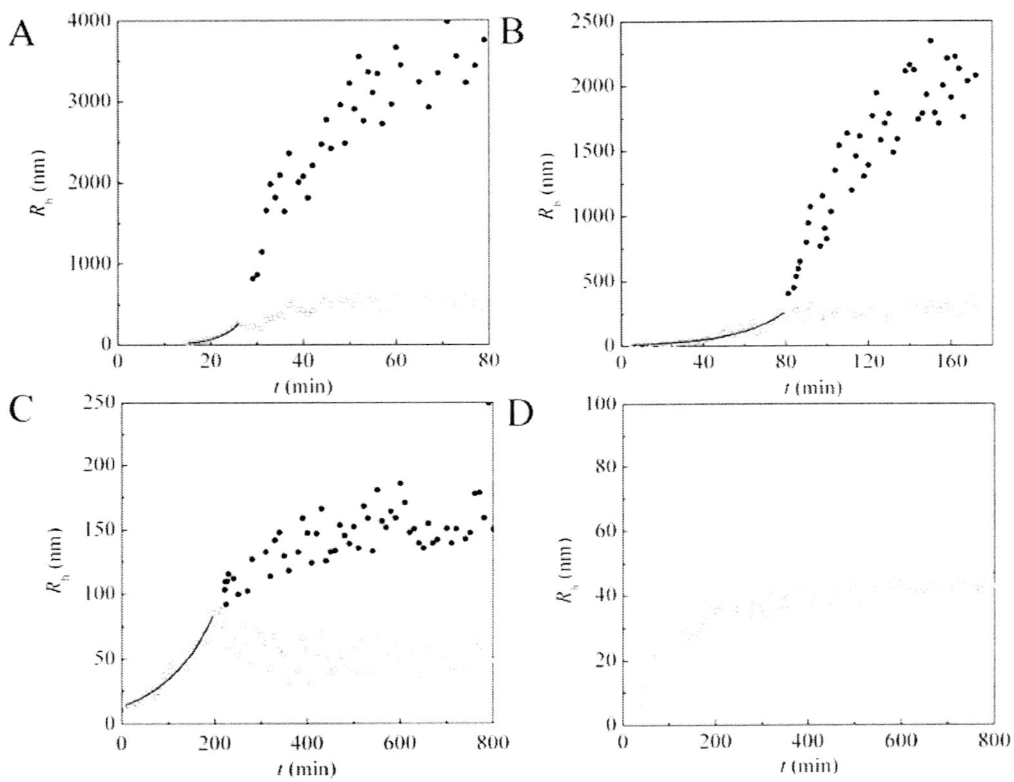

Figure 23. Effect of α-crystallin on the size of aggregates formed in the course of heating of ADH (0.2 mg/ml) at 56°C. The dependences of the hydrodynamic radius R_h on time obtained in the absence of α-crystallin (A) and in the presence of 0.015, 0.03, and 0.045 mg/ml of α-crystallin (B, C, and D, respectively). The solid curves for the initial parts of the dependences of R_h on time were drawn using Eq. (9).

The construction of the light scattering intensity versus R_h plots allows us to make a conclusion about the character of the effect of α-crystallin on the size of the start aggregates (Figure 24). For aggregation of ADH (0.2 mg/ml) in the absence of α-crystallin the $R_{h,0}$ value was found to be 23 ± 2 nm (Figure 20A). At the concentration of α-crystallin 0.015 mg/ml the $R_{h,0}$ value decreases to 12 ± 3 nm (Figure 23B). At a higher concentration of α-crystallin (0.045 mg/ml) the $R_{h,0}$ value was 16 ± 1 nm. Thus, the start aggregates of lesser size are formed in the presence of α-crystallin.

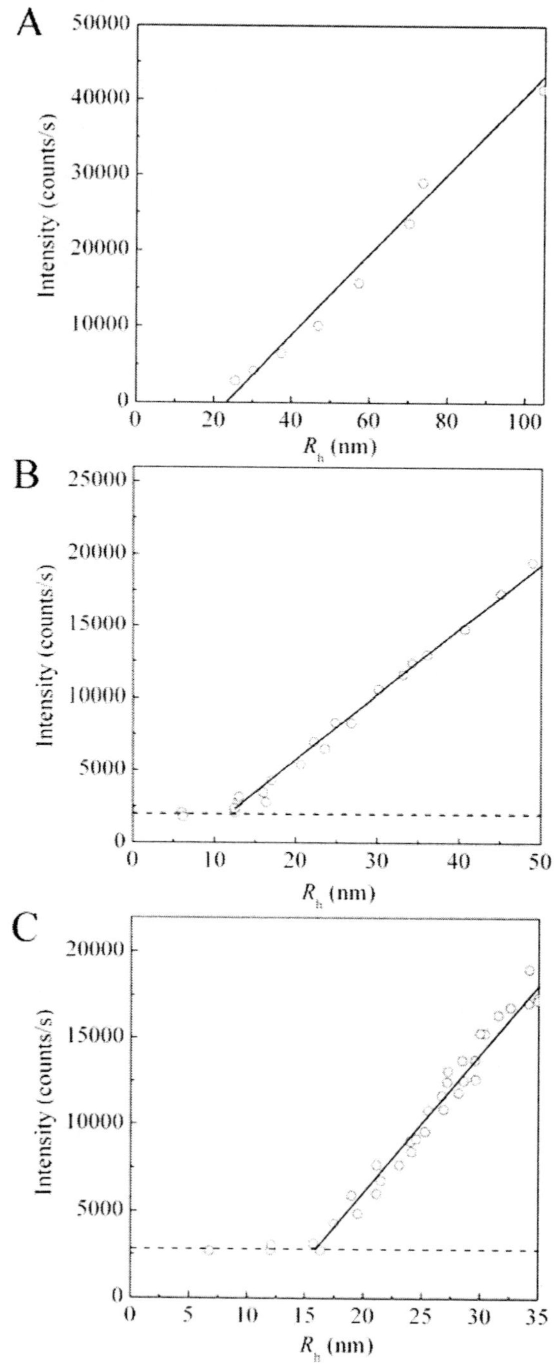

Figure 24. The dependences of the light scattering intensity on the hydrodynamic radius (R_h) obtained for aggregation of preheated ADH (0.2 mg/ml) at 56°C in the presence of various concentrations of α-crystallin: (A) control, in the absence of α-crystallin; (B) and (C) in the presence of 0.015 and 0.045 mg/ml of α-crystallin, respectively. The dotted horizontal lines correspond to the initial values of the light scattering intensity.

It should be noted that the protective action of α-crystallin on ADH aggregation is realized at lesser concentrations of α-crystallin than in the case of aggregation of β_L-crystallin. This is because the ADH molecules in the unfolded state reveal the chaperone-like activity. A hydrophobic region in the yeast ADH molecule that binds to the hydrophobic probe bis-ANS (4,4'-dianilino-1,1'-binaphtyl-5,5'-disulfonic acid) and is mostly present in a random coil conformation has been identified [Bhattacharyya et al., 2003]. This region includes the YSGVCHTDLHAWHGDWPLPVK sequence. This peptide reveals a chaperone-like activity by preventing dithiothreitol-induced aggregation of insulin at 27°C, oxidation-induced aggregation of γ-crystallin at 37°C, and aggregation of thermally denatured ADH and β_L-crystallin at 52°C. One can assume that the unfolded form of the ADH molecule can prevent aggregation of ADH itself owing to exposure of the peptide sequence YSGVCHTDLHAWHGDWPLPVK (40–60) as a result of unfolding of the protein molecule.

Thermal Denaturation and Aggregation of Rabbit Muscle Glyceraldehyde-3-Phosphate Dehydrogenase

Glyceraldehyde-3-phosphate dehydrogenase (GAPDH; EC 1.2.1.12) catalyses the conversion of glyceraldehyde 3-phosphate into 1,3-diphosphoglycerate. GAPDH is a tetrameric enzyme of 144 kDa composed of identical subunits. The polypeptide chain of GAPDH is folded in two domains, the NAD^+-binding and catalytic domains. [Levashov et al., 1999]. The two GAPDH domains are relatively independent, as suggested by the fact that a complete NAD^+-binding domain capable of autonomous folding into a native-like structure could be obtained by protein engineering as a continuous polypeptide chain [Levashov et al., 1999]. At the same time, specific interdomain interactions established upon folding of the whole polypeptide chain into native conformation are of critical importance in the organization of the active center and stabilization of its functionally competent structure.

GAPDH has been extensively studied for structural changes during denaturation. The enzyme renatures spontaneously to a small extent, although there is extensive aggregation, as assessed by turbidity measurements [Li and Wang, 1999]. The chaperone GroEL, with or without GroES, decreased the aggregation of GAPDH but impaired its reactivation. Stable chaperone complexes were identified by SDS-PAGE [Li and Wang, 1999]. α-Crystallin has been shown to specifically increase the reactivation of GAPDH denatured by guanidine hydrochloride with most of its activity being recovered [Ganea and Harding, 2000]. While glycolytic function of GAPDH is well-known, recent evidence suggests that the enzyme plays several diverse roles in living systems. Mammalian GAPDH is involved in membrane fusion, microtubule bundling, phosphotransferase activity, nuclear RNA export, prostate cancer progression, programmed neuronal cell death, DNA replication, and DNA repair. It is of interest that rabbit muscle GAPDH shares 91% sequence identity with the human enzyme; human GAPDH is a potential target for the development of anti-apoptotic drugs [Cowan-Jacob et al., 2003].

Thermal Denaturation of Glyceraldehyde-3-Phosphate* Dehydrogenase *as Studied by DSC

First of all, we analyzed the thermal denaturation of GAPDH by DSC. The thermal unfolding of GAPDH was fully irreversible, and the heat sorption curve was represented by a sharp thermal transition (Figure 25). It has been shown that the maximum of the GAPDH thermal transition (T_m) strongly depends on the concentration of the protein: it increases by 3.5°C, from 60.7 to 64.2°C, as the protein concentration rises from 0.5 to 3.0 mg/ml (Figure 25). Such dependence of T_m on the protein concentration is believed to be characteristic for thermal denaturation of oligomeric proteins and denotes the presence of reversible stage of dissociation of subunits before their irreversible thermal denaturation [Sanchez-Ruiz, 1992; Kurganov et al., 2000]. Indeed, it seems very likely that in the course of heating tetrameric molecule of GAPDH (which is so called "dimer of dimers") dissociates into dimers before their irreversible denaturation.

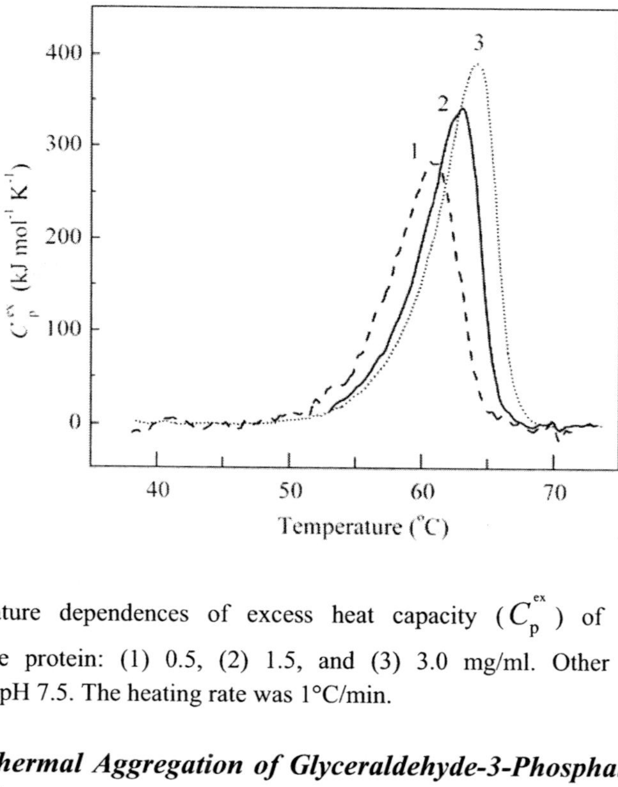

Figure 25. Temperature dependences of excess heat capacity (C_p^{ex}) of GAPDH at various concentrations of the protein: (1) 0.5, (2) 1.5, and (3) 3.0 mg/ml. Other conditions: 10 mM Na-phosphate buffer, pH 7.5. The heating rate was 1°C/min.

The Kinetics of Thermal Aggregation of Glyceraldehyde-3-Phosphate Dehydrogenase as Studied by DLS

Thermal aggregation of GAPDH was studied by DLS in the temperature interval from 37 to 55°C. Figure 26 shows the dependences of the light scattering intensity (I) and the hydrodynamic radius (R_h) on time (A and B, respectively). As can be seen from this Figure, the kinetic curves are characterized by the presence of lag period. At a rather high temperature (55°C) the light scattering intensity increases and reaches the maximum value following which the I value decreases because of precipitation of large-sized aggregates. The effect of the protein concentration on the kinetics of GAPDH aggregation was studied at this temperature. Figure 27 shows the dependence of the light scattering intensity on time (A), the dependence of R_h on time (B), and the dependence of the light scattering intensity on R_h at various protein concentrations in the range from 0.05 to 0.4 mg/ml. The higher the protein concentration, the lower the time value at which precipitation occurs (Figure 27A).

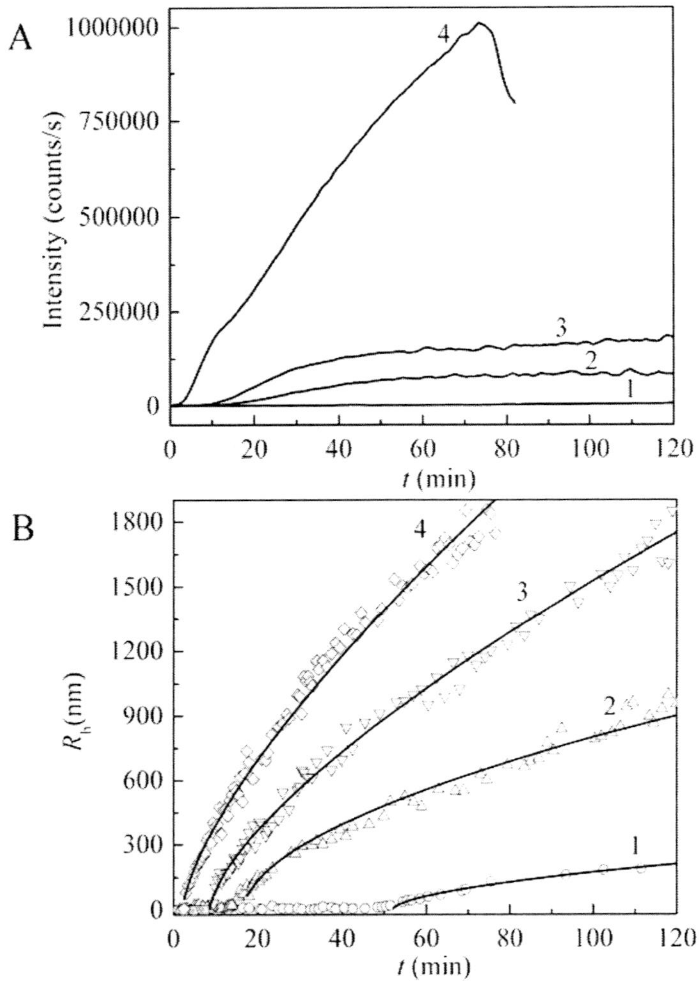

Figure 26. Kinetics of thermal aggregation of GAPDH (0.4 mg/ml; 10 mM Na-phosphate buffer, pH 7.5) registered by DLS at various temperatures: (1) 37, (2) 45, (3) 47.5, and (4) 55°C. The dependences of the light scattering intensity and R_h on time (A and B, respectively). Solid curves in Figure B were drawn using Eq. (7).

The dependences of the light scattering intensity on R_h were linear and enabled to estimate the $R_{h,0}$ value for the start aggregates (as a length cut off on the abscissa axis by straight lines). The $R_{h,0}$ value was independent of the protein concentration and was found to be 22.3 ± 0.6 nm. The rough estimation of the number of the denatured monomers of GAPDH in the start aggregate performed by Eq. (5) gave the value of 135 ± 10. Analysis of the dependences of R_h on time shows that starting from a certain value of time, the experimental data are satisfactorily described by Eq. (7) at $R_{h,0}$ = 22.3 nm. Parameters of Eq. (7) are given in Table 3. The fact that the d_f value is close to 1.8 means that aggregation of GAPDH under studied conditions proceeds in the kinetic regime corresponding to the diffusion-limited aggregation.

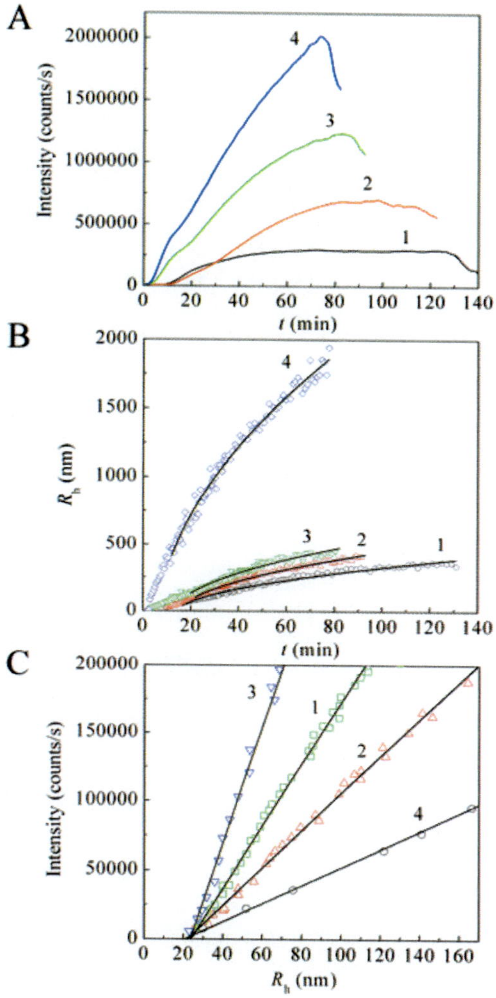

Figure 27. Kinetics of thermal aggregation of GAPDH (0.4 mg/ml) at 55°C registered by DLS. The dependences of the light scattering intensity on time (A), R_h on time (B), and the light scattering intensity on R_h (C) were obtained at various concentrations of the enzyme: (1) 0.05, (2) 0.2, (3) 0.3, and (4) 0.4 mg/ml. Solid curves in Figure B were drawn using Eq. (7) at $R_{h,0}$ = 22.3 nm.

Table 3. Parameters of Eq. (7) Used for Description of the Dependences of R_h on Time for Aggregation of GAPDH (Na-phosphate buffer, pH 7.5; 55°C)

Concentration of GAPDH, mg/ml	t^*, min	K, min^{-1}	t_0, min	d_f
0.05	17	1.4 ± 0.2	15.5 ± 0.7	1.80 ± 0.06
0.2	18	2.6 ± 0.3	16.4 ± 0.5	1.80 ± 0.05
0.3	17	3.6 ± 1.0	13.5 ± 0.9	1.81 ± 0.09
0.4	12	45 ± 14	7.5 ± 0.9	1.82 ± 0.07

Eq. (7) is fulfilled at $t \geq t^*$.

Effect of α-Crystallin on Thermal Denaturation and Aggregation of Glyceraldehyde-3-Phosphate Dehydrogenase as Studied by Measuring Light Scattering by Fluorescence Spectrophotometer

When the mixture of GAPDH and α-crystallin was subjected to DSC analysis, the thermal transition of GAPDH shifted by 2.5°C to a lower temperature (Figure 28A). This pronounced shift cannot be explained by simple superposition of the thermal transition of GAPDH and α-crystallin, and therefore, it suggests that some interaction between GAPDH and α-crystallin occurs before the thermal unfolding of GAPDH. In this respect, GAPDH cardinally differs from other proteins studied by DSC under the same conditions (β_L-crystallin and ADH described above, see Figures 3 and 13), for which addition of α-crystallin had no influence on the thermal unfolding process. It seems most likely that α-crystallin can interact with GAPDH dimers produced from tetrameric GAPDH molecule due to its dissociation during the heating.

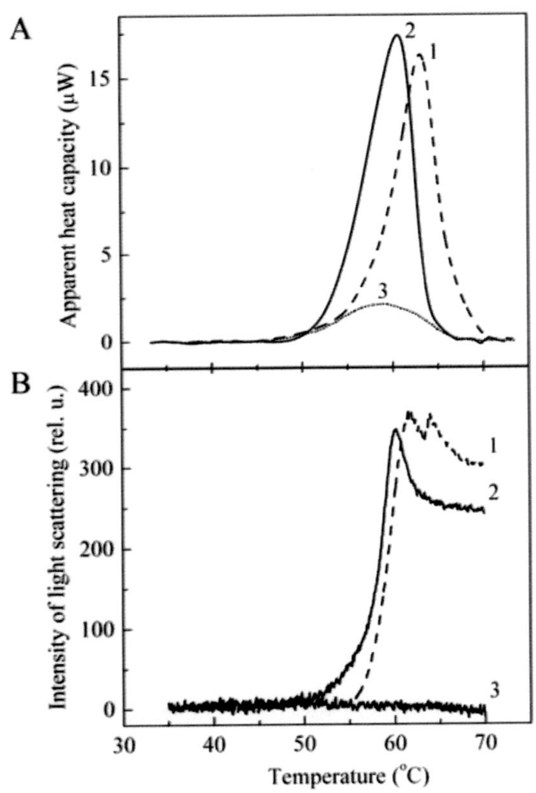

Figure 28. The effect of α–crystallin on thermal denaturation and aggregation of GAPDH. (A) DSC profiles for GAPDH (1.0 mg/ml) in the absence (curve 1) and in the presence (curve 2) of α-crystallin (1.0 mg/ml). Curve 3 represents the profile for isolated α-crystallin (1.0 mg/ml). Other conditions were identical to those in Figure 25. (B) Temperature dependences of the heat-induced aggregation of GAPDH (measuring of light scattering by fluorescence spectrophotometer) in the absence or in the presence of α-crystallin. GAPDH was heated with the constant rate of 1°C/min in the absence (dashed line curves 1 in A and B) or in the presence of α-crystallin, and aggregation was followed by light scattering at 350 nm.

Figure 28B represents the temperature dependences of the heat-induced aggregation of GAPDH in the absence and in the presence of α-crystallin. It is important to note that these measurements of light scattering by fluorescence spectrophotometer were performed on the same samples, under the same conditions, and at the same heating rate as DSC experiments shown in Figure 28A. It is clearly seen from Figure 28 that thermal denaturation of GAPDH is accompanied by aggregation of the protein, which is expressed in a pronounced increase of light scattering. However, no significant difference was observed between the aggregation curves obtained in the presence and in the absence of α-crystallin (Figure 28B). In this respect, GAPDH is quite different from other proteins, β_L-crystallin and ADH, whose thermally induced aggregation was studied under similar conditions (see above). For these proteins, addition of α-crystallin resulted in the significant shift of the aggregation curves towards a higher temperature (see Figures 4 and 15). In contrast, the addition of α-crystallin at weight ratio α-crystallin/GAPDH equal to 1:1 had no appreciable influence of the heat-induced aggregation of GAPDH (Figure 28B). Some appreciable changes in the temperature dependence of light scattering were only observed in the presence of excess of α-crystallin. In this case, in the presence of 1.5 to 2-fold weight excess of α-crystallin, we observed significant decrease in the amplitude of light scattering of GAPDH (Figure 28). However, even in this case we did not observe any noticeable shift of the GAPDH light scattering profile towards higher temperature.

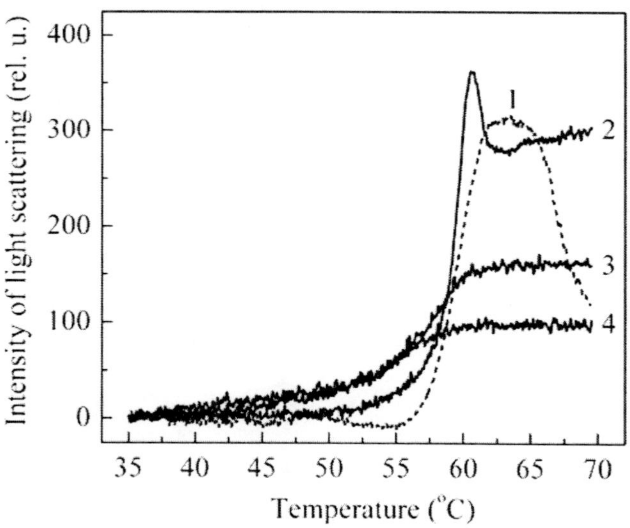

Figure 29. Concentration dependent effect of α-crystallin on the heat-induced aggregation of GAPDH. GAPDH (0.5 mg/ml) was heated with constant rate of 1°C/min in the absence or in the presence of α-crystallin, and aggregation was followed by light scattering at 350 nm by fluorescence spectrophotometer. Concentrations of α-crystallin were equal to 0, 0.5, 0.75, and 1.0 mg/ml for the curves 1, 2, 3, and 4, respectively.

Thus, at first glance, the results of these experiments show that α-crystallin has no appreciable protective effect on the aggregation of thermally denatured GAPDH, as it does not induce the shift of the aggregation curve to higher temperature that is characteristic for other proteins studied by this way (β_L-crystallin (Figure 4), ADH (Figure 15), and F-actin [Pivovarova et al., 2005]. However, some our observations suggest that α-crystallin also can very effectively prevent the aggregation of thermally denatured GAPDH. We have observed that solution of fully denatured GAPDH remained clear after heating up to 70°C in the presence of α-crystallin (curves 2–4 in Figure 29), whereas in the absence of α-crystallin (curves 1 in Figures 28B and 29) solution of GAPDH became very turbid after the heating. After cooling, these samples were subjected to DLS analysis to estimate the size of the aggregates. The R_h values obtained from these measurements for the complexes of fully denatured GAPDH with α-crystallin were equal to 20.7 ± 0.1 and 15.5 ± 0.1 nm at weight ratio α-crystallin/GAPDH equal to 1:1 and 2:1, respectively. These R_h values were much less than those of aggregated GAPDH in the absence of α-crystallin, which were measured in hundreds of nm, and they were comparable with the R_h values of native unheated GAPDH (4.7 nm) and α-crystallin (10 nm).

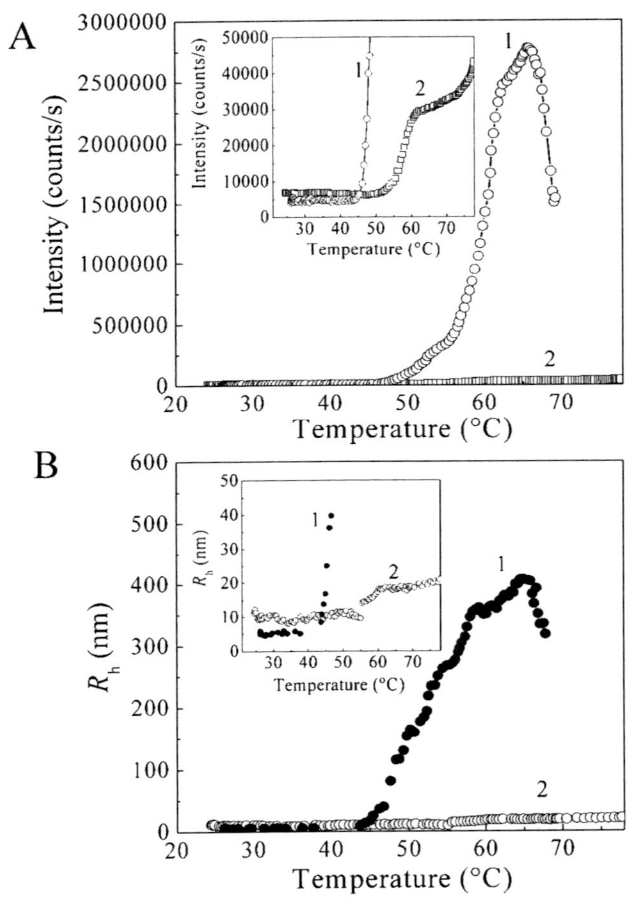

Figure 30. Effect of α-crystallin (0.4 mg/ml) on thermal aggregation of GAPDH (0.4 mg/ml) registered by DLS. Temperature was elevated with the constant rate (1°C/min). The dependences of the light scattering intensity and R_h on temperature (A and B, respectively) obtained in the absence (curves 1) and in the presence of α-crystallin (curves 2). Insets in Figures A and B show the dependences of the light scattering intensity and R_h on temperature with the extended ordinate axes.

The question has arisen: why such a significant difference in the size between aggregates formed by thermally denatured GAPDH in the presence and in the absence of α-crystallin cannot be detected by measuring the temperature dependences of light scattering? The point is that these measurements were performed on highly sensitive fluorescence spectrophotometer Cary Eclipse (Varian), which is unsuitable for analysis of light scattering in turbid media. This approach is quite applicable to analyze the first stage of aggregation that occurs during thermal denaturation of the protein, but it is probably non-applicable to investigate the following stages of aggregation, when the protein solution becomes turbid due to the formation of very large aggregates.

To check this assumption, we performed an experiment on the effect of α-crystallin on aggregation of GAPDH in DLS experiments, in which temperature was elevated with a constant rate. This method is more applicable for measuring protein aggregation in turbid media. Figure 30 shows the dependences of the light scattering intensity and R_h value on temperature (Figure 30A and B, respectively), obtained in the absence (curve 1) or in the presence of α-crystallin (0.4 mg/ml, curves 2). The analysis of data obtained shows that aggregation of GAPDH alone becomes considerable at temperatures higher than 45°C. The addition of α-crystallin resulted in reduction of the increment of the light scattering intensity and formation of aggregates of lesser size. The results show a significant difference in the intensity of light scattering and in the R_h values between GAPDH samples heated in the presence and in the absence of α-crystallin (Figure 30). This means that α-crystallin indeed effectively prevents the thermally denatured GAPDH from formation of large aggregates.

Effect of α-Crystallin on the Kinetics of Thermal Aggregation of Glyceraldehyde-3-Phosphate Dehydrogenase as Studied by DLS

Figure 31 demonstrates the effect of α-crystallin on the kinetics of aggregation of GAPDH at 45°C. The addition of α-crystallin reduced the increment of the light scattering intensity and suppressed precipitation of large-sized aggregates of GAPDH (Figure 31A). The calculations of the hydrodynamic radius showed that the aggregates of the lesser size were formed in the presence of α-crystallin (Figure 31B-F). The initial part of the dependence of R_h on time obtained in the presence of α-crystallin at the concentration of 0.025 mg/ml obey the exponential law (see Eq. (9)).

As in the case of thermal aggregation of β_L-crystallin, aggregation of GAPDH in the presence of α-crystallin was accompanied by splitting the aggregate population into two components at rather high values of time ($t > t_{crit}$). Such a picture was observed at the concentrations of α-crystallin equal to 0.025–0.1 mg/ml. However, at higher concentrations of α-crystallin the distribution of aggregates with their size remained unimodal over the overall period of registration of the process (1200 min; Figure 31E, F).

It was unexpected that at the concentration of α-crystallin equal to 0.8 mg/ml the R_h value decreased in the initial stages of the registration of the aggregation process. Further heating of the GAPDH and α-crystallin mixture resulted in the increase of the R_h value, and at rather high values of incubation time (600-1200 min) the hydrodynamic radius approached the value close to the R_h value typical of α-crystallin alone (R_h = 10.5 nm). To explain such a behavior of the GAPDH and α-crystallin mixture with high content of α-crystallin, we studied the DLS characteristics of α-crystallin under heating at 45°C. As can be seen from

Figure 32, long-term heating of α-crystallin was accompanied by the decrease in both the light scattering intensity and R_h value. At rather high times of incubation (600-800 min) R_h reached the value near 7.0 ± 0.1 nm. These data indicate that heating at 45°C resulted in dissociation of the α-crystallin oligomers into oligomeric forms of lesser size. Thus, the initial decrease in the R_h value in the course of GAPDH aggregation in the presence of high concentration of α-crystallin (0.8 mg/ml, Figure 32F) may be connected with partial dissociation of the α-crystallin oligomers. The increase in the R_h value at $t > 100$ min was due to the development of the aggregation process in the system.

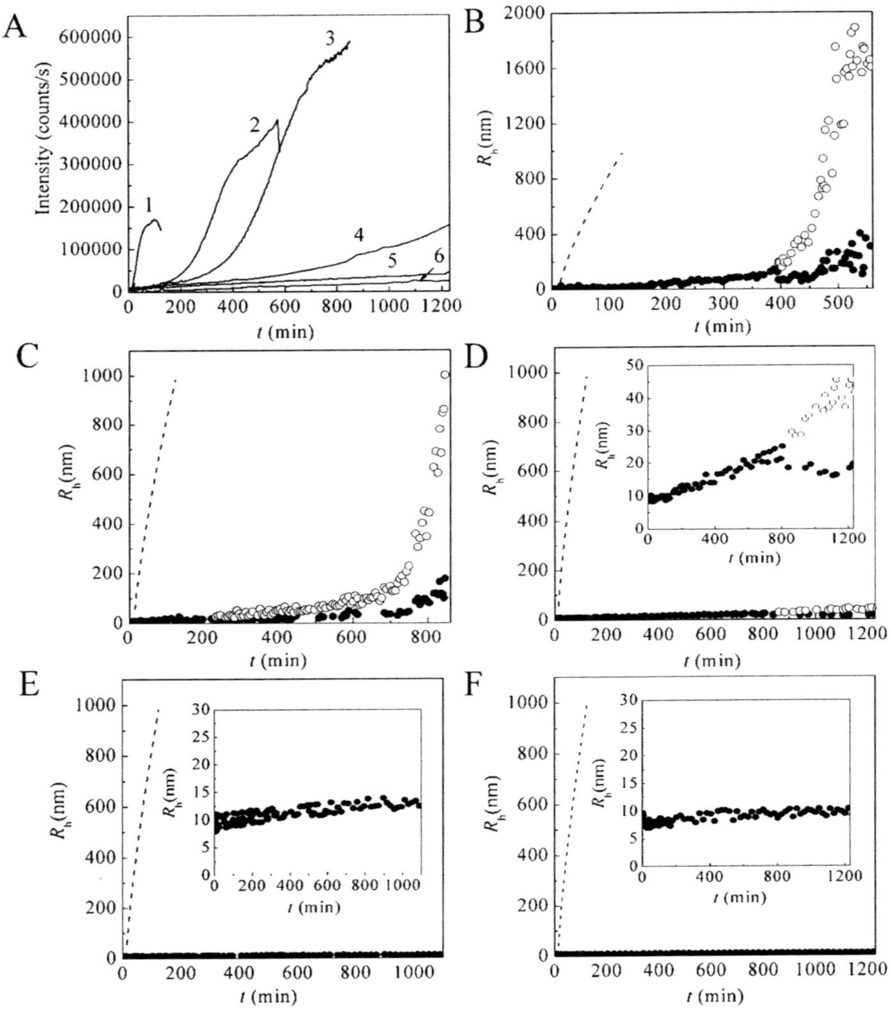

Figure 31. Effect of various concentrations of α-crystallin on thermal aggregation of GAPDH (0.4 mg/ml) at 45°C registered by DLS. The dependences of the light scattering intensity on time (A) obtained in the absence of α-crystallin (1) and in the presence of various concentrations of α-crystallin: (2) 0.025, (3) 0.05, (4) 0.1, (5) 0.4, and (6) 0.8 mg/ml. The dependences of R_h on time obtained at various concentrations of α-crystallin: (B) 0.025, (C) 0.05, (D) 0.1, (E) 0.4, and (F) 0.8 mg/ml. The dotted lines in Figures B–F correspond to the control (aggregation in the absence of α-crystallin). Inset shows the dependence of R_h on time with the extended coordinate axis.

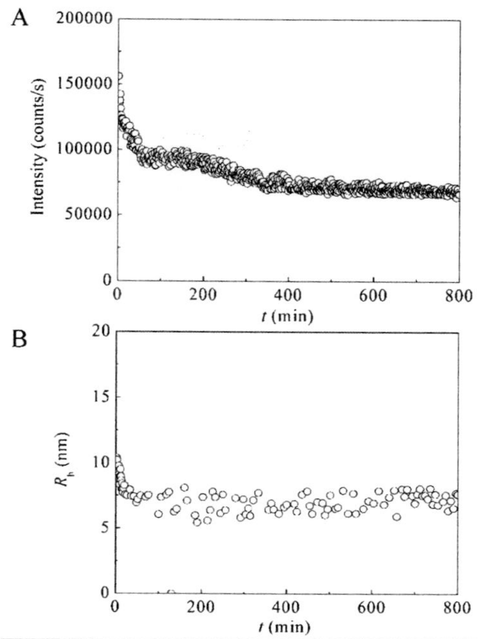

Figure 32. The changes in the light scattering intensity and R_h with time (A and B, respectively) registered by DLS at heating of α-crystallin (1 mg/ml) at 45°C (10 mM Na-phosphate buffer, ph 7.5).

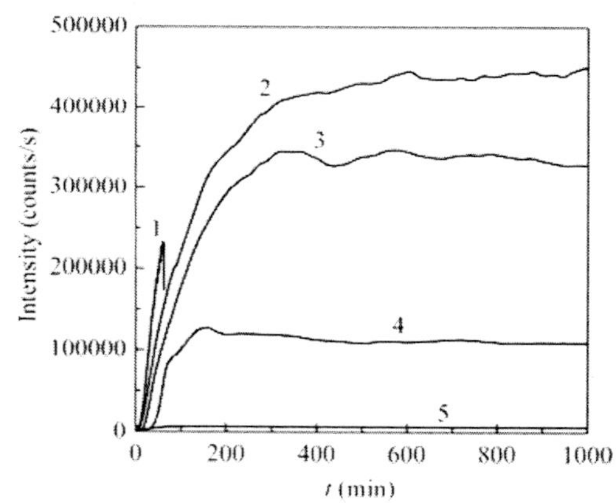

Figure 33. Effect of α-crystallin on thermal aggregation of GAPDH (0.4 mg/ml) at 55°C registered by DLS. The dependences of the light scattering intensity on time obtained in the absence of α-crystallin (1) and in the presence of various concentrations of α-crystallin: (2) 0.025, (3) 0.05, (4) 0.1, and (5) 0.4 mg/ml.

The results of the study of the effect of α-crystallin on the kinetics of GAPDH aggregation at 55°C are presented in Fig. 33 (the time course of the light scattering intensity) and Fig. 34 (the time course of the R_h value). At rather high concentrations of α-crystallin (0.05 and 0.1 mg/ml) the splitting of the aggregate populations into two components occurred in the course of aggregation (Fig. 34B, C). It is of interest that at the addition of low concentration of α-crystallin (0.025 mg/ml) the values of R_h in the initial stage of aggregation were markedly lower than the R_h values obtained for aggregation of GAPDH in the absence of α-crystallin (Fig. 34A). However, at $t > 30$ min inverse relationship was observed. So far this fact remains obscure.

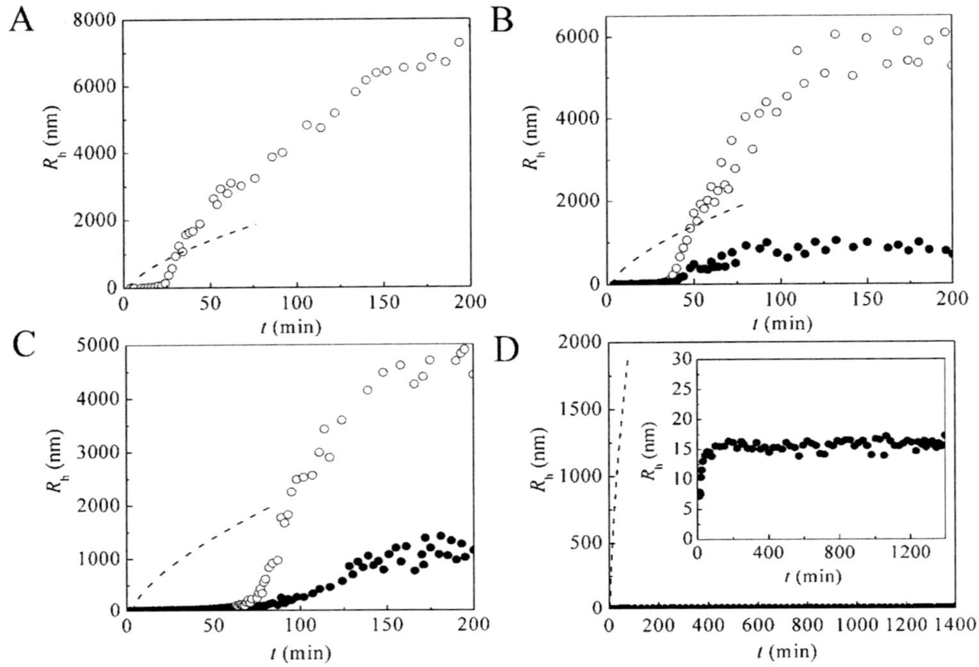

Figure 34. Effect of α-crystallin on the size of aggregates formed in the course of heating of GAPDH (0.4 mg/ml) at 55°C. The dependences of R_h on time obtained at various concentrations of α-crystallin: (A) 0.025, (B) 0.05, (C) 0.1, and (D) 0.4 mg/ml. The dotted lines in Figures A-D correspond to the control (aggregation in the absence of α-crystallin). Inset shows the dependence of R_h on time with the extended coordinate axis.

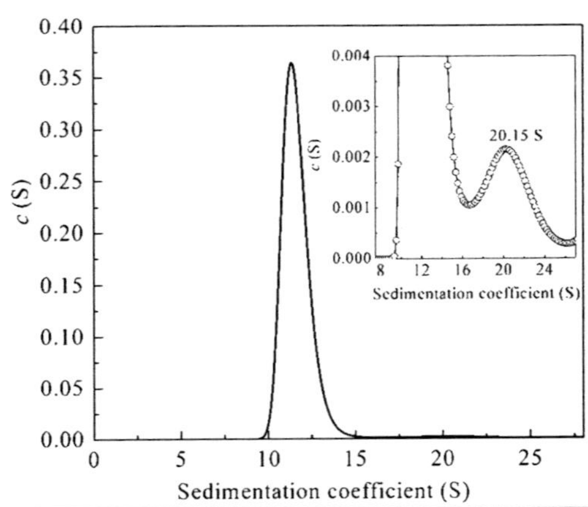

Figure 35. Sedimentation coefficient distribution $c(s)$ for GAPDH (0.4 mg/ml, 10 mM Na-phosphate buffer, pH 7.5) at 37°C, 40000 rpm. The inset shows a minor peak. The enzyme preparation was heated for 7 h at 37°C.

The results obtained by all the methods used allow to conclude that, during the heating, α-crystallin forms small and highly soluble complexes with denatured GAPDH and prevents the following formation of large protein aggregates. In order to understand in more detail the mechanism of protective effect of α-crystallin on heat-induced aggregation of GAPDH, the kinetic experiments were performed by DLS at constant temperature (37, 45, 47.5, and 55°C), i. e., under the conditions where GAPDH unfolds and aggregates rather slowly. For example, after incubation at 45°C for 14 h, only about 50% of GAPDH became denatured, whereas another 50% of the protein remained in the folded state, as was shown from a 50% decrease in the unfolding enthalpy measured in DSC experiments.

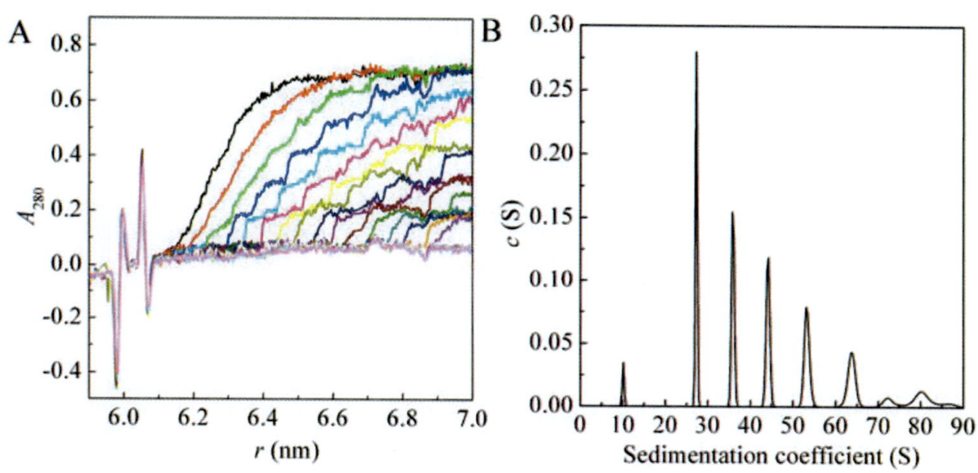

Figure 36. Sedimentation behavior of mixture of α-crystallin and GAPDH at 45°C. (A) Sedimentation velocity patterns of mixture of α-crystallin (0.4 mg/ml) and GAPDH (0.4 mg/ml) at 40000 rpm. Time interval was 3 min. (B) Sedimentation coefficient distribution *c*(*s*) calculated from data in Figure A. The mixture of α-crystallin and GAPDH was heated for 14 h at 45°C (10 mM Na-phosphate buffer, pH 7.5).

Analytical Ultracentrifugation of Glyceraldehyde-3-Phosphate Dehydrogenase

Sedimentation velocity studies of GAPDH at 37°C show that the original oligomeric state is retained during a long time. Figure 35 demonstrates one major peak in the differential sedimentation-coefficient distribution *c*(*s*) for GAPDH, which was preincubated at 37°C during 7 h. Sedimentation coefficient obtained (11.4 S) was normalized to the standard conditions ($s_{20,w}$ = 6.9 S). This value corresponds to the tetrameric form of GAPDH. The minor peak (inset in Figure 35) with $s_{20,w}$ = 12.2 S corresponds to the octameric form of GAPDH. Increase of temperature up to 45°C and the period of the protein incubation at 45°C to 14 h promotes aggregation of GAPDH. It was shown by the sedimentation velocity method that large aggregates of GAPDH precipitated prior to the attainment of the maximum rotor speed (40000 rpm). It was of interest to clarify whether the presence of α-crystallin would protect GAPDH against aggregation under the same conditions. GAPDH was preincubated with α-crystallin for 14 h at 45°C. The sedimentation behavior of the mixture of α-crystallin (0.4 mg/ml) and GAPDH (0.4 mg/ml) at 45°C (40000 rpm) is shown in Figure 36A and B. The sedimentation profiles are given in Figure 36A. The absorbance in the region of plateau coincides with the initial value of absorbance for the mixture of GAPDH and α-crystallin. In contrast to experiments with GAPDH alone, there were no large-sized aggregates in the presence of α-crystallin. The *c*(*s*) distribution calculated from data in Figure 36A is indicative of a set of aggregated forms (Figure 36B). Sedimentation coefficients of the main peaks are equal to 26.9, 35.5, 43.6, 52.6, 63, and 80 S at 45°C. Figure 37 shows the *c*(*s*) distribution for α-crystallin under the same conditions. The sedimentation coefficients for two main peaks are equal to 15.1 and 18.9 S ($s_{20,w}$ = 9.1 S and 11.5 S). A comparison of the *c*(*s*) distributions from Figure 36B and 37 allows us to conclude that α-crystallin forms complexes (or aggregates) with GAPDH. It should be noted that α-crystallin dissociates under study conditions (45°C), as at 20°C only one asymmetric peak with $s_{20,w}$ = 23.5 S was observed.

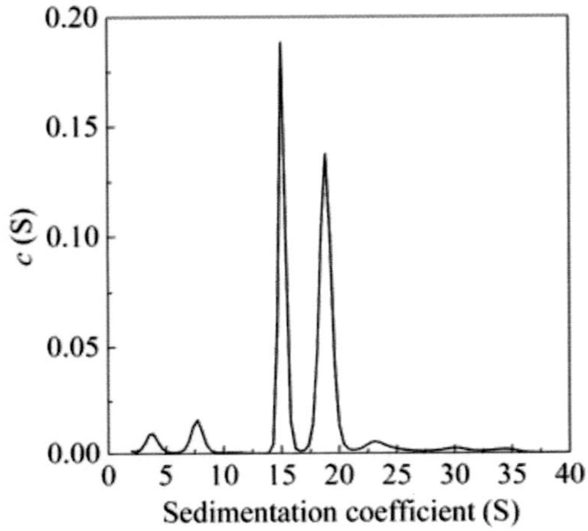

Figure 37. Sedimentation coefficient distribution *c*(*s*) for α-crystallin (0.4 mg/ml) at 45°C, 40000 rpm. α-Crystallin was heated for 14 h at 45°C (10 mM Na-phosphate buffer, pH 7.5).

Effect of GroEL on the Kinetics of Thermal Aggregation of Glyceraldehyde-3-Phosphate Dehydrogenase as Studied by DLS

Figure 38 demonstrates the effect of GroEL on the kinetics of thermal aggregation of GAPDH (0.4 mg/ml) at 45°C. The addition of GroEL resulted in the reduction of the initial increment of the light scattering intensity in the course of GAPDH aggregation and the increase in the duration of lag period (Figure 38A). Such an effect of GroEL became evident at its concentration of 0.4 mg/ml and remained unchanged with further increase in the GroEL concentration. However, it is worth noting that the higher the GroEL concentration, the more pronounced the effect of suppression of the precipitation stage (Figure 38A).

The calculations of the R_h value for the aggregates formed in the course of heating of GAPDH in the presence of GroEL showed that the addition of GroEL was accompanied by the formation of aggregates of lesser size, distribution of aggregates with their size becoming bimodal in the course of aggregation (Figure 38B-D).

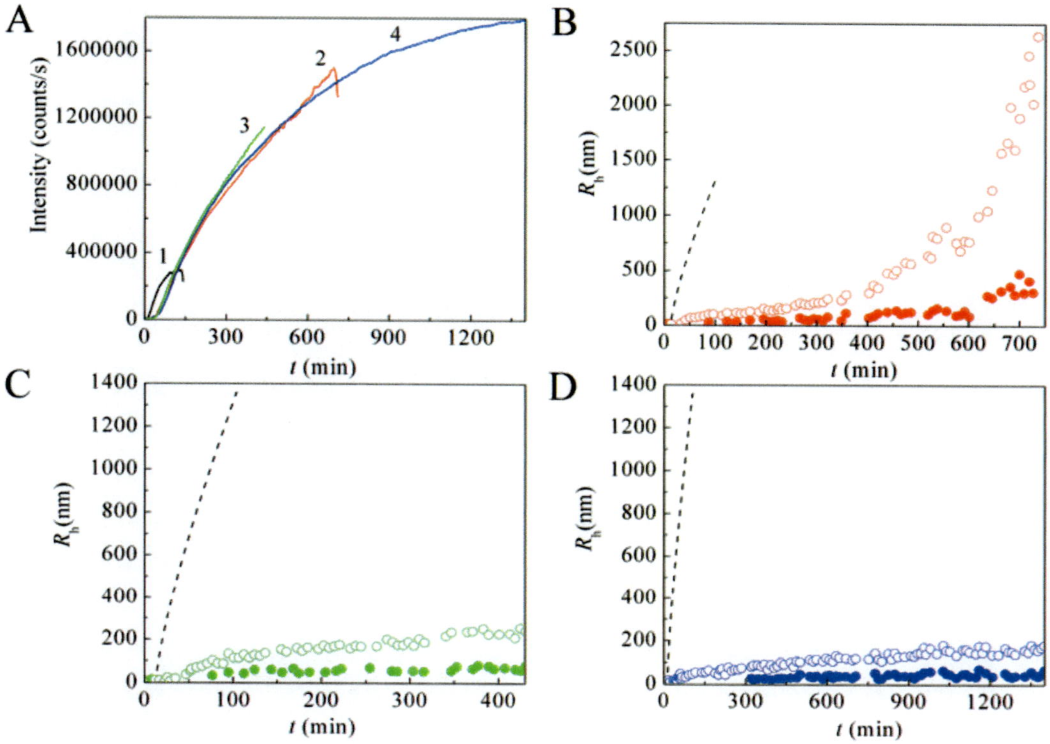

Figure 38. Effect of GroEL on thermal aggregation of GAPDH (0.4 mg/ml; 10 mM Na-phosphate buffer, pH 7.5) registered by DLS at 45°C. The dependences of the light scattering intensity on time (A) obtained in the absence of GroEL (1) and in the presence of various concentrations of GroEL: (2) 0.4, (3) 0.8, and (4) 1.8 mg/ml. The dependences of R_h on time obtained at various concentrations of GroEL: (B) 0.4, (C) 0.8, and (D) 1.8 mg/ml. The dotted lines in Figures B-D correspond to the control (aggregation in the absence of GroEL).

Thermal Denaturation and Aggregation of Phosphorylase *b*

Glycogen phosphorylase *b* (1,4-α-D–glucan: orthophosphate-α-D-glucosyltransferase; EC 2.4.1.1, Ph*b*) is a key enzyme of glycogen metabolism in skeletal muscle, which catalyzes the first step in the pathway of degradation of glycogen, the principal storage form of carbohydrate in muscle. The catalytically active form of Ph*b* is a dimer composing of two identical subunits (97 kDa) [Barford and Johnson, 1989]. Previously we investigated the thermal stability of rabbit skeletal muscle Ph*b* using the enzyme inactivation studies, DSC, analytical ultracentrifugation [Kurganov et al., 2000], and stability of the enzyme in the presence of guanidine hydrochloride [Eronina et al., 2005].

Thermal Denaturation of Phosphorylase b

Figure 39 shows the thermal stability of Ph*b* characterized by DSC. The maximum value of the excess heat capacity $C^{ex}_{p,max}$ was observed at 59°C.

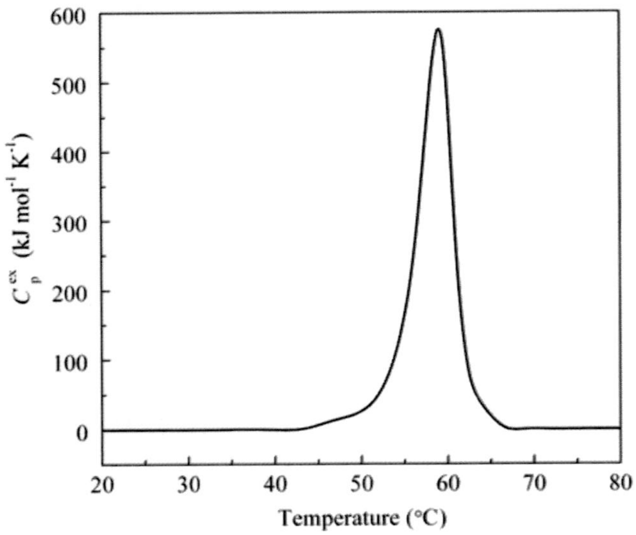

Figure 39. Thermal denaturation of Ph*b* (2 mg/ml; 30 mM Hepes-KOH buffer, pH 7.0). The dependence of excess heat capacity (C_p^{ex}) of a dimer on temperature. The scanning rate was 1°C/min.

Thermal Aggregation of Phosphorylase b

The kinetics of Ph*b* aggregation were studied at 48°C. As can be seen in Figure 39, this temperature corresponds to the beginning of the denaturation process. We have used DLS to characterize the size of aggregates formed in the course of thermal aggregation of Ph*b*. The distribution of the protein aggregates with their size at various times of incubation of the enzyme in 80 mM Hepes buffer, pH 6.8, containing 0.2 mM EDTA at 48°C is represented in Figure 40.

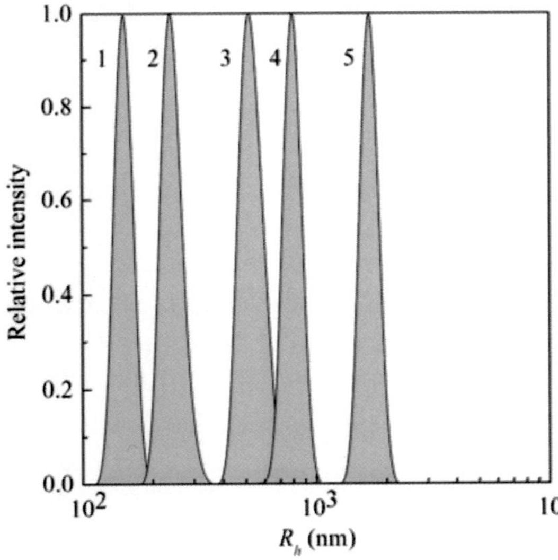

Figure 40. Thermal aggregation of Ph*b* at 48°C (80 mM Hepes, pH 6.8, containing 0.2 mM EDTA). Distribution of the particles by their size registered at various times of incubation: (1) 2, (2) 10, (3) 13, (4) 17, and (5) 43 min.

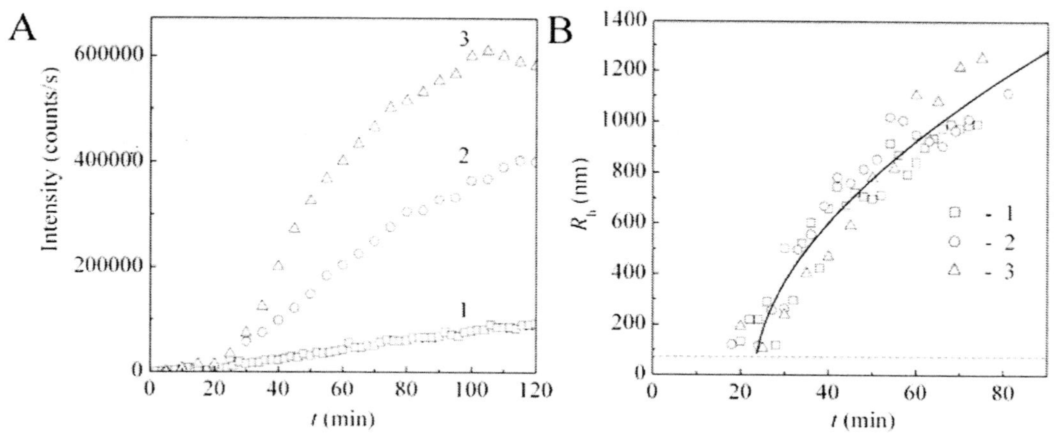

Figure 41. Thermal aggregation of Ph*b* at 48°C (80 mM Hepes, pH 6.8, containing 0.2 mM EDTA). (A) The dependences of the light scattering intensity on time (t). (B) The dependences of the hydrodynamic radius (R_h) on time (t). The solid curve was calculated from Eq. (7) at d_f equal 1.83 at $t > 23.5$ min. The dotted horizontal line corresponds to the value of R_h for the start aggregates ($R_{h,0}$ = 71 nm). Concentrations of Ph*b*: (1) 0.09, (2) 1.77, and (3) 10.5 mg/ml.

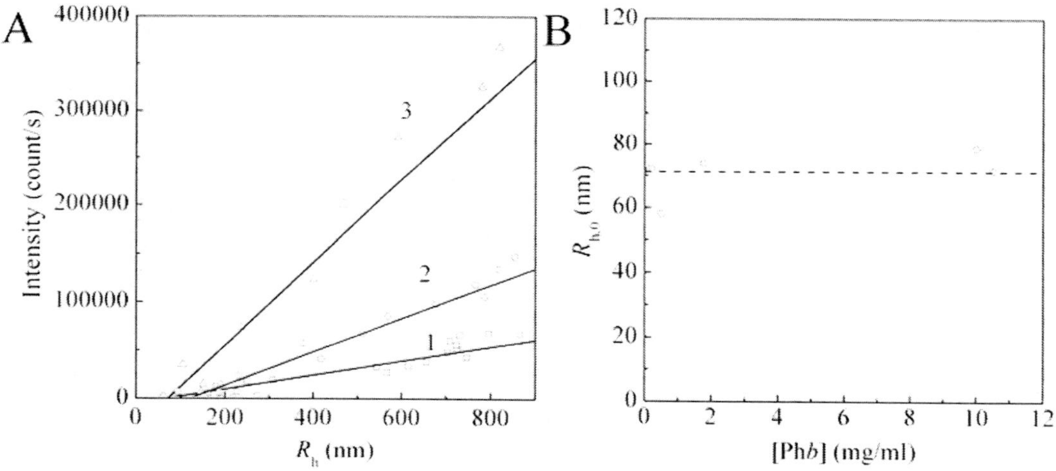

Figure 42. Thermal aggregation of Ph*b* at 48°C (80 mM Hepes, pH 6.8, containing 0.2 mM EDTA). (A) The dependences of the intensity of light scattering on the hydrodynamic radius (R_h) obtained at various concentrations of Ph*b*: (1) 0.22, (2) 1.77, and (3) 10.5 mg/ml. (B) The dependence of the R_h value of start aggregates ($R_{h,0}$) on concentration of Ph*b*. The dotted line corresponds to the average value of $R_{h,0}$ equal to 71 nm.

The dependences of the light scattering intensity (I) on time (Figure 41A) and the dependences of the hydrodynamic radius (R_h) on time (Figure 41B) were obtained at 48°C in the interval of Ph*b* concentrations from 0.09 to 10.5 mg/ml in 80 mM Hepes, pH 6.8, containing 0.2 mM EDTA. The higher the concentration of the enzyme, the higher the intensity increment (Figure 41A). The dependences of R_h on time (Figure 41B) were independent of the concentration of Ph *b*. This fact indicates that the rate of the general process of aggregation is limited by the stage of unfolding of the protein molecule.

Figure 42A shows the dependences of I on R_h obtained at various concentration of Ph *b*. All the dependences cut off the same length on the abscissa axis (Figure 42A). The values of the size of the start aggregates ($R_{h,0}$) for various concentration of Ph*b* (in the interval from 0.09 to 10.5 mg/ml) are presented in Figure 42B. The mean value of R_h for the start aggregates was equal to 71 ± 2 nm. Thus, the size of the start aggregates remains constant at variation of Ph*b* concentrations.

The dependences of the R_h on time represented in Figure 41 were analysed with Eq. (7) at $R_{h,0}$ = 71 nm. The equation described satisfactorily the experimental points at time values higher than 23.5 min. The parameter d_f was found to be 1.83 ± 0.18. The satisfiability of Eq. (7) with the d_f value close to 1.8 indicated that aggregation process proceeded in the kinetic regime of diffusion-limited aggregation.

Thermal Aggregation of Tobacco Mosaic Virus Coat Protein

For many years, tobacco mosaic virus (TMV) coat protein (CP) has served as a model in different kinds of structural studies and is well-known for its ability to produce ordered assemblies (Butler, 1984). At room temperature, pH values in the range from 7.5 to 9.0 and ionic strengths in the range from 10 to 100 mM, the TMV CP exists as a dynamic mixture of pentamers and trimers, with a minor amount of monomers, this being called the 4S-protein. At pH of about 7.0 and ionic strength of about 100 mM, 60–80% of the TMV CP is in the form of the 20S-aggregate (two-layer disk or short helix), with the other 40 to 20% being the 4S-protein. At pH ≤ 6.0 the protein produces long virus-like helical aggregates called repolymerized protein (Butler, 1984). However, TMV CP also turned out to be a good model for studies of thermal amorphous (unordered) aggregation (Orlov et al., 2001; Kurganov et al., 2002; Rafikova et al., 2003; Rafikova et al., 2004). The process of TMV CP heat-induced aggregation is irreversible and highly reproducible. Its rate can be easily manipulated by changing solution ionic strength, the protein concentration, and temperature.

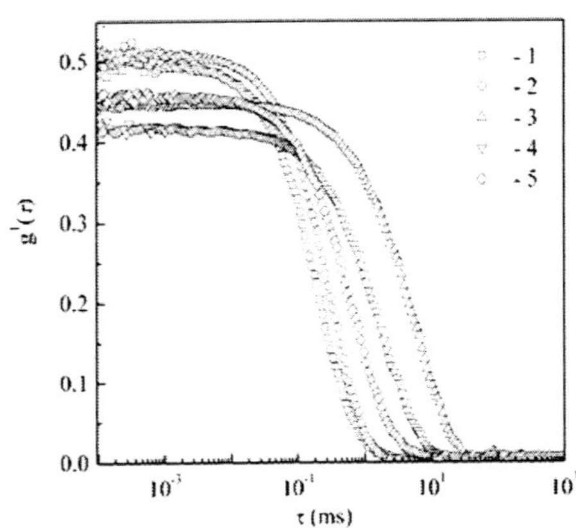

Figure 43. Autocorrelation functions measured at various times of incubation of TMV CP (0.1 mg/ml; 50 mM Na-phosphate buffer, pH 8.0) at 52°C: (1) 5, (2) 10, (3) 22, (4) 45, (5) 75 min. All curves were measured at scattering angle of 90°.

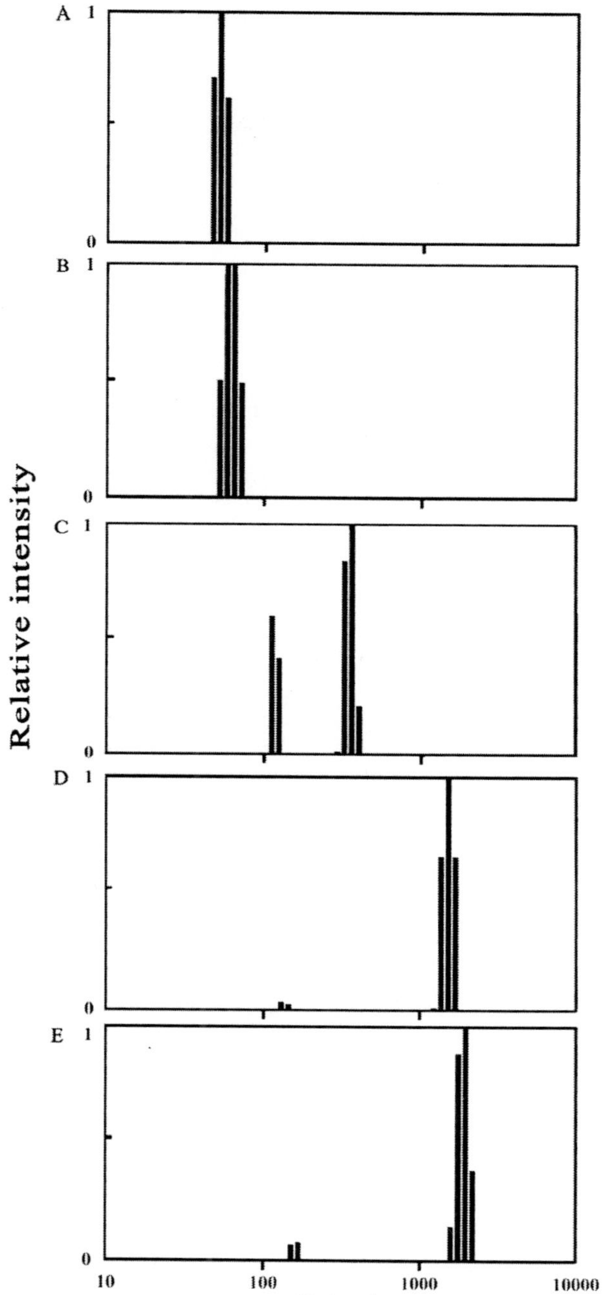

Figure 44. Aggregation of TMV CP (0.1 mg/ml) at 52°C. The distribution of the particles by their size registered at various times of incubation: (A) 5, (B) 10, (C) 22, (D) 45, (E) 75 min. R_h is the hydrodynamic radius.

In the present work, thermal aggregation of TMV CP has been studied using dynamic light scattering. Figure 43 shows the typical autocorrelation functions measured at various times of incubation of 0.1 mg/ml TMV CP in 50 mM Na-phosphate buffer, pH 8.0, at 52°C. Using the DynaLS software we calculated the size distribution of particles formed during aggregation. At sufficiently low times of incubation the distribution function was unimodal (Figure 44A, B). The mean value of the hydrodynamic radius (R_h) increased with the time of incubation. At times of incubation longer than 22 min, in addition to the main TMV CP aggregates, the aggregates of a larger size appeared and the aggregate R_h distribution became bimodal (Figure 44C-E). The R_h value of the large-sized aggregates increased monotonously with the time of incubation.

The process of thermal amorphous aggregation of TMV CP is accompanied by a large increase in the light scattering intensity (I). Figures 45A and C show the time-course of the light scattering intensity obtained at two concentrations of TMV CP (0.05 and 0.1 mg/ml); the kinetic curves are shown in the time interval 0-180 and 0-60 min, respectively. At higher values of time the decrease in the light scattering intensity takes place (the data are not shown) because of precipitation of large-sized aggregates.

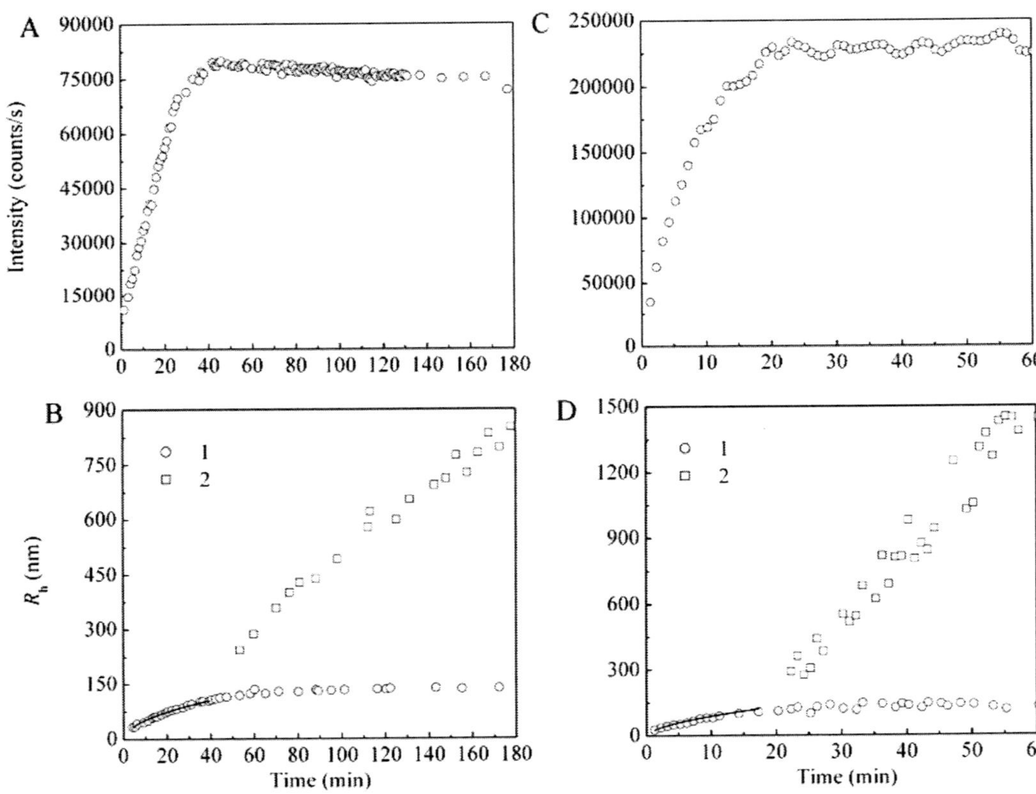

Figure 45. The kinetics of thermal aggregation of TMV CP at 52°C. The protein concentration: (A and B) 0.05 mg/ml, (C and D) 0.1 mg/ml. (A and C) the dependences of the intensity of light scattering on time. (B and D) the dependences of the hydrodynamic radius (R_h) of the basic aggregates (1) and superaggregates (2) on time. The solid curves were drawn in accordance with Eq. (6).

In the time interval where the increase in the light scattering intensity with time was observed the distribution of aggregates by their size remained unimodal and the R_h value increased with increasing the time of incubation. We call «basic aggregates» the initially formed aggregates (Figures 45B, D). It is of interest that in the time region where the light scattering intensity ceased to increase the splitting of the population of the aggregates into two components occurred. The size of the aggregates of one kind remained constant in time (R_h = 135 nm). The size of the aggregates of other kind (the superaggregates) increased monotonously till the values (R_h = 900-1500 nm) characteristic of the large-sized aggregates prone to precipitation.

The initial parts of the dependences of R_h on time obtained at the concentrations of TMV CP equal to 0.05 and 0.1 mg/ml (Figure 45B, D) obey Eq. (6). The value of d_f was found to be 1.84 ± 0.13 and 1.82 ± 0.08, respectively. Thus, the d_f value is close to 1.8. This fact allows us to suggest that the sticking of the start aggregates of TMV CP proceeds in the regime of diffusion-limited aggregation.

Figure 46 shows the dependences of the light scattering intensity on the R_h obtained at various concentrations of TMV CP (from 0.025 to 0.15 mg/ml). Those dependences are linear. As can be seen from Figure 46 the rather large aggregates, which may be called the start aggregates, exist in the system at the instant the initial increase in the light scattering intensity is observed. The hydrodynamic radius of the start aggregates ($R_{h,0}$) is simply estimated as a length cut off on the abscissa axis by the linear dependence of I on R_h. The $R_{h,0}$ value is independent of the protein concentration and the mean value of $R_{h,0}$ was found to be 21 ± 2 nm. Taking into account the molecular mass of TMV CP monomer (17.5 kDa), we can calculate the number of denatured monomers in the start aggregate from Eq. (5). This number is equal to 240 ± 50.

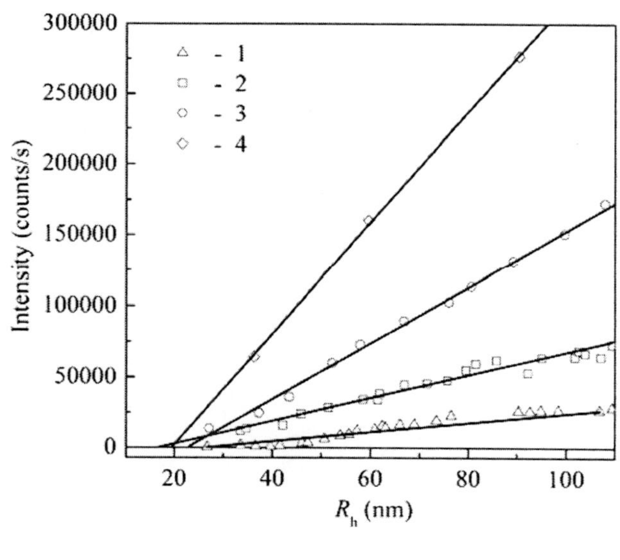

Figure 46. The dependences of the light scattering intensity on the hydrodynamic radius (R_h) obtained at various concentrations of TMV CP: (1) 0.025, (2) 0.05, (3) 0.1, (4) 0.15 mg/ml (50 mM Na-phosphate buffer, pH 8.0, 52°C).

To check the stability of the basic aggregates of TMV CP the following experiments were carried out. The incubation times were chosen so as to be in the interval where only the basic aggregates are formed: 2.5 min (Figure 47A, B) and 6 min (Figure 47C, D). After heating of 0.1 mg/ml TMV CP (50 mM Na-phosphate buffer, pH 8.0) at 52°C for the defined periods of time the protein samples were quickly cooled to 25°C and the DLS measurements were performed for 15 min at 25°C. Cooling the protein samples from 52 to 25°C resulted in the marked increase in the light scattering intensity (compare Figure 45C and Figures 47A and C). As can be seen in Figure 47B and D, this increase in the I value is determined by the formation of the large-sized aggregates. The aggregates of a lesser size (curves 1 in Figure 47B and D) are basic aggregates. The R_h value for the basic aggregates increased only slightly with the time of incubation at 25°C while the size of superaggregates rose rather strongly (curves 2 in Figure 47B and D). It is reasonable to assume that the large-sized aggregates are formed by sticking the basic aggregates together. As can be seen in Figure 47, smaller basic aggregates (2.5 min at 52°C; R_h = 54 nm) displayed a lower tendency for the formation of superaggregates than the larger ones (6.5 min at 52°C; R_h = 89 nm). In our DLS experiments we never observed any breakdown of the basic TMV CP aggregates on cooling from 25 to 52°C. This confirms the irreversible character of amorphous aggregation of TMV CP (Orlov et al., 2001). However, the basic aggregates can easily stick together with the formation of the large-sized particles.

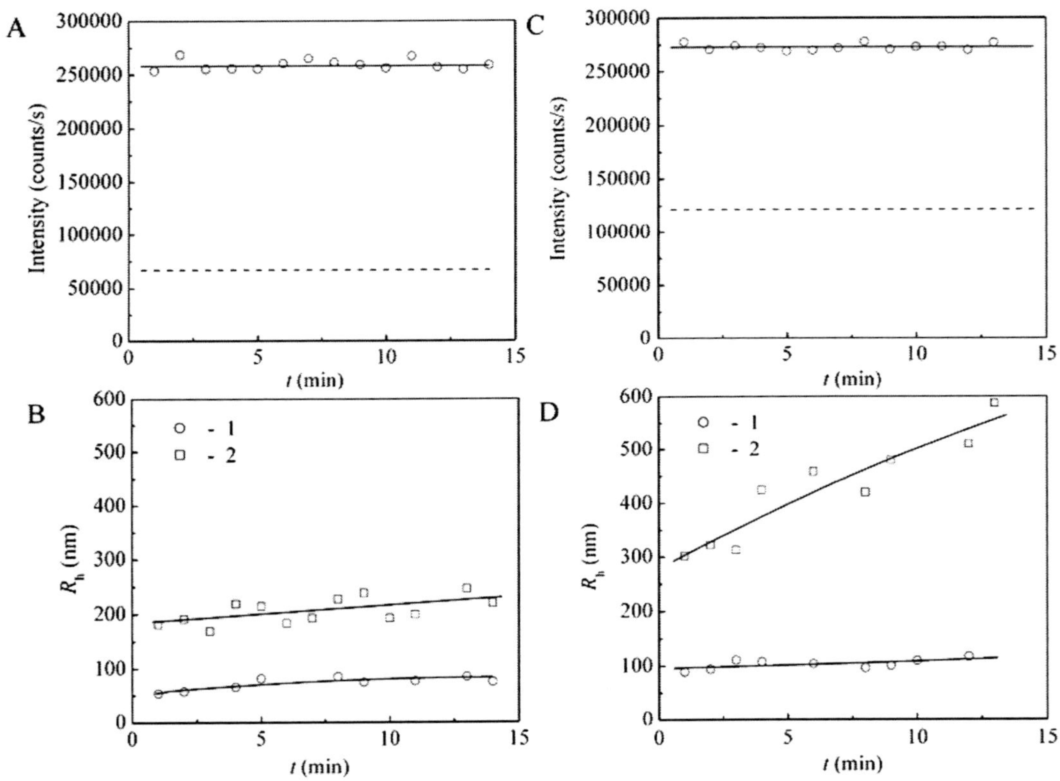

Figure 47. The stability of the TMV CP basic aggregates at 25°C. TMV CP (0.1 mg/ml) was incubated for 2.5 min (A and B) and 6 min (C and D) at 52°C in 50 mM Na-phosphate buffer, pH 8.0, and then quickly cooled to 25°C. The time-dependences of the light scattering intensity (A and C) and the hydrodynamic radius (B and D) for the cooled samples were measured at 25°C. The dotted lines in Figures A and C correspond to the initial values of the light scattering intensity of the protein samples after 2.5 and 6 min incubation at 52°C. Curves 1 and 2 in Figures B and D correspond to the basic aggregates and superaggregates, respectively.

It was a special interest to test the effect of α-crystallin on the TMV CP thermal amorphous aggregation. The kinetics of aggregation of 0.1 mg/ml TMV CP at 52°C (50 mM Na-phosphate buffer, pH 8.0) in the absence and in the presence of α-crystallin (1 mg/ml) are shown in Figure 48. As can be seen from this Figure, the time-courses of the light scattering intensity and hydrodynamic radii of the basic aggregates or superaggregates are the same in the absence and in the presence of α-crystallin. Thus, α-crystallin does not affect the thermal amorphous aggregation of TMV CP.

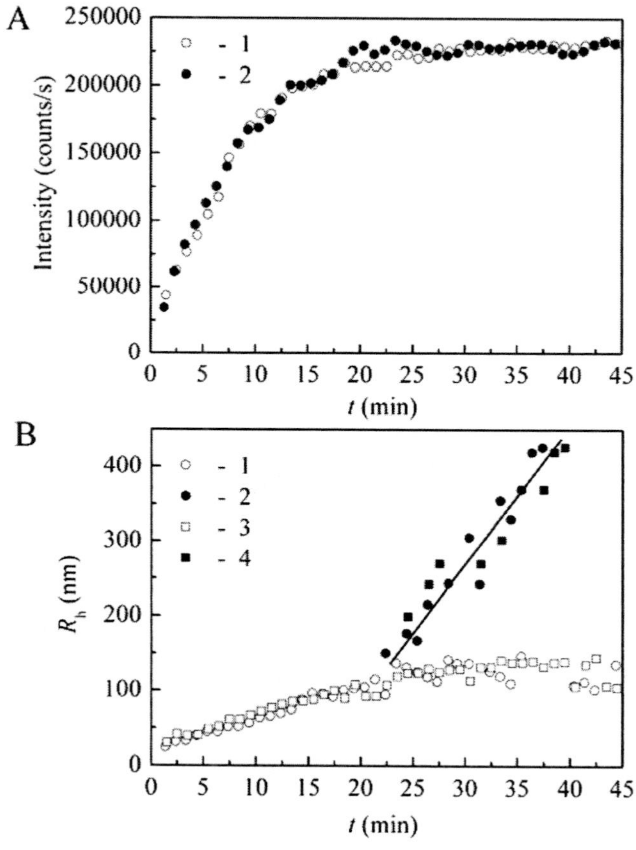

Figure 48. Effect of α-crystallin on kinetics of thermal aggregation of TMV CP (0.1 mg/ml, 50 mM Na-phosphate buffer, pH 8.0) at 52°C. (A) The dependence of the light scattering intensity on time in the absence of α-crystallin (curve 1) and in the presence of α-crystallin (1 mg/ml; curve 2). (B) The dependence of the hydrodynamic radius (R_h) of the basic aggregates (1 and 2) and superaggregates (2 and 4) on time. The concentrations of α-crystallin: (1 and 2) 0 and (3 and 4) 1 mg/ml.

The ability of α-crystallin to suppress protein aggregation is generally due to its interaction with hydrophobic patches exposed to the solvent upon protein unfolding. The fact that α-crystallin does not affect the kinetics of thermal amorphous aggregation of TMV CP may be indicative of the important role of specific interactions in the formation of TMV CP aggregates. This data support our previous idea (Rafikova et al., 2003; Rafikova et al., 2004) that the TMV CP thermal amorphous aggregation is driven by distorted *inter*subunit interactions of those regions of the molecules which in the native state participate in very strong *inter*subunit interactions leading to the formation of the ordered aggregates (helical "polymers" and virions) and that a delicate balance between strong repulsive electrostatic interaction and strong attractive hydrophobic interactions takes place on the surface of the TMV CP molecules. This does not agree too well with the predictions of the Goldberg–Wetzel model (London et al., 1974; Wetzel, 1994), that protein amorphous aggregates are formed due to specific *inter*molecular interactions of hydrophobic surfaces of the protein molecule subdomains, which are normally involved in tertiary *intra*molecular interactions between the same surfaces within one molecule. However, the capacity to produce highly stable ordered aggregates is the most prominent feature of the TMV CP, and the Goldberg–Wetzel model still can be true for a vast majority of proteins which in their native state do not display such strong propensity for intermolecular interactions.

Self-Association of Phosphorylase Kinase as a Model of Protein Aggregation

Phosphorylase kinase (PhK; EC 2.7.1.38) catalyzing phosphorylation and activation of glycogen phosphorylase b (Phb) plays a key role in the cascade system of regulation of glycogen metabolism [Krebs et al., 1959; Brushia and Walsh, 1999; Livanova, 1993]. The PhK molecule is a hexadecamer with subunit composition $(\alpha\beta\gamma\delta)_4$ and molecular mass of 1320 kDa [Cohen, 1973]. The oligomeric state of the native enzyme is dependent on concentrations of the protein, Ca^{2+}, and Mg^{2+}. Ca^{2+} and Mg^{2+} ions stimulate the PhK activity by inducing tertiary and subsequent quaternary structural changes in the enzyme molecule [Nadeaw et al., 1999; Wilkinson et al., 1999]. In the absence of Ca^{2+} and Mg^{2+}, the enzyme exists in the monomeric and dimeric forms with $s_{20,w}$ = 23 S (that corresponding to a molecular mass of 1320 kDa) and $s_{20,w}$ = 36.5 S, respectively [Cohen, 1973; Chebotareva et al., 2002]. However, the addition of 0.1 mM Ca^{2+} and 10 mM Mg^{2+} results in the appearance of higher order associates [Carlson and King, 1982; Chebotareva et al., 2002].

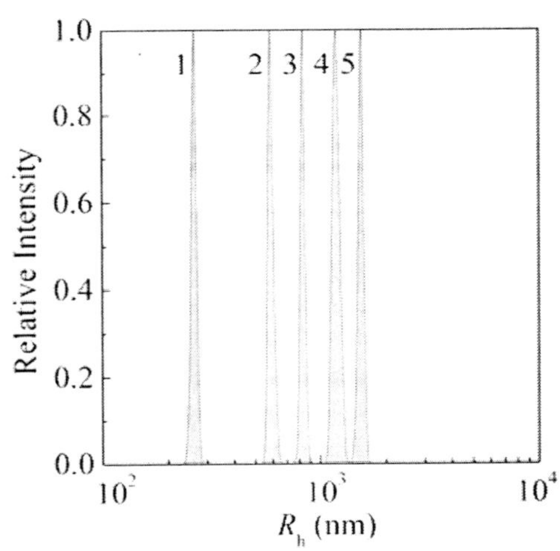

Figure 49. Self-association of phosphorylase kinase at 25°C (40 mM Hepes, pH 6.8, containing 10 mM NaCl, 0.1 mM Ca^{2+}, 10 mM Mg^{2+}). Distribution of the particles by their size registered at various times of incubation: (1) 11, (2) 23, (3) 36, (4) 44, and (5) 64 min.

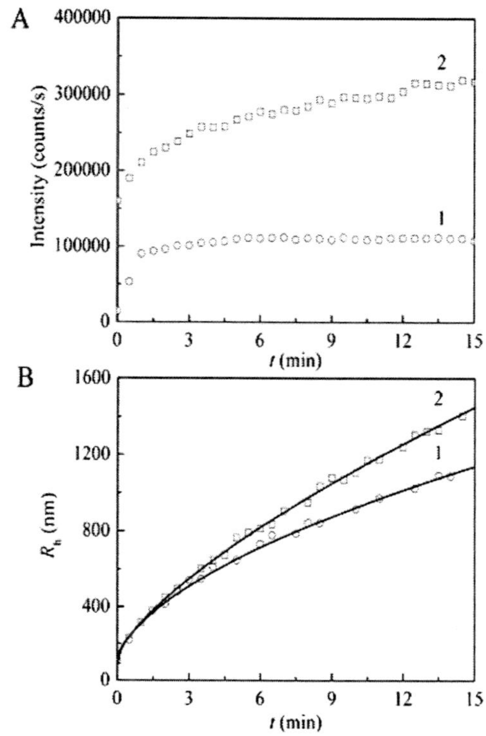

Figure 50. Kinetics of self-association of PhK; the effect of TMAO on PhK (0.3 mg/ml) association. The dependences of the light scattering intensity (I) on time (A) and the dependences of the hydrodynamic radius (R_h) on time (B) obtained in the absence of TMAO (curve 1) (points are the experimental data and the solid curve was drawn in accordance with Eq. (6)), and in the presence of TMAO (curve 2).

Study of Self-Association of Phosphorylase Kinase by DLS

Kinetics of self-association of PhK induced by Ca^{2+} and Mg^{2+} were studied by DLS. Figure 49 shows the change in the distribution of PhK associates by their size in the course of PhK association. As can be seen, the distribution remained monomodal in all time intervals used. The dependences of the light scattering intensity and mean values of hydrodynamic radius (R_h) on time are represented in Figure 50 (curves 1 in A and B). The dependence of R_h on time obeys the power law, which was established for diffusion-limited colloidal aggregation (see Eq. (6)) [Lin et al., 1989]. The following values of parameters were obtained for the dependence of R_h on t under discussion: $R_{h,0} = 82 \pm 3$ nm and $d_f = 1.78 \pm 0.04$. The radius of the PhK molecule was 13 ± 1 nm. The distinctive feature of self-association of PhK was the fact that the size of primary associates (in the following, we shall denote them as "start associates") exceeded substantially the dimension of the PhK molecule. To make an estimate of the number of the PhK molecules forming start associate, we can use an empirical relationship between the molecular mass and the hydrodynamic radius of the protein [Creighton, 1993] (see Eq. (5)). If we take into account the molecular mass of the PhK molecule (1320 kDa), the start aggregate with $R_{h,0} = 82 \pm 3$ nm should contain 76 ± 7 PhK molecules. Thus, the first stage of self-association of PhK is the stage of formation of the start aggregates which proceeds according to "all-or-nothing" principle. The associates with the size lesser than the size of the start associate ($R_{h,0}$) were not detected by DLS. The fact that d_f value is close to 1.8 indicates that the self-association of PhK proceeds in the kinetic regime of the diffusion-limited association, where the start aggregates are the interacting particles.

It has been assumed that the self-association of PhK results in the decrease of the specific activity of the enzyme [Andreeva et al., 1995; Livanova et al., 1995]. Therefore, it is of special interest to find cellular factors capable of preventing association of PhK. According to recent data obtained in this work, heat-induced protein aggregation is considered to be a process involving the sticking together of start aggregates having a hydrodynamic radius of several tens of nanometers. Since there is an analogy between the self-association of PhK and aggregation of unfolded states of the proteins, we decided to test the effect of α-crystallin, a protein with a well-studied chaperone-like activity, on the self-association of PhK in the region where large associates of PhK are formed (R_h > 82 nm). As can be seen from Figure 51, sufficiently high concentrations of α-crystallin completely suppressed self-association of PhK induced by Ca^{2+} and Mg^{2+}. The addition of α-crystallin resulted in the reduction of the increment of the light scattering intensity (Figure 51A) and the formation of the particles of lesser size (Figure 51B). When the concentration of α-crystallin was rather high (0.9 mg/ml), only start associates were registered (R_h = 100 ± 4 nm). α-Crystallin was probably incorporated into the start associates and reduced their propensity for sticking together.

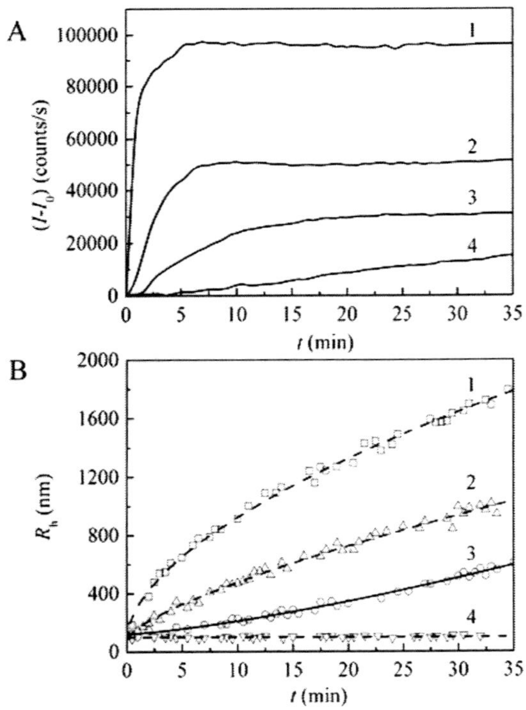

Figure 51. Effect of α-crystallin on self-association of PhK (0.3 mg/ml). The dependences of the light scattering intensity increment ($I - I_0$) on time (A) and the dependences of the hydrodynamic radius (R_h) on time (B) were obtained in the absence of α-crystallin (1) and in the presence of various concentrations of α-crystallin: (2) 0.3 mg/ml, (3) 0.6 mg/ml, (solid curve was drawn in accordance with Eq. (7)) and 0.9 mg/ml (4). I_0 is the value of the light scattering intensity at t = 0.

It is well known that molecular crowding influences the conformation and degree of association and aggregation of macromolecules [Ellis, 2001; Ellis and Minton, 2003; Minton, 1997, 1998, 2001; Ralston, 1990; Zimmerman and Minton, 1993; Chebotareva et al., 2004]. Osmolytes, small organic molecules, stabilize proteins and therefore protect organisms against different stresses [Bolen and Baskakov, 2001; Yancey et al., 1982]. For instance, the tissues of sharks and rays contain urea in high concentration. It is known that urea causes denaturation of the proteins, but this effect could be compensated through supporting of the high concentration of the counteracting osmolytes, especially trimethylamine N-oxide (TMAO), betaine, and sarcosine [Yancey and Somero, 1979; Wang and Bolen, 1997; Burg and Peters, 1997]. Among organisms, concentrating proline, are those that have adapted to live in high salt environments, and they use the osmolyte to offset the high external osmotic pressure [19]. Using high concentrations of osmolytes *in vitro* permits the simulation of molecular crowding conditions [Chebotareva et al., 2001, 2002, 2004, 2005].

As was shown by us previously [Chebotareva et al., 2002], TMAO-stimulated self-association of PhK in the presence of Ca^{2+} and Mg^{2+} is accompanied by an increase in apparent absorbance in the visible region of the spectrum. The study of self-association of PhK by DLS gives information on the size of the protein particles whose formation results in the enhancement of turbidity of the enzyme solution. Curve 1 in Figure 50A shows the dependence of the light scattering intensity of the PhK solution (0.3 g/l) after the addition of Ca^{2+} and Mg^{2+}. The more marked increase in the light scattering intensity in the presence of 0.5 M TMAO (curve 2) means that TMAO favours self-association of PhK. The estimation of the values of the hydrodynamic radius of the particles formed in the process of PhK association suggests that associates of larger size are formed in the presence of this osmolyte (Figure 50B). In Figure 50B only the radii of the PhK associates are shown. The hydrodynamic radii of the start associates determined by extrapolation of the R_h values to zero time in the absence and in the presence of TMAO were equal to 82 ± 3 and 117 ± 4 nm, respectively. It should be noted that DLS does not allow particles with intermediate size, i.e., with size between the values corresponding to the PhK molecule and the start associates, to be registered because of low concentrations of the intermediate forms. The increase in the light scattering intensity in the course of the self-association of PhK is probably connected with the sticking together of the start associates.

Enhancement of self-association of PhK in the presence of TMAO may be explained in terms of the thermodynamic nonideality produced by the osmolyte. From the theory of absolute reaction rate, the second order rate constant (k) characterising the interaction of two particles ($P_i + P_j \rightarrow P_{i+j}$) is expressed as follows [Glasstone et al., 1941; Johnson et al., 1954]:

$$k = \frac{k_B T}{h} K^{\neq} \; ; \; K^{\neq} = \frac{c^{\neq}}{c_i c_j}, \tag{15}$$

where k is Boltzmann's constant, T is the absolute temperature, $K^{\neq}$ is the constant of equilibrium between the initial components (P_i and P_j, concentrations c_i and c_j respectively) and the activated complex ($P^{\neq}$, concentration $c^{\neq}$). In the presence of the crowding-agent the equilibrium constant $K^{\neq}$ is considered as an apparent equilibrium constant:

$$K^{\neq} = K_0^{\neq} \frac{\gamma_i \gamma_j}{\gamma^{\neq}}, \tag{16}$$

where $K_0^{\neq}$ is the true equilibrium constant, γ_i and γ_j are the thermodynamic activity coefficients for the particles P_i and P_j, and $\gamma^{\neq}$ is the thermodynamic activity coefficient for the activated complex. Thermodynamic activities (a) and concentrations (c) are connected by the following relationships: $a_i = \gamma_i c_i$, $a_j = \gamma_j c_j$, and $a^{\neq} = \gamma^{\neq} c^{\neq}$.

The reaction rate constant k measured in the presence of the crowding-agent is described by the expression:

$$k = k_0 \Gamma = k_0 \frac{\gamma_i \gamma_j}{\gamma^{\neq}}, \tag{17}$$

where k_0 is the rate constant in the absence of the crowding-agent and Γ is the nonideality factor ($\Gamma = \gamma_i\gamma_j/\gamma^{\neq}$). The thermodynamic activity coefficient for the solute of m-th kind is determined by the fraction of the total volume available to this solute [Hall and Minton, 2003]:

$$\gamma_m = \frac{v_{\text{total}}}{v_m}, \tag{18}$$

where v_{total} is the total volume and v_m is the volume available to the solute m. It is evident that γ_m exceeds unity, inasmuch as $v_m < v_{\text{total}}$. Because the size of the activated complex is higher than that for the particle P_i or P_j, the value of $v^{\neq}$ (the volume available to the activated complex) is less than the values of v_i or v_j (the volumes available to the particles P_i and P_j, respectively). Therefore, the thermodynamic activity coefficient of the activated complex ($\gamma^{\neq}$) is greater than the thermodynamic activity coefficients of the particles P_i and P_j (γ_i and γ_j). Since the values of the thermodynamic activity coefficients exceeds unity, the product $\gamma_i\gamma_j$ appears to be greater than $\gamma^{\neq}$ and consequently $k > k_0$. This means that thermodynamic nonideality produced by osmolyte should result in the acceleration of association of the protein particles. Such considerations explain the enhancement of the rate of self-association of PhK in presence of TMAO.

Since TMAO facilitates self-association of PhK, it is of interest to elucidate whether α-crystallin is able to counteract such an action of this osmolyte. As can be seen from Figure 52, α-crystallin retained its ability to suppress self-association of PhK in the presence of TMAO.

It has been demonstrated that proline possesses a chaperone-like activity and favors a protein folding [Samuel et al., 2000]. In this connection we also studied the influence of proline on the size of the particles formed in the course of self-association of PhK. Proline suppressed self-association of PhK as detected by the reduction of the increment in the light scattering intensity (Figure 53A) and by diminishing of the size of the particles formed in the course of PhK association (Figure 53B). It is worth noting that the size of the start aggregates remained the same in the presence of proline.

The action of proline on the rate of self-association of PhK is opposite to that revealed by TMAO. In contrast to TMAO, proline hampers association of PhK molecules. Samuel et al. [Samuel et al., 2000] have shown that proline prevents aggregation during lysozyme refolding. Other crowing-agents such as ethylene glycol, glycine, glycerol, and sucrose were ineffective in preventing protein aggregation. The authors suggest that proline inhibits protein aggregation by binding to folding intermediates and trapping the folding intermediates into "aggregation-insensitive" states. It was demonstrated [Samuel et al., 2000] that proline forms supramolecular assemblies in the solution. The results of the study of interaction of supramolecular assemblies with fluorescence probe (1-anilino-8-naphthalene sulfonic acid) are indicative of hydrophobic character of such assemblies. Owing to their hydrophobic properties, supramolecular assemblies of proline interact with the nonpolar portions of the unfolded states of the proteins and consequently prevent the aggregation process.

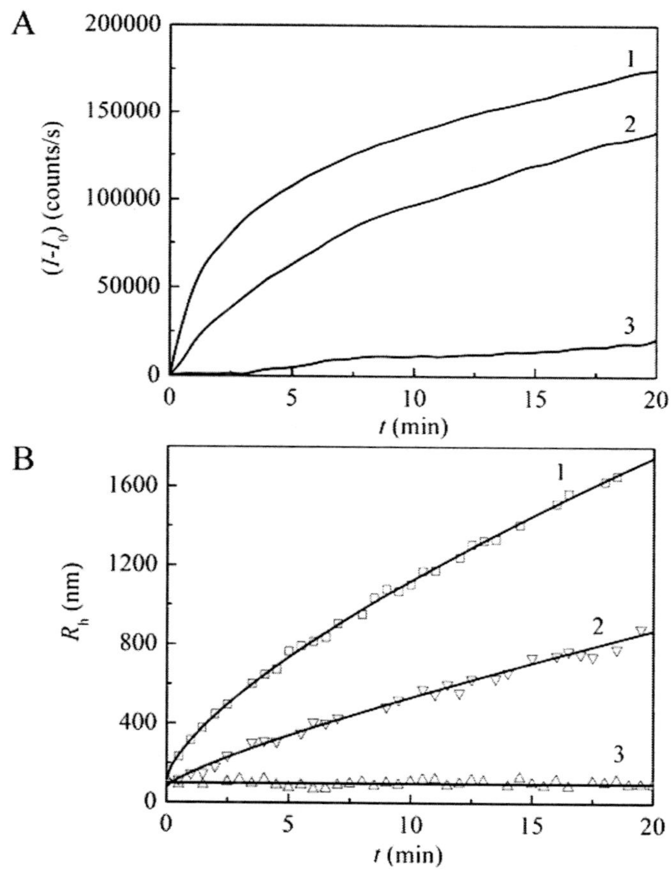

Figure 52. Effect of α-crystallin on kinetics of PhK self-association under molecular crowding conditions arising from the presence of 0.5 M TMAO. The dependences of the light scattering intensity increment ($I - I_0$) on time (A) and the dependences of the hydrodynamic radius (R_h) on time (B) were obtained in the absence of α-crystallin (1) and in the presence of various concentrations of α-crystallin: (2) 0.3, and (3) 0.9 mg/ml.

The ability of proline to reduce the rate of self-association of PhK may be explained by direct incorporation of proline into the start associates. The start associates modified in this way would have a lower sticking probability than the initial start associates. Such a change in the reactivity of PhK associates implies the transition from a regime of diffusion-limited association to a regime of reaction-limited association [Weitz et al., 1985].

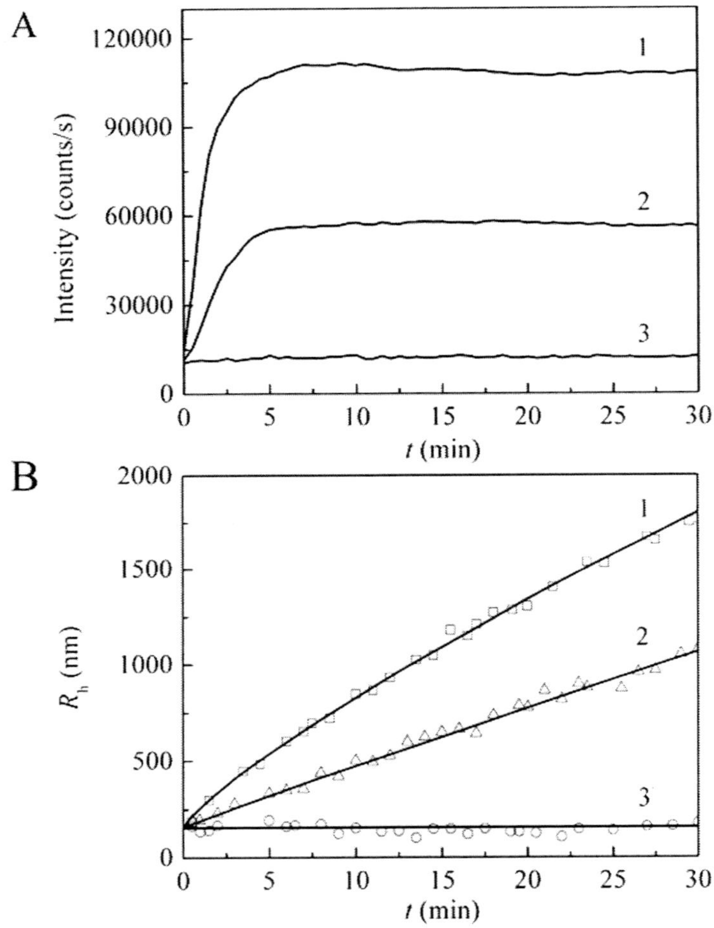

Figure 53. Effect of proline on self-association of PhK (0.3 mg/ml). The dependences of the light scattering intensity (I) on time (A) and the dependences of the hydrodynamic radius (R_h) on time (B) were obtained in the absence of proline (1) and in the presence of various concentrations of proline: (2) 0.08 M, and (3) 0.15 M.

Sedimentation Velocity Analysis of Self-Association of Phosphorylase Kinase

It was of special interest to study the effect of α-crystallin on PhK association by analytical ultracentrifugation. The differential sedimentation coefficient distributions c(s) of a self-association PhK, α-crystallin and their mixture are shown in Figure 54. Interactions can be detected through the change in the ratio of the peak areas and shifts in the peak positions to lesser s values. Analysis of the sedimentation behavior of the PhK and α-crystallin mixture was performed under different conditions (different concentration of α-crystallin, rotor speed, and temperatures), but the system was too complex to calculate the stoichiometry of the complex formed. We can only suggest that PhK binds with α-crystallin.

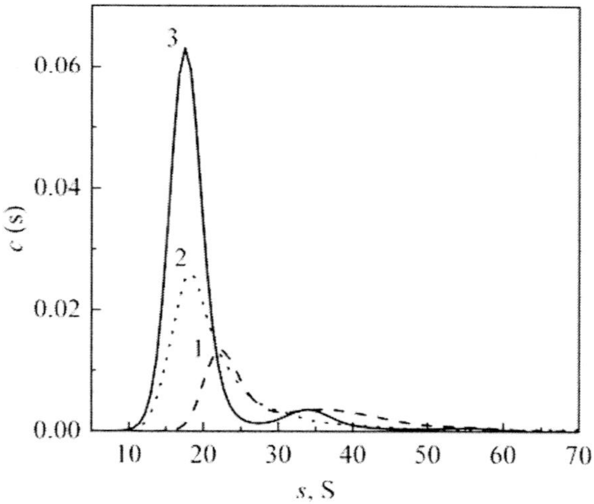

Figure 54. The $c(s)$ distributions for PhK (0.3 mg/ml; curve 1), α-crystallin (0.3 mg/ml; curve 2) and their mixture at the same concentrations (curve 3).

Sedimentation velocity studies of self-association of PhK also showed that the formation of very large associates took place under molecular crowding conditions. Species with the sedimentation coefficients of 23700 S were registered at rotor speed 2000 rpm for PhK in presence of 1 M TMAO [Chebotareva et al., 2004]. The self-association of PhK is a reversible process. Addition of 1 mM EGTA causes an appreciable disintegration of PhK associates formed in the presence of TMAO [Chebotareva et al., 2002].

The differential sedimentation-coefficient distributions $c(s)$ for a self-associating system of PhK (40 mM Hepes, pH 6.8, containing 0.1 mM Ca^{2+}, 10 mM Mg^{2+}, and 10 mM NaCl at 15°C) in the absence (A) and in the presence (B) of 0.5 M TMAO are shown in Figure 55. In the absence of TMAO the enzyme (0.3 mg/ml) existed mainly in the monomeric, dimeric, trimeric, and tetrameric forms with $s_{20,w}$ = 23.0 ± 1.5, 37 ± 2, 49.0 ± 2.5, and 64.0 ± 2.2 S (Figure 55A). In the presence of 0.5 M TMAO one can see the change in the ratio of peak areas and the shift of peak positions to the higher s with average $s_{20,w}$ = 38.0 ± 2.2, 61.0 ± 1.9, 106.0 ± 1.8, 131.0 ± 1.5, 148 ± 1, 218 ± 1 and 327 ± 1 S (Figure 55B). It is worth noting that according to molecular crowding theory compact states of macromolecules are favored over asymmetric ones [Minton, 2000]. This allowed us to use the relationship $s_n = s_1 n^{2/3}$ to characterize the dimension of large oligomeric forms. The peak with $s_{20,w}$= 327 S corresponded to a 53-mer of PhK.

Figure 56 shows the effect of proline on self-association of PhK (0.3 mg/ml; 40 mM Hepes, pH 6.8; 0.1 mM Ca^{2+}, 10 mM Mg^{2+}, and 10 mM NaCl; 20°C). The $c(s)$ distributions obtained in the absence of proline (A) and in the presence of 0.15 M (B), 0.3 M (C), and 0.6 M proline (D) demonstrate that the addition of proline to the PhK solution does not result in the appearance of new large associates. On the contrary, proline suppresses self-association of PhK, probably, due to its specific interaction with the monomeric form of PhK. With increasing concentration of proline, the equilibrium state shifts toward a monomeric state: $s_{20,w}$ = 23.0 ± 1.9 S (A), 20.0 ± 0.6 S (B), 19.0 ± 0.6 S (C and D).

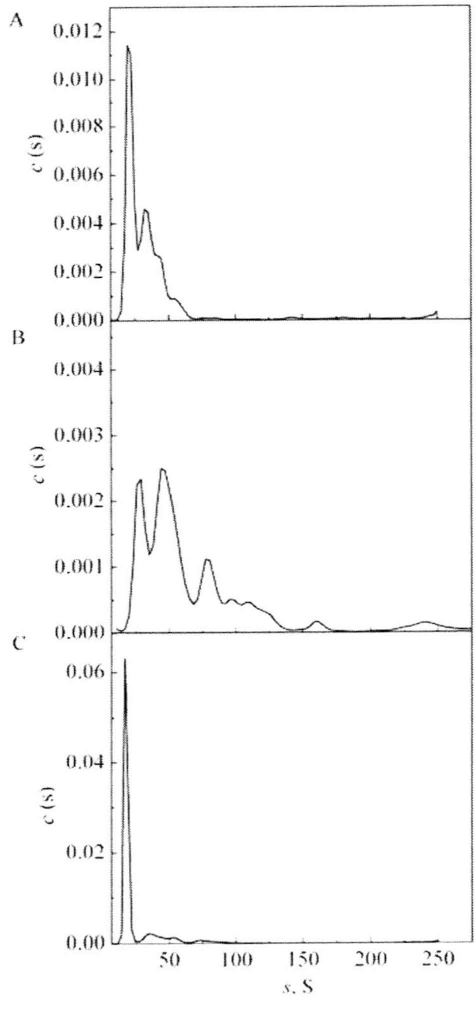

Figure 55. Self-association of PhK (0.3 mg/ml; 40 mM Hepes, pH 6.8; 0.1 mM Ca^{2+}, 10 mM Mg^{2+}; and 10 mM NaCl; 15°C) under molecular crowding conditions arised from the presence of 0.5 M TMAO. Differential sedimentation coefficient distributions *c*(*s*) obtained in the absence of TMAO (A), in the presence of 0.5 M TMAO (B), and in the presence of 0.5 M TMAO and α-crystallin 0.3 mg/ml (C). Rotor speed was 20000 rpm.

In order to check whether α-crystallin as well as proline are able to counteract the enhancement of self-association of PhK under molecular crowding conditions, we studied the effects of α-crystallin and proline on the PhK association in the presence of TMAO (Figure 57). Comparison of *c*(*s*) distributions obtained without proline (Figure 57A) and in the presence of 0.6 M proline (Figure 57B) demonstrates that the equilibrium state shifts toward smaller oligomeric forms. Thus, the effect of proline counteracts the effect of molecular crowding. Figures 57B and C demonstrate the counteracting effects of proline and α-crystallin under the same conditions. There are only two main peaks with $s_{20,w}$ = 15.4 ± 0.3 and 23.3 ± 1.5 S in the presence α-crystallin. Thus, α-crystallin, a protein possessing the chaperone-like activity, and proline suppress the PhK self-association under molecular crowding conditions.

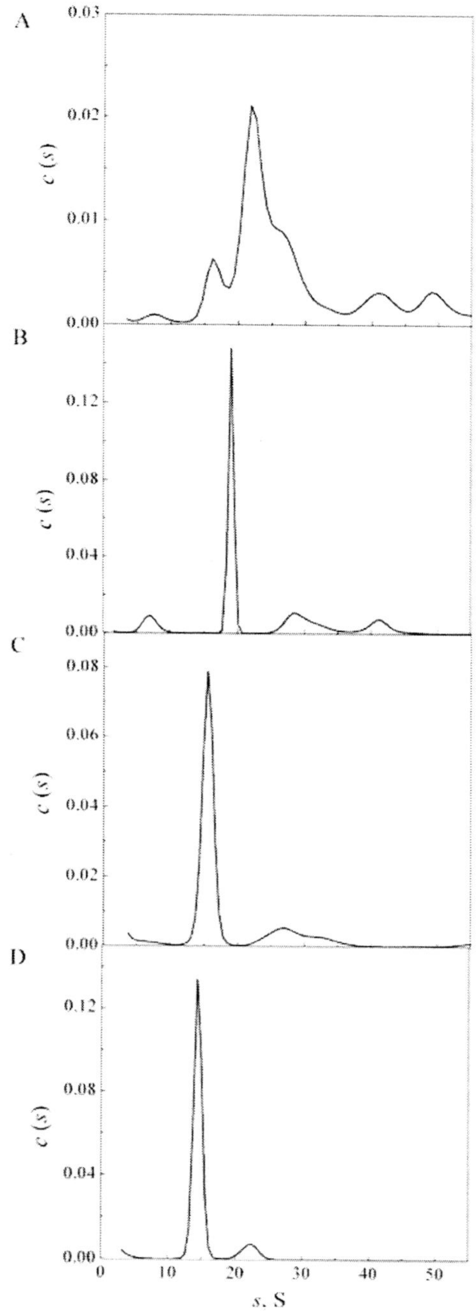

Figure 56. Effect of proline on self-association of PhK (0.3 mg/ml; 40 mM Hepes, pH 6.8; 0.1 mM Ca^{2+}, 10 mM Mg^{2+}; and 10 mM NaCl; 20°C). The *c*(*s*) distributions obtained (A) in the absence of proline and in the presence of (B) 0.15 M, (C) 0.3 M, and (D) 0.6 M proline. Rotor speed was 30000 rpm.

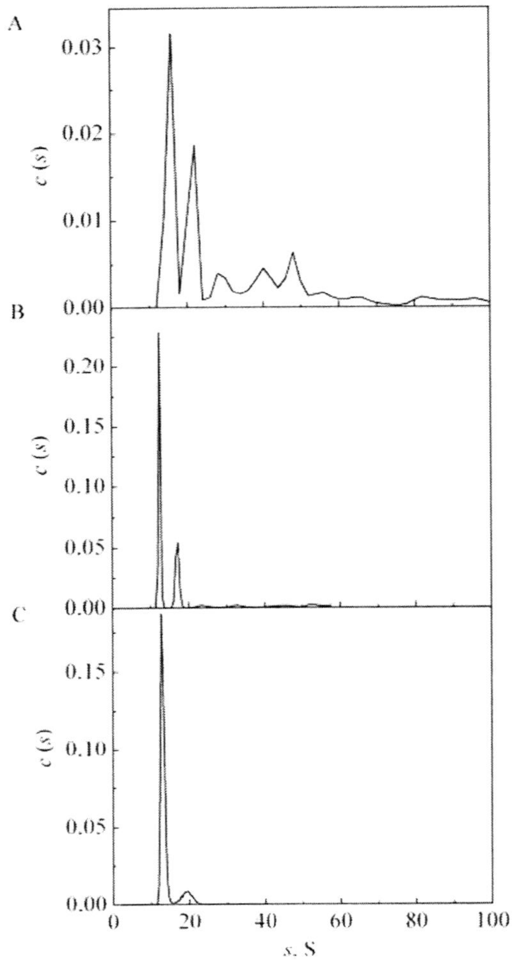

Figure 57. Effect of proline and α-crystallin on self-association of PhK (0.3 mg/ml; 40 mM Hepes, pH 6.8; 0.1 mM Ca^{2+}, 10 mM Mg^{2+}; and 10 mM NaCl; 20°C) under molecular crowding conditions arised from the presence of 0.5 M TMAO. The $c(s)$ distributions for the PhK self-association were obtained in the absence of proline (A), in the presence of 0.6 M proline (B), and in the presence of 0.6 mg/ml α-crystallin (C). Rotor speed was 30000 rpm.

The results obtained by sedimentation velocity analysis show that TMAO greatly favors self-association of PhK. This is consistent with the general notion about molecular crowding as a factor favoring protein oligomerization and the formation of supramolecular structures [Shtilerman et al., 2002; Zimmerman and Minton, 1993; Patel et al., 2002]. The suppression of these processes by proline is unexpected and is probably due to the specific interaction of proline with PhK. The specific interaction of proline with PhK supported by the fact that proline inhibits oligomerization even at relatively low concentrations.

The results of the study of self-association of PhK by two methods (sedimentation velocity and dynamic light scattering) indicate that there are two stages of protein association. The first stage corresponds to the formation of associates with lesser size than that of the start associates. The second stage includes the formation of superassociates from the start associates.

The initial association of PhK is a step-wise process as evidenced by the data presented in Figure 55B. A set of oligomeric forms with $s_{20,w}$ = 38, 61, 106, 131, 148, 218 and 327 S was obtained. The results of the sedimentation velocity analysis of PhK self-association carried out by us [Chebotareva et al., 2004] at lower Mg^{2+} concentration (2 mM) also indicate that initial association of PhK is characterized by the formation of discrete oligomeric forms with $s_{20,w}$ = 189 and 385 S and lesser values. It should be noted that the empirical relationship (5) between the molecular mass of the protein associate and its hydrodynamic radius is valid only for initial associates of PhK including the start associates.

Although the initial associates of PhK really exist, the formation of the start associates proceeds substantially as a process of cooperative association and the concentrations of the intermediate forms are too low to be registered by DLS. In contrast to analytical ultracentrifugation, DLS is a very suitable method for the detection of the superassociates which are formed by the sticking the start associates together. Judging from the size of the start associate, it contains about 80 PhK molecules. It is significant that the crowding-agent (TMAO) exerts a similar effect on both stages of PhK self-association. TMAO favors the formation of prestart associates as well as the formation of superassociates. Proline and α-crystallin exert a similar counteracting effect on all the stages of PhK association. The results obtained imply that proline α-crystallin bind directly to the PhK molecule.

CONCLUSION

In the present work dynamic light scattering was used to study the kinetics of protein aggregation at elevated temperatures. This method allows the size of particles formed in the process of protein aggregation to be determined. If the system contains particles varying markedly in size, the characteristics of the particles of each type may also be obtained.

Study of kinetics of thermal aggregation of different protein substrates (bovine lens β_L-crystallin; yeast alcohol dehydrogenase; rabbit skeletal muscle glycogen phosphorylase *b* and glyceraldehydes 3-phosphate dehydrogenase; coat protein of tobacco mosaic virus). The first stage of the aggregation process is formation of the start aggregates containing hundreds and thousands denatured monomers (Table 4).

The main pathway of further aggregation of the protein is the sticking together of the start aggregates, which proceeds in the regime of diffusion-limited aggregation; that is each collision results in sticking together of interacting particles. This pathway of aggregation brings about the formation of the large-sized aggregates prone to precipitation. There is an additional pathway of aggregation, which is realized by the addition of the denatured protein molecules to growing aggregate.

Using α-crystallin, a protein possessing a chaperone-like activity, we have developed a mechanim of suppression of protein aggregation by chaperones. This mechanims explains formation of aggregates of lesser size in the presence of chaperones. Incorporation of a chaperone in the start aggregate results in decrease of the probability in sticking together of interacting particles and change-over to the regime of the reaction-limited aggregation.

Table 4. The Size of the Start Aggregates for Thermal Aggregation of the Proteins

Protein	Molecular mass of monomer, kDa	Conditions of aggregation	The hydrodynamic radius ($R_{h,0}$), nm	The number of denatured monomers in the start aggregate
Calf lens β-crystallin	22-28	40 mM Na-phosphate buffer, pH 6.8, 100 mM NaCl, 10 mM EDTA; 60°C	84 ± 4	3800-4900
Yeast alcohol dehydrogenase (preheated for 13 min at 52°C)	37.5	50 mM Na-phosphate buffer, pH 7.4, 100 mM NaCl; 56°C	24 ± 1	170 ± 10
Rabbit muscle glyceraldehyde 3-phosphate dehydrogenase	36	10 mM Na-phosphate buffer, pH 7.5; 55°C	22.3 ± 0.6	35 ± 10
Rabbit muscle glycogen phosphorylase *b*	97.4	80 mM Hepes, pH 6.8, 0.2 mM EDTA; 48°C	71 ± 2	740 ± 50
Tobacco mosaic virus coat protein	17.5	50 mM Na-phosphate buffer, pH 8.0; 52°C	21 ± 2	240 ± 50

It has been shown that the analysis of the dependence of the hydrodynamic radius on time allows the protein, which act as chaperones in the unfolded state (i.e. suppress own aggregation) to be revealed. Yeast alcohol dehydrogenase may serve as an example of proteins of such a type.

It has been discovered that the reversible association of proteins may proceeds through the mechanism developed for the mechanism of protein aggregation, and involving formation of the start aggregates followed by sticking together. This mechanism of protein association has been demonstrated for rabbit skeletal muscle phosphorylase kinase induced by Ca^{2+} and Mg^{2+}.

ACKNOWLEDGEMENTS

This study was funded by the Russian Foundation for Basic Research (grants 05-04-48691, 05-04-48955, 05-04-49503, and grant 04-04-81038 for collaborative studies with Byelorussia), Programs "Molecular and Cell Biology" and "Basic Sciences to Medicine" of the Presidium of the Russian Academy of Sciences, by the Program for the Support of the Leading Scientific Schools in Russia (grant 813.2003.4), by grants INTAS (03-51-4813) and NATO (LST.CLG. 979533).

REFERENCES

Abgar, S., Vanhoudt, J., Aerts, T. and Clauwaert, J. (2001) Study of the chaperoning mechanism of bovine lens α-crystallin, a member of the a small heat shock superfamily. *Biophys. J.*, *80*, 1986-1995.

Ajaz, M. S., Ma, Z., Smith, D. L. and Smith, J. B. (1997) Size of human lens beta-crystallin aggregates are distinguished by N-terminal truncation of beta B1. *J. Biol. Chem*, *272,* 11250–11255.

Andreeva, I. E., Makeeva, V. F., Livanova, N. B. and Kurganov, B. I. (1995) Kinetics of action of phosphorylase kinase in a cascade enzymatic system. III. Hysteretic properties of phosphorylase kinase from skeletal muscles. *Biochemistry* (*Moscow*), *60*, 1326–1335.

Anfinsen, C. B. (1973) Principles that govern the folding of protein chains. *Science*, 181, 223-230.

Augusteyn, A. and Stevens, A. (1998) Macromolecular structure of the eye lens. *Prog. Polymer. Sci.*, *23*, 375-413.

Augusteyn, R. C. (2004) Dissociation is not required for alpha-crystallin's chaperone function. *Exp.Eye Res.*, *79*, 781-784.

Avilov, S., Aleksandrova, N. A. and Demchenko, A. P. (2004) Quaternary structure of α-crystallin is necessary for the binding of unfolded proteins. A surface plasmon resonance study *Prot. Pept. Lett.*, *11*, 1-8.

Barford, D. and Johnson, L. H. (1989) The allosteric transition of glycogen phosphorylase. *Nature*, *340*, 609–616.

Bateman, O. A., Sarra, R., van Genesen, S. T., Kappe, G., Lubsen, N. H. and Slingsby C. (2003) The stability of human acidic β-crystallin oligomers and hetero-oligomers. *Exp. Eye Res.*, *77*, 409–422.

Becker, J., and Craig, E. A. (1994) Heat-shock proteins as molecular chaperones. *Eur. J. Biochem.*, *219*, 11-23.

Berbers, G. A. M., Boermann, O. C., Bloemendal, H. and de Jong, W. W. (1982) Primary gene products of bovine beta-crystallin and reassociation behaviour of its aggregates. *Eur. J. Biochem.*, *128*, 495–502.

Berbers, G. A., Hoekman, W. A., Bloemendal H., de Jong W. W., Kleinschmidt, T. and Braunitzer, G. (1984) Homology between the primary structures of the major bovine beta-crystallin chains. *Eur. J. Biochem.*, *139*, 467-479.

Bettelheim, F. A., Ansari, R., Cheng, Q. F. and Zigler, J. S. Jr. (1999) The mode of chaperoning of dithiothreitol-denatured alpha-lactalbumin by alpha-crystallin. *Biochem. Biophys. Res. Commun.*, *261*, 292-297.

Bhat, S. P. and Nagineni, C. N. (1989) alpha B subunit of lens-specific protein alpha-crystallin is present in other ocular and non-ocular tissues. *Biochem. Biophys. Res. Commun.*, *158*, 319-325.

Bhattacharyya, J., Santhoshkumar, P. and Sharma K. K. (2003) A peptide sequence — YSGVCHTDLHAWHGDWPLPVK [40–60] — in yeast alcohol dehydrogenase prevents the aggregation of denatured substrate proteins. *Biochem. Biophys. Res. Commun.*, *307*, 1–7.

Bindels, J. G., Koppers, A. and Hoenders, H. J. (1981) Structural aspects of bovine β-crystallins: Physical characterization including dissociation-association behavior. *Exp. Eye Res.*, *33*, 333–343.

Bloemendal, H., de Jonga, W., Jaenickeb, R., Lubsena N. H., Slingsby, C. and Tardieu A. (2004) Ageing and vision: structure, stability and function of lens crystallins. *Progr. Biophys. Mol. Biol. 86*, 407-485.

Bolen, D. W. and Baskakov, I. V. (2001) The osmophobic effect: natural selection of a thermodynamic force in protein folding. *J. Mol. Biol.*, *310*, 955–963.

Borges J. C. and Ramos C. H. (2005) Protein folding assisted by chaperones. *Protein Pept. Lett. 12*, 257-261.

Bova, M. P., Ding, L. L., Horwitz, J. and Fung, B. K. (1997) Subunit exchange of αA-crystallin. *J. Biol. Chem.*, *272*, 29511-29517.

Boyle D., Gopalakrishnan, S. and Takemoto, L. (1993) Localization of the chaperone binding site. *Biochem. Biophys. Res. Commun.*, *192*, 1147-1154.

Boyle, D. and Takemoto, L. (1994) Characterization of the alpha-gamma and alpha-beta complex: evidence for an in vivo functional role of alpha-crystallin as a molecular chaperone. *Exp. Eye Res.*, *58*, 9-16.

Braig, K., Otwinowski, Z., Hedge, R., Boisvert, D. C., Joachimiak, A., Horwich, A. L. and Sigler, P. B. (1994) The crystal structure of the bacterial chaperonin GroEL at 2.8 A. *Nature*, *371*, 578–586.

Brodsky, J. L. and McCracken, A. A. (1999) ER protein quality control and proteasome-mediated protein degradation. *Semin. Cell Dev. Biol.*, *10*, 507-513.

Brushia, R. J. and Walsh, D. A. (1999) Factors affecting the activity of muscle phosphorylase *b* kinase. *Frontiers Biosci.*, *4*, 618–641.

Bukau, B. and Horwich, A. L. (1998) The Hsp70 and Hsp60 chaperone machines. *Cell*, *92*, 351–366.

Burg, M. B. and Peters E. M. (1997) Urea and methylamines have similar effects on aldose reductase activity. *Am. J. Physiology*, *273*, F1048–1053.

Burgio, M. R., Kim, C. J. and Koretz, J. F. (2000a). Characterization of the heat-induced quaternary transition of α-crystallin aggregates. *Invest. Ophthalmol. Vis. Sci.*, *41,* S581.

Burgio, M. R., Kim, C. J., Dow, C. C. and Koretz, J. F. (2000b) Correlation between the chaperone-like activity and aggregate size of alpha-crystallin with increasing temperature. *Biochem. Biophys. Res. Commun.*, *268*, 426-432.

Butler, P. J. G. (1984). The current picture of the structure and assembly of tobacco mosaic virus. *J. Gen. Virol., 65*, 253-279.

Carlson, G. M. and King, M. M. (1982) Aggregation of phosphorylase kinase induced by Ca^{2+} and Mg^{2+}. *FASEB J*, *41*, 869.

Carrell, R. W. and Lomas, D. A. (1997) Conformational disease. *Lancet*, *350*, 134-138. Busch, A., Engemann, S., Lurz, R., Okazawa, H., Lehrach, H. and Wanker, E. E. (2003) Mutant huntingtin promotes the fibrillogenesis of wild-type huntingtin: a potential mechanism for loss of huntingtin function in Huntington's disease. *J. Biol. Chem.*, 278, 41452-41461.

Carrio, M. M., and Villaverde, A. (2002) Construction and deconstruction of bacterial inclusion bodies. *J. Biotechnol.*, *96*, 3-12.

Carver, J. A. Aquilina, J. A. and Truscott, R. J. (1994a) On the interaction of α-crystallin with unfolded proteins. *Biochim. Biophys. Acta, 1164*, 24-28.

Carver, J. A. Aquilina, J. A., Cooper, P. G. and Williams, G. A. (1994b) Alpha-crystallin: molecular chaperone and protein surfactant. *Biochim. Biophys. Acta, 1204*, 195-206.

Chebotareva, N. A, Andreeva, I. E., Makeeva, V. F., Kurganov, B. I., Livanova, N. B. and Harding, S. E. (2002) Self-association of phosphorylase kinase from rabbit skeletal muscle in the presence of natural osmolyte, trimethylamine N-oxide. *Progr. Colloid. Polym. Sci.*, *119,* 70–76.

Chebotareva, N. A., Harding, S. E. and Winzor, D. J. (2001) Ultracentrifugal studies of the effect of molecular crowding by trimethylamine N-oxide on the self-association of muscle glycogen phosphorylase *b*. *Eur. J. Biochem.*, *268*, 506–513.

Chebotareva, N. A., Kurganov, B. I. and Livanova, N. B. (2004) Biochemical effects of molecular crowding. *Biochemistry* (*Moscow*), *69*, 1239-1251.

Chebotareva, N. A., Kurganov, B. I., Harding, S. E. and Winzor, D. J. (2005) Effect of osmolytes on the interaction of flavin adenine dinucleotide with muscle glycogen phosphorylase *b*. *Biophys. Chem.*, *113*, (1), 61–66.

Chiou, S. H., Azari, P., Himmel, M. E. and Squire, P. G. (1979). Isolation and physical characterization of bovine lens crystallins. *Int. J. Pept. Protein Res.*, *13*, 409-417.

Clark, J. I. and Huang Q. L. (1996) Modulation of the chaperone-like activity of bovine α-crystallin. *Proc. Natl. Acad. Sci. USA*, *93*, 15185–15189.

Clark, J. I. and Muchowski, P. J. (2000) Small heat-shock proteins and their potential role in human disease. *Curr. Opin. Struct. Biol.*, *10*, 52–59.

Cohen P. (1973) The subunit structure of rabbit-skeletal-muscle phosphorylase kinase, and the molecular basis of its activation reactions. *Eur. J. Biochem.*, *34*, 1-14.

Corrales, F. J. and Fersht, A. R. (1996) Kinetic significance of GroEL14.(GroES7)2 complexes in molecular chaperone activity. *Fold. Des.*, *1*, 265-273.

Cowan-Jacob, S. W., Kaufmann, M., Anselmo, A. N., Stark, W. and Grutter, M. G. (2003) Structure of rabbit-muscle glyceraldehyde-3-phosphate dehydrogenase. *Acta Crystallogr. D. Biol. Crystallogr.*, *59*, 2218-2227.

Creighton, T. E. (1993) *Proteins. Structures and Molecular Properties* (W. H. Freeman and Co, New York).

Das, B. K., Liang J. J. and Chakrabarti, B. (1997) Heat-induced conformational change and increased chaperone activity of lens alpha-crystallin. *Curr. Eye. Res.*, 16, 303-309.

Das, K. P., Choo-Smith, L. P., Petrash, J. M. and Surewicz, W. K. (1999) Insight into the secondary structure of non-native proteins bound to a molecular chaperone alpha-crystallin. An isotope-edited infrared spectroscopic study. *J. Biol. Chem.*, *274*, 33209–33212.

Delaye, M. and Tardieu, A. (1983) Short-range order of crystallin proteins accounts for eye lens transparency. *Nature*, *302*, 415–417.

Devlin, J. G., Carver, L. A. and Bottomley, S. P. (2003) The selective inhibition of serpin aggregation by the molecular chaperone, α-crystallin, indicates a nucleation-dependent specificity. *J. Biol. Chem.*, *278*, 48644–48650.

Dobrov, E. N., Abu-Eid, M. M., Solovyev, A. G., Kust, S. V. and Novikov, V. K. (1997). Properties of the coat protein of a new tobacco mosaic virus coat protein ts-mutant. *J. Protein Chem.*, *16*, 27-36.

Dobrov, E., Kust, S., Yakovleva, O., and Tikhonenko, T. (1977). Structure of single-stranded virus RNA in situ. II. Optical activity of five tobacco mosaic-like viruses and their components. *Biochim. Biophys. Acta*, *475*, 623-637.

Dobson, C. M. (1999) Protein misfolding, evolution and disease. *Trends Biochem. Sci.*, *24*, 329–332.

Ellis, R. J. and Minton, A. P. (2003) Join the crowd. *Nature*, *425*, 27–28.

Ellis, R. J. (2001) Macromolecular crowding: obvious but underappreciated. *Trends Biochem. Sci.*, *26*, 597–604.

Eronina, T. B., Chebotareva, N. A. and Kurganov, B. I. (2005) Influence of osmolytes on inactivation and aggregation of muscle glycogen phosphorylase *b* by guanidine hydrochloride. Stimulation of protein aggregation under crowding conditions. *Biochemistry (Moscow)*, *70*, 1020-1026.

Farahbakhsh, Z., Huang, Q., Ding, L., Altenbach, C., Steinhoff, H. J., Horwitz, J. and Hubbell, W. L. (1995) Interaction of alpha-crystallin with spin-labeled peptides. *Biochemistry*, *34*, 509-514.

Feng, J., Smith, D. L. and Smith, J. B. (2000) Human lens β-crystallin solubility. *J. Biol. Chem.*, *275*, 11585–11590.

Fink, A. L. (1998) Protein aggregation: folding aggregates, inclusion bodies and amyloid. *Folding Des. 3*, R9–R23.

Fink, A. L. (1999) Chaperone-mediated protein folding. *Physiol. Rev.*, *79*, 425–449.

Fisher, E. H. and Krebs, E. G. (1962) Muscle phosphorylase *b*. *Meth. Enzymol.*, *5*, 368–373.

Fraenkel-Conrat, H. (1957). Degradation of tobacco mosaic virus with acetic acid. *Virology*, *1*, 1-4.

Frydman, J. (2001) Folding of newly translated proteins in vivo: The role of molecular chaperones. *Annu. Rev. Biochem.*, *70*, 603–647.

Ganea, E. and Harding, J. J. (2000) α-Crystallin assists the renaturation of glyceraldehyde-3-phosphate dehydrogenase. *Biochem. J.*, *345*, 467-472.

Ganzhorn, A. J. and Plapp, B. V. (1988) Carboxyl groups near the active site zinc contribute to catalysis in yeast alcohol dehydrogenase. *J. Biol. Chem.*, *263*, 5446-5454.

Giese, K. C. and Vierling, E. (2002) Changes in oligomerization are essential for the chaperone activity of a small heat shock protein *in vivo* and *in vitro*. *J. Biol. Chem.*, *277*, 46310–46318.

Glasstone, S. K., Laidler, J. and Eyring, H. (1941) The theory of rate processes: The kinetics of chemical reactions, viscosity, diffusion and electrochemical phenomena. McGraw-Hill, New York.

Goti, D., Katzen, S. M., Mez, J., Kurtis, N., Kiluk, J., Ben-Haiem, L., Jenkins, N. A., Copeland, N.G., Kakizuka, A., Sharp, A. H., Ross, C. A., Mouton, P. R. and Colomer, V. (2004) A mutant ataxin-3 putative-cleavage fragment in brains of Machado-Joseph disease patients and transgenic mice is cytotoxic above a critical concentration. *J. Neurosci., 24*, 10266-10279.

Groenen, P. J., Merck, K. B., de Jong, W. W. and Bloemendal, H. (1994) Structure and modifications of the junior chaperone alpha-crystallin. From lens transparency to molecular pathology. *Eur. J. Biochem., 225*, 1-19.

Gu, Y., Verghese, S., Mishra, R. S., Xu. X., Shi. Y. and Singh N. (2003) Mutant prion protein-mediated aggregation of normal prion protein in the endoplasmic reticulum: implications for prion propagation and neurotoxicity. *J. Neurochem., 84*, 10-22.

Haase-Pettingell, C. A. and King, J. (1988) Formation of aggregates from a thermolabile in vivo folding intermediate in P22 tailspike maturation. A model for inclusion body formation. *J. Biol. Chem., 263*, 4977–4983.

Haley, D. A., Horwitz, J. and Stewart, P. L. (1998) The small heat-shock protein, alphaB-crystallin, has a variable quaternary structure. *J. Mol. Biol., 277*, 27-35.

Hall, D. and Minton, A. P. (2003) Macromolecular crowding: qualitative and semiquantitative successes, quantitative challenges. *Biochim. Biophys. Acta, 1649*, 127-139.

Hammond, C. and Helenius, A. (1995) Quality control in the secretory pathway. *Curr. Opin. Cell. Biol., 7*, 523-529.

Hartl, F. U. and Hayer-Hartl, M. (2002) Molecular chaperones in the cytosol: from nascent chain to folded protein. *Science, 295,* 1852-1858.

Hartl, F. U. (1996) Molecular chaperones in cellular protein folding. *Nature, 381*, 571–579.

Haslbeck, M. (2002) sHsps and their role in the chaperone network. *Cell. Mol. Life Sci., 59*, 1649-1657.

Hayes, J. E. and Velick, S. F. (1954) Yeast alcohol dehydrogenase: molecular weight, coenzyme binding, and reaction equilibria. *J. Biol. Chem., 207*, 225-244.

He, B. Bai, J. H. and Zhou H. M. (1997) Comparison of inactivation and unfolding of yeast alcohol dehydrogenase during thermal denaturation. *Int. J. Biochem. Cell Biol. 29*, 1021-1028.

Hendrick, J. P., and Hartl, F. U. (1993) Molecular chaperone functions of heat-shock proteins. *Ann. Rev. Biochem., 62*, 349-384.

Herbrink, P., Van Westreenen, H. and Bloemendal, H. (1975) Further studies on the polypeptide chains of beta-crystallin. *Exp. Eye. Res., 20*, 541-548.

Horwitz, J. (1992) α-Crystallin can function as a molecular chaperone. *Proc. Natl Acad. Sci. USA, 89*, 10449–10453.

Horwitz, J. (2000) The function of alpha-crystallin in vision. *Sem. Cell Devel. Biol., 11*, 53-60.

Horwitz, J., Huang, Q. and Ding, L. (2004) The native oligomeric organization of alpha-crystallin, is it necessary for its chaperone function? *Exp.Eye Res., 79*, 817-821.

Hurtley, S. M. and Helenius, A. (1989) Protein oligomerization in the endoplasmic reticulum. *Annu. Rev. Cell. Biol., 5*, 277–307.

Jaenicke, R. (1995) Folding and association versus misfolding and aggreation of proteins. *Philos. Trans. R. Soc. Lond. B Biol. Sci., 348*, 97-105.

Jaenicke, R. (1998) Protein self-organization in vitro and in vivo: partitioning between physical biochemistry and cell biology. *Biol. Chem., 379*, 237–243.

Johnson, F. H., Eyring, H. and . Polisar, M. J. (1954) The kinetic basis of molecular biology. Wiley and Sons, New York.

Johnston, J. A., Dalton, M. J., Gurney, M. E. and Kopito, R. R. (2000) Formation of high molecular weight complexes of mutant Cu, Zn-superoxide dismutase in a mouse model for familial amyotrophic lateral sclerosis. *Proc. Natl. Acad. Sci. USA*, *97*, 12571-12576.

Johnston, J. A., Ward, C. L. and Kopito, R. R. (1998) Aggresomes: a cellular response to misfolded proteins. *J. Cell Biol.*, 143, 1883-1898.

Julien, J. P. (2001) Amyotrophic lateral sclerosis: unfolding the toxicity of the misfolded the *SOD1* gene. *Cell*, *104*, 581-591.

Kane, J. F. and Hartley, D. L. (1991) Properties of recombinant protein-containing inclusion bodies in *Escherichia coli*. *Bioprocess Technol.*, *12*, 121-145.

Kastenschmidt, L. L., Kastenschmidt, J. and Helmreich, E. (1968) Subunit interactions and their relationship to the allosteric properties of rabbit skeletal muscle phosphorylase *b*. *Biochemistry*, *7*, 3590–3607.

Kirschenbaum, D. M. (1972) Molar absorptivity and $A_{1cm}^{1\%}$ values for proteins at elected wavelengths of the ultraviolet and visible region. *Int. J. Protein Research*, *4*, 63-73.

Kopito, R. R. (2000) Aggresomes, inclusion bodies and protein aggregation. *Trends Cell Biol.*, *10*, 524–530.

Koretz, J. F. (1999) Quaternary structural changes in native bovine alphacrystallin aggregates with temperature. *Invest. Ophthalmol. Vis. Sci.*, *40*, S214.

Krebs, E. G, Graves, D. J. and Fisher, E. H. (1959) Factors affecting the activity of muscle phosphorylase *b* kinase. *J. Biol. Chem.*, *234*, 2867–2873.

Krivandin, A. V., Muranov, K. O. and Ostrovsky, M. A. (2004a) Heat-induced complex formation in solutions of alpha- and beta L-crystallins: a small-angle X-ray scattering study. *Dokl. Biochem. Biophys. (Moscow) 394*, 1-4.

Krivandin, A. V., Muranov, K. O., and Ostrovsky, M. A. (2004b) Study of complexing between α- and β-crystallins in solutions at 60°C. *Mol. Biol. (Moscow) 38*, 1-15.

Kurganov, B. I. (1998) Kinetics of heat aggregation of proteins. *Biochemistry (Moscow)*, *63*, 364–366.

Kurganov, B. I. (2002) Estimation of the activity of molecular chaperones in test-systems based on suppression of protein aggregation. *Uspekhi Biol. Khim.* (*Moscow*), *42*, 89-138.

Kurganov, B. I., Kornilaev, B. A., Chebotareva, N. A., Malikov, V. Ph., Orlov, V. N., Lyubarev, A. E. and Livanova, N. B. (2000) Dissociative mechanism of thermal denaturation of rabbit skeletal muscle glycogen phosphorylase *b*. *Biochemistry*, *39*, 13144-13152.

Kurganov, B. I., Rafikova, E. R. and Dobrov, E. N. (2002) Kinetics of thermal aggregation of tobacco mosaic virus coat protein. *Biochemistry* (*Moscow*), *67*, 631–640.

Laemmli, U. K. (1970) Cleavage of structural proteins during the assembly of the head of bacteriophage T4, *Nature*, *227*, 680-685.

Lampi, K. J., Ma, Z., Shih, M., Shearer, T. R., Smith, J. B., Smith, D. L. and David, L. L. (1997) Sequence analysis of betaA3, betaB3, and betaA4 crystallins completes the identification of the major proteins in young human lens. *J. Biol. Chem.*, *272*, 2268–2275.

Levashov, P., Orlov, V., Boschi-Muller, S., Talfournier, F., Asryants, R., Bulatnikov, I., Muronetz, V., Branlant, G. and Nagradova, N. (1999) Thermal unfolding of phosphorylating D-glyceraldehyde-3-phosphate dehydrogenase studied by differential scanning calorimetry. *Biochim. Biophys. Acta*, *1433*, 294-306.

Li, J. and Wang, C. C. (1999) "Half of the sites" binding of D-glyceraldehyde-3-phosphate dehydrogenase folding intermediate with GroEL. *J. Biol. Chem.*, *274*, 10790-10794.

Lin, M. Y., Linsday, H. M., Weitz, D. A., Ball, R. C., Klein, R. and Meakin, P. (1989) Universality of fractal aggregates as probed by light scattering. *Proc. R. Soc. Lond. A.*, *423*, 71-87.

Livanova, N. B. (1993) Structure and regulation of the activity of muscle phosphorylase kinase. *Biochemistry (Moscow)*, *58*, 1677–1684.

Livanova, N. B., Kurganov, B. I., Andreeva, I. E. and Makeeva, V. F. (1995): *Evolutionary Biochemistry and Related Areas of Physicochemical Biology* (Poglazov, B. F., Kurganov, B. I. and Kritsky, M.S., eds), Bach Institute of Biochemistry and ANKO, Moscow.

London, J., Skrzyna, C., and Goldberg, M. E. (1974). Renaturation of *Escherichia coli* tryptophanase after exposure to 8 M urea. Evidence for the existence of nucleation centers. *Eur. J. Biochem., 47,* 409-415.

Ma, Z., Hanson, S. R., Lampi, K., David, L., Smith, D. L. and Smith, J. B. (1998) Age-related changes in human lens crystallins identified by HPLC and mass spectrometry. *Exp. Eye Res.*, *67,* 21–30.

Mach, H., Trautman, P. A., Thomson, J. A., Lewis, R. V. and Middaugh, C. R. (1990) Inhibition of alpha-crystallin aggregation by gamma-crystallin. *J. Biol. Chem.*, *265*, 4844-4848.

MacRae, T. H. (2000) Structure and function of small heat shock/alpha-crystallin proteins: established concepts and emerging ideas. *Cell. Mol. Life Sci.,* *57*, 899-913.

Magonet, E., Hayen, P., Delforge, D., Delaive, E., Remacle, J. (1992) Importance of the structural zinc atom for the stability of yeast alcohol dehydrogenase. *Biochem. J.*, *287*, 361–365.

Maiti, M., Kono, M. and Chakrabarti, B. (1988) Heat-induced changes in the conformation of alpha- and beta-crystallins: unique thermal stability of alpha-crystallin. *FEBS Lett.*, *236,* 109–114.

Mandal, K., Dillon, J. and Gaillard, E. R. (2000) Heat and concentration effects on the small heat shock protein, α-crystallin. *Photochem. Photobiol.*, *71*, 470-475.

Markossian, K. A. and Kurganov, B. I. (2004) Protein Folding, Misfolding, and Aggregation. Formation of Inclusion Bodies and Aggresomes. *Biochemistry* (*Moscow*), *69*, 971-984.

Mayer, M. P. and Bukau, B. (2005) Hsp70 chaperones: cellular functions and molecular mechanism. *Cell Mol. Life Sci.* *62*, 670-684.

Merlini, G., Bellotti, V., Andreola, A., Palladini, G., Obici, L., Casarini, S. and Perfetti, V. (2001) Protein aggregation. *Clin. Chem. Lab. Med.*, *39*, 1065-1075.

Militello, V., Casarino, C., Emanuele, A., Giostra, A., Pullara, F. and Leone, M. (2004) Aggregation kinetics of bovine serum albumin studied by FTIR spectroscopy and light scattering. *Biophys. Chem.*, *107*, 175-187.

Minami, Y., Hohfeld, J., Ohtsuka, K. and Hartl, F.U. (1996) Regulation of the heat-shock protein 70 reaction cycle by the mammalian DnaJ homolog, Hsp40. *J. Biol. Chem.*, *271*, 19617–19624.

Minton, A. P. (1997) Influence of excluded volume upon macromolecular structure and associations in crowded media. *Curr. Opin. Biotechnol.*, *8*, 65–69.

Minton, A. P. (1998) Molecular crowding: analysis of effects of high concentrations of inert cosolutes on biochemical equilibria and rates in terms of volume exclusion. *Methods Enzymol.*, *295,* 127–149.

Minton, A. P. (2001) The influence of macromolecular crowding and macromolecular confinement on biochemical reactions in physiological media. *J. Biol. Chem.*, *76*, 577–10580.

Morozov, V. E., Eronina, T. B., Andreeva, I. E., Silonova, G. V., Soloviyova, N. V., Schors, E. I., Livanova, N. B. and Poglazov, B. F. (1989) Purification, quaternary structure and regulatory properties of phosphorylase kinase from pigeon skeletal muscle. *Biochemistry (Moscow)*, *54*, 448–455 (in Russian).

Nadeau, O. W., Traxler, K. W., Fee, L. R., Baldwin, B. A. and Carlson, G. M. (1999) Activators of phosphorylase kinase alter the cross-linking of its catalytic one-sixth subunit to the C-terminal of its regulatory alpha subunit. *Biochemistry*, *38*, 2551–2559.

Orlov, V. N., Arutyunyan, A. M., Kust, S. V., Litmanovich, E. A., Drachev, V. A., and Dobrov, E. N. (2001). Macroscopic aggregation of tobacco mosaic virus coat protein. *Biochemistry (Moscow)*, *66*, 154-162.

Panasenko, O. O., Seit-Nebi, A., Bukach, O. V., Marston, S. B. and Gusev, N. B. (2002) Structure and properties of avian small heat shock protein with molecular weight 25 kDa. *Biochim. Biophys. Acta*, *1601*, 64–74.

Patel, C. N., Noble, S. M., Weatherly, G. T., Trypathy, A., Winzor, D. J. and Pielak, G. J. (2002) Effect of molecular crowding by saccharides on α-chymotrypsin dimerization. *Protein Sci.*, *11*, 997–1003.

Perutz, M. F. (1997) Amyloid fibrils – mutations make enzyme polymerize. *Nature*, *385*, 773-775.

Perutz, M. F. (1999) Glutamine repeats and neurodegenerative diseases: molecular aspects. *Trends Biochem. Sci.*, *4*,8-63.

Photon Correlation and Light Beating Spectroscopy (1974) (Cummins, H. Z. and Pike, E. R., Eds) Plenum, New York.

Pivovarova, A. V., Mikhailova, V. V., Chernik, I. S., Chebotareva, N. A., Levitsky, D. I. and Gusev, N. B. (2005) Effects of small heat shock proteins on the thermal denaturation and aggregation of F-actin. *Biochem. Biophys. Res. Commun.*, *331*, 1548–1553.

Prusiner, S. B. and Hsiao, K. K. (1994) Human prion diseases. *Ann. Neurol.*, *35*, 385-395.

Putilina, T., Skouri-Panet, F., Prat, K., Lubsen, N. H. and Tardieu, A. (2003) Subunit exchange demonstrates a differential chaperone activity of calf α-crystallin toward β_{LOW} - and individual γ-crystallins. *J. Biol. Chem.*, *278*, 13747-13756.

Rafikova, E. R., Kurganov, B. I., Arutyunyan, A. M., Kust, S. V., Drachev, V. A., and Dobrov, E. N. (2003). A mechanism of macroscopic (amorphous) aggregation of the tobacco mosaic virus coat protein. *Intern. J. Biochem. Cell Biol.*, *35*, 1452-1460.

Rafikova, E. R., Panyukov, Yu. V., Arutyunyan, A. M., Yaguzhinsky, L. S., Drachev, V. A., and Dobrov E. N. (2004). Low sodium dodecyl sulfate concentrations inhibit tobacco mosaic virus coat protein amorphous aggregation and change the protein stability. *Biochemistry (Moscow)*, *69*, 1372-1378.

Ralston, G. B. (1990) The effect of "crowding" in protein solutions. *J. Chem. Educ.*, *67*, 857–860.

Raman, B. and Rao, C. M. (1994) Chaperone-like activity and quaternary structure of alpha-crystallin. *J. Biol. Chem.*, *269*, 27264-27284.

Raman, B., Ramakrishna, T. and Rao, C. M. (1995) Rapid refolding studies on the chaperone-like alpha-crystallin. Effect of alpha-crystallin on refolding of beta- and gamma-crystallins. *J. Biol. Chem.*, *270*, 19888-19921.

Rao, P. V., Huang, Q. L., Horwitz, J. and Zigler, J. S., Jr. (1995) Evidence that alpha-crystallin prevents non-specific protein aggregation in the intact eye lens. *Biochim. Biophys. Acta*, *1245*, 439-447.

Reddy, G. B., Das, K. P., Petrash, J. M. and Surewicz, W. K. (2000) Temperature-dependent chaperone activity and structural properties of human αA- and αB-crystallins. *J. Biol. Chem.*, 275, 4565-4570.

Regini, J. W. and Grossman, J. G. (2003) Structural changes of α-crystallin during heatingand comparisons with other small heat shock proteins. *Fibre Diffr. Rev.*, *11*, 95-101.

Samuel, D., Kumar, T. K. S., Ganesh, G., Jayaraman, G., Yang, P. W., Chang, M. M., Trivedi, V. D., Wang, S. L., Hwang, K. C., Chang, D. K. and Yu, C. (2000) Proline inhibits aggregation during protein refolding. *Protein Sci.*, *9*, 344–352.

Sanchez-Ruiz, J. M. (1992) Theoretical analysis of Lumry-Eyring models in differential scanning calorimetry. *Biophys. J.*, *61*, 921-935.

Saso, L., Grippa, E., Gatto, M. T., Leone, M. G. and Silvestrini, B. (2000) Inhibition of heat-induced aggregation of beta- and gamma-crystallin by alpha-crystallin evaluated by gel permeation HPLC. *Biochemistry* (*Moscow*), *65*, 208-212.

Schuck, P. (2000) Size-distribution analysis of macromolecules by sedimentation velocity ultracentrifugation and Lamm equation modeling. *Biophys. J., 78*, 1606–1619.

Schuck, P., Perugini, M. A., Gonzales, N. R., Howlett, G. J., Schubert, D. (2002) Size-distribution analysis of proteins by analytical ultracentrifugation: strategies and application to model systems. *Biophys. J., 82,* 1096–1111.

Scopes, R. K. and Stoter, A. (1982) Purification of all glycolytic enzymes from one muscle extract. *Meth. Enzymol.*, *90*, 479-490.

Sergeev, Y.V., Hejtmancik, J.F. and Wingfield P.T. (2004) Energetics of domain-domain interactions and entropy driven association of β-crystallins. *Biochemistry*, *43*, 415-424.

Sharma, K. K., Kumar, R. S., Kumar, G. S. and Quinn, P. T. (2000) Synthesis and characterization of a peptide identified as a functional element in αA-crystallin. *J. Biol. Chem.*, *275*, 3767-3771.

Shtilerman, M. D., Ding, T. T. and Lansbury, P. T., Jr. (2002) Molecular crowding accelerates fibrillization of α-synuclein: could an increase in the cytoplasmic proteinconcentration induce Parkinson's disease? *Biochemistry*, *41*, 3855–3860.

Siezen, R. J., Bindels, J. G. and Hoenders, H. J. (1980) The quaternary structure of bovine α-crystallin: effects of variation in alkaline pH, ionic strength, temperature and calcium ion concentration. *Eur. J.Biochem.*, *111*, 435-444.

Slingsby, C. and Bateman, O.A. (1990) Quaternary interactions in eye lens β-crystallins: Basic and acidic subunits of β-crystallins favor heterologous association. *Biochemistry*, *29,* 6592–6599.

Smith, D. F., Whitesell, L. and Katsanis, E. (1998) Molecular chaperones: biology and prospects for pharmacological intervention. *Pharmacol. Rev.*, *50*, 493–514.

Smulders, R. H., van Boekel, M. A. and de Jong, W. W. (1998) Mutations and modifications support a 'pitted-flexiball' model for alpha-crystallin. *Int. J. Biol. Macromol.*, *22*, 187-196.

Soti, C., Pal, C., Papp, B. and Csermely, P. (2005) Molecular chaperones as regulatory elements of cellular networks. *Curr. Opin. Cell Biol. 17*, 210-215.

Sparrer, H., Lilie, H. and Buchner, J. (1996) Dynamics of the GroEL-protein complex: effect of nucleotides and folding mutants. *J. Mol. Biol.*, *258*, 74-87.

Speed, M. A., King, J. and Wang, D. J. (1997) Polymerization mechanism of polypeptide chain aggregation. *Biotechnol. Bioeng.*, *54*, 333-343.

Speed, M. A., Wang, D. I. and King, J. (1996) Specific aggregation of partially folded polypeptide chains: the molecular basis of inclusion body composition. *Nat. Biotechnol.*, *14*, 1283-1287.

Stromer, T., Ehrnsperger, M., Gaestel, M. and Buchner, J. (2003) Analysis of the interaction of small heat shock proteins with unfolding proteins. *J. Biol. Chem.*, *278*, 18015–18021.

Surewicz, W. K. and Olesen, P. R. (1995) On the thermal stability of alpha-crystallin: a new insight from infrared spectroscopy. *Biochemistry*, *34*, 9655–9660.

Thurston, G. M., Sun, T. X. and Liang, J.N. (1998) Relationship between molecular weight and hydrodynamic radius during heat-induced aggregation of recombinant human αA and αB crystallin. *Invest. Ophthalmol. Vis. Sci.*, *39*, S870.

Treweek, T. M., Morris, A. M. and Carver, J. A. (2003) Intracellular protein unfolding and aggregation: the role of small heat-shock chaperone proteins. *Aust. J. Chem.*, *56*, 357-367.

van den Ijssel P. R., Smulders, R. H., de Jong, W. W. and Bloemendal, H. (1996) alpha-Crystallin: molecular chaperone and heat shock protein. *Ophthalmic Res.*, *28*, 39-43.

van den Oetelaar, P. J., van Someren, P. F., Thomson, J. A., Siezen, R. J. and Hoenders, H. J. (1990) A dynamic quaternary structure of bovine α-crystallin as indicated from intermolecular exchange of subunits. *Biochemistry*, *29*, 3488-3493.

Vanhoudt, J., Abgar, S., Aerts, T. and Clauwaert, J. (2000) A small-angle X-ray solution scattering study of bovine a-crystallin. *Eur. J. Biochem.*, *267*, 3848-3858.

Vanhoudt, J., Aerts, T., Abgar, S. and Clauwaert, J. (1997) Quaternary structure and interaction parameters of bovine α-crystallin: influence of isolation conditions. *Progr. Colloid. Polym. Sci.*, *107*, 88-93.

Veillon, C. and Sitkowsky, A. J. (1975) The intrinsic zinc atoms of yeast alcohol dehydrogenase. *Biochem. Biophys. Res. Commun.*, *67*, 1494–1500.

Wang, A. and Bolen, D. W. (1997) A naturally occurring protective system in urea-rich cells: mechanism of osmolyte protection of proteins against urea denaturation. *Biochemistry*, *36*, 9101–9108.

Wang, K. and Kurganov, B. I. (2003) Kinetics of heat- and acidification-induced aggregation of firefly luciferase. *Biophys. Chem.*, *106*, 97–109.

Wang, K. and Spector, A. (1994) The chaperone activity of bovine α-crystallin. Interaction with other lens crystallins in native and denatured states. *J. Biol. Chem.*, *269*, 13601-13608.

Wegele, H., Muller, L. and Buchner, J. (2004) Hsp70 and Hsp90 - a relay team for protein folding. *Rev. Physiol. Biochem. Pharmacol. 151*, 1-44.

Weitz, D. A. and Lin, M. Y. (1986) Dynamic scaling of cluster-mass distributions in kinetic colloid aggregation. *Phys. Rev. Lett.*, *57*, 2037–2040.

Weitz, D. A., Huang, J. S., Lin, M. Y. and Sung, J. (1985) Limits of the fractal dimension for irreversible kinetic aggregation of gold colloids. *Phys. Rev. Lett.*, *54*, 1416–1419.

Wetzel, R. (1994) Mutations and off-pathway aggregation of proteins. *Trends Biotechnol., 12*, 193–198.

Wilkinson, D. A., Fitzgerald, T. J., Marion, T. N. and Carlson, G. M. (1999) Mg^{2+} induces conformational changes in the catalytic subunit of phosphorylase kinase, whether by itself or as part of the holoenzyme complex. *J. Protein. Chem.*, *18*, 157–164.

Wistow, G. J. and Piatigorsky, J. (1988) Lens crystallins: The evolution and expression of proteins for a highly specialized tissue. *Ann. Rev. Biochem.*, *57*, 479–504.

Wood, J. D., Beaujeux, T. P. and Shaw, P. J. (2003) Protein aggregation in motor neurone disorders. *Neuropathol. Appl. Neurobiol., 29*, 529–545.

Yancey, P. H. and Somero, G. N. (1979) Counteraction of urea destabilization of protein structure by methylamine osmoregulatory compounds of elasmobranch fishes. *Biochem. J.*, *183*, 317–323.

Yancey, P. H., Clark, M. E., Hand, S. C., Bowlus, R. D. and Somero, G. N. (1982) Living with water stress: evolution of osmolyte systems. *Science*, *217*, 1214–1222.

Young, J. C. and Hartl, F. U. (2002) Chaperones and transcriptional regulation by nuclear receptors. *Nature Struct. Biol.*, *9*, 640–642

Yudin, I. K., Nikolaenko, G. L., Kosov, V. I., Agayan, V. A., Anisimov, M. A. and Sengers, J. V. (1997) Simple photon-correlation spectrometer for research and education. *Int. J. Thermophys.*, *18*, 1237-1248.

Zigler J. S., Horwitz, J. and Kinoshita, J. H. (1980). Human β-crystallin I. Comparative studies on the β_1, β_2 and β_3-crystallins. *Exp. Eye Res.*, *31*, 41-55.

Zigler, J. S. (1978) Age-related changes in the polypeptide composition of beta-crystallin from bovine lens. *Exp. Eye Res.*, *26*, 537-546.

Zimmerman, S. B. and Minton, A. P. (1993) Macromolecular crowding: biochemical, biophysical, and physiological consequences. *Annu. Rev. Biophys. Biomol. Struct.*, *22*, 27–65.

In: Protein Folding: New Research
Editor: Tony R. Obalinsky, pp. 173-194
ISBN 1-59454-835-8

Chapter 4

EXISTENCE OF CONDENSED STRUCTURES IN DENATURED LYSOZYME AND THEIR CONTRIBUTIONS TO THE FOLDING

***Takatoshi Ohkuri*[1], *Tadashi Ueda*[1] *and Taiji Imoto*[2]**
[1]Graduate School of Pharmaceutical Sciences, Kyushu University, Fukuoka, Japan
[2]Faculty of Biotechnology and Life Science, Sojo University, Kumamoto, Japan

ABSTRACT

Recently, it has been shown that residual structures are present even in the denatured state of a protein. If these residual structures are related to the initial structures in the folding of the denatured protein, they should affect the protein folding. However, there have been few reports on the effect of the residual structures of a protein on the protein folding. Here, we focus on the relationship between the residual structure in denatured lysozyme and the protein folding. It has been demonstrated that the reduced lysozyme forms six residual hydrophobic clusters under non-denaturing conditions. In particular, Trp62, which is exposed to solvent in the native structure and is involved in substrate binding, is located in the third residual hydrophobic cluster. When Trp62 was replaced by glycine (W62G), the hydrophobic clusters in the denatured protein were simultaneously disrupted. This result means that the other residual structures of the denatured state are retained by long-range nonnative interaction with Trp62. From the analysis of oxidative-renaturation of reduced W62G lysozyme, it was suggested that the disruption of the hydrophobic cluster led to the random folding at the early stages in the process of folding of the reduced lysozyme, resulting in aggregation. On the other hand, from the analysis of the disulfide bond formations in W62G lysozyme secreted from yeast, misfolded species were partially detected in the secreted protein. Therefore, it was concluded that Trp62 is not only involved in the formation of the hydrophobic clusters in the denatured state but also contributes to the correct folding in the early folding stages of the reduced lysozyme. Finally, the contributions of the residual structures of the denatured state to the conventional and amyloid aggregations were considered.

INTRODUCTION

There are numerous proteins in nature, each of which has a different function and structure. It has been estimated that the total number of protein superfamilies is limited to several thousand [1-3]. Recently, the various protein structural folds have been defined by determining the three-dimensional structure of the proteins. However, it is hard to predict the three-dimensional structure based on the primary amino acid sequence, because protein folding includes not only native interactions but also nonnative interactions [4-7]. Thus, the elucidation of the factors in the protein folding process is pivotal in understanding how proteins maintain their unique native conformations. Although the protein structure is generally analyzed according to the behavior between the denatured state and the native state, it has been shown that the residual structures are present even in the denatured state of a protein. Therefore, the residual structures may be related with the initial structures in the folding of the denatured protein. Thus, we have focused here on the relationship between the residual structures in the denatured state and the early events in the folding. This knowledge is also of vital importance in the designing of *de novo* proteins.

FOLDING OF NON-REDUCED LYSOZYME

Hen egg-white lysozyme was the first enzyme whose three-dimensional structure was elucidated using X-ray crystallography [8] and for whom a detailed mechanism of action was proposed [9]. Accordingly, this enzyme has been one of the proteins whose structure-function relationships have been most vigorously investigated. Its three-dimensional structure is composed of two domains, an alpha domain and a beta domain, and has four disulfide bonds, Cys6-Cys127, Cys30-Cys115, Cys64-Cys80, and Cys76-Cys94 (Figure 1). The folding reaction of the non-reduced lysozyme has been investigated by a variety of techniques, including hydrogen exchange analysis with nuclear magnetic resonance spectroscopy (NMR) [10], electrospray mass spectrometry (ESMS) [11], stopped-flow fluorescence measurements [12], and circular dichroism (CD) [13]. These results indicated that the alpha domain is formed before the beta domain in the folding of the non-reduced lysozyme.

FOLDING OF REDUCED LYSOZYME

Several studies on the folding process of hen lysozyme from the reduced and denatured state have been reported [14-16]. In a biological system of cells, a newly synthesized protein is produced as a fully reduced form in the endoplasmic reticulum (ER) and folds after translocation across the ER membrane [17]. Therefore, experiments on the folding process from the reduced form are very important for elucidating the general rules of protein folding. Anderson and Wetlaufar suggested that the disulfide bonds involving Cys64, Cys76, Cys80, and Cys94 formed faster than those involving Cys6, Cys30, Cys115, and Cys127 in the folding of reduced lysozyme [14]. The peptide fragment 59-105 involving the cysteines, Cys64, Cys76, Cys80, and Cys94, could correctly form the disulfide bonds from the reduced form [18]. It was also suggested that Trp62 in the peptide fragment 59-105 was a key residue for the formation of correct disulfide bonds [18]. Moreover, the chemical modification of Trp62 affected the folding of the reduced lysozyme [19]. These results indicated that Trp62 is important for the early events in lysozyme folding. In the native structure, however, Trp62 is located on the protein surface, where it is exposed to solvent and where it plays a role in the substrate binding (Figure 1). It is interesting that such an amino acid residue is intimately involved in the protein folding.

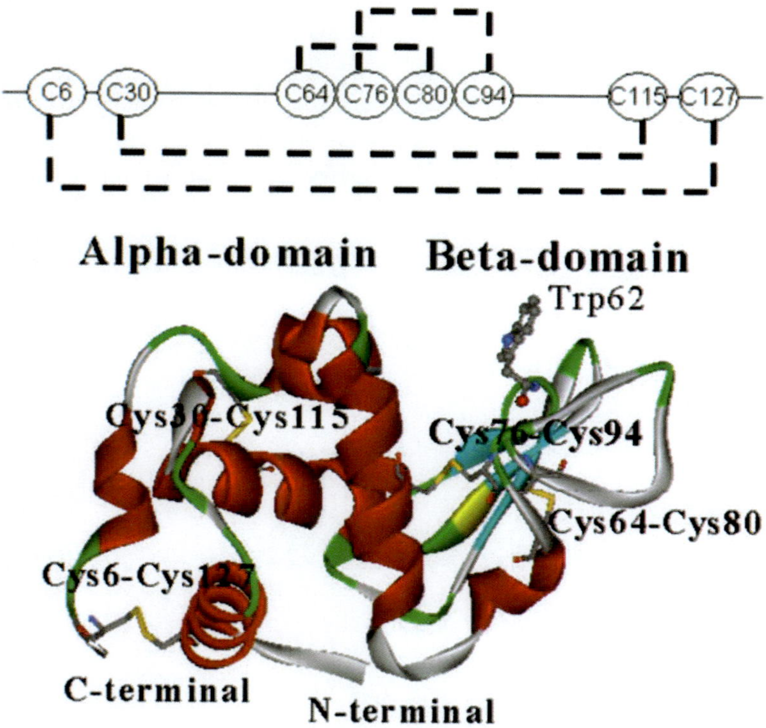

Figure 1. Schematic presentation of disulfide bonds and the three-dimensional structure of hen egg-white lysozyme. Four disulfide bonds and Trp62 are shown. The structure of the lysozyme consists of two domains, an alpha-domain and a beta-domain.

Disruption of the Residual Structure by W62G Mutation

Elements of the secondary structure have been detected in several unfolded proteins [20-22]. Moreover, the formation of the hydrophobic clusters in the denatured protein has been detected [23, 24]. Recently, using NMR techniques, residual structures were detected in the denatured hen lysozyme without disulfide bonds [25]. Transverse relaxation rates (R2), which are measured by ^{15}N-^{1}H heteronuclear NMR, show conformational exchange in the millisecond time scale [26]. The measurement of the R2 of each residue in the denatured protein can be used to probe for the presence of the residual structure [25]. Figure 2a shows the R2 values in the reduced lysozyme at pH 2, in which all reduced sulfhydryl groups are blocked by methylation. Six regions of elevated values of R2 were found to correlate with the location of hydrophobic residues, indicating the existence of hydrophobic clusters [25]. Tryptophan residues were involved in four clusters, Trp28 (cluster 2), Trp62 and Trp63 (cluster 3), Trp108 and Trp111 (cluster 5), and Trp123 (cluster 6). Moreover, the hydrophobic clusters were maintained even in the presence of 8 M urea at pH 2, which creates denaturing conditions (Figure 2b). We focused particular attention on Trp62, which is important for the early events of lysozyme folding, as described above. When Trp62 was replaced by glycine, the plotting of the R2 values yielded a horizontal line (Figure 2c). These results indicated that the hydrophobic clusters were all disrupted by a single-point mutation, W62G [27]. On the other hand, the hydrodynamic radius (Rh) can be defined as the radius of a sphere that has the same diffusion coefficient as the protein molecule [28]. As shown in Figure 3, the Rh of reduced lysozyme and W62G lysozyme were larger than that of native lysozyme, indicating that both reduced states were extended. Moreover, the large difference in Rh between the reduced lysozyme and W62G lysozyme indicated that a residual structure consisting of the hydrophobic clusters existed in the reduced lysozyme. Thus, the residual structure of lysozyme in the denatured state maintained the overall compactness by long-range interaction involving Trp62.

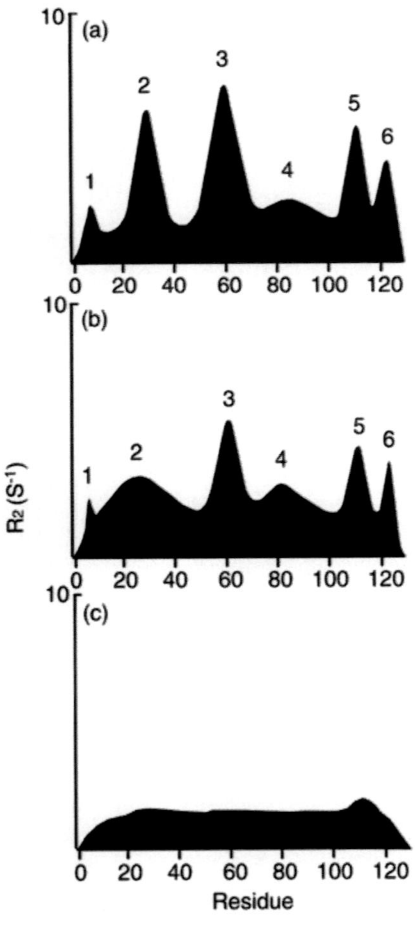

Figure 2. Transverse relaxation rates (R2) in the reduced lysozymes at pH 2, in which the free sulfhydryl groups are blocked by methylation; wild-type (a), wild-type in 8 M urea (b), and W62G (c). The six clusters are detected in the wild-type lysozyme. (Schematically redrawn from ref 27.)

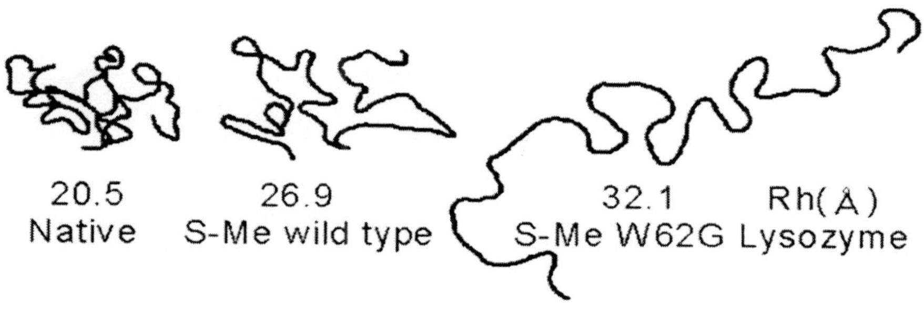

Figure 3. The hydrodynamic radius (Rh) of the native structure of lysozyme, reduced-methylated wild-type, and reduced-methylated W62G lysozyme at pH 2. (Schematically redrawn from ref 29.)

THE RESIDUAL STRUCTURES DERIVED FROM VARIOUS SINGLE MUTATIONS

The effects of single-point mutations on the compactness and interaction of clusters were investigated [29]. The R2 values of denatured variant lysozymes, A9G (cluster 1), W62G (clusters 3), W111G (cluster 5), and W123G (cluster 6), in which four native disulfide bonds were reduced and methylated, were measured at pH 2. Table 1 shows the range of R2 values for each cluster region. W62G mutation abolished not only its own cluster 3 but also clusters 1-4 and attenuated clusters 5 and 6 as described above. In contrast, A9G mutation did not affect even its own cluster 1. Since there were few hydrophobic residues in cluster 1, it was assumed that Ala9 would be responsible to the formation of cluster 1 [27]. However, it was found that Ala9 was not important for the stabilization of cluster 1. On the other hand, W111G and W123G lysozyme showed unique behaviors. W111G mutation abolished clusters 4, 5, and 6, and attenuated clusters 1, 2, and 3. Similarly, W123G mutation abolished clusters 4 and 6, and attenuated cluster 1, 2, 3, and 5. These results indicated that the hydrophobic clusters in the residual structure were hierarchically built up. It is expected that the various residual structures in the denatured lysozyme would affect the early events in the folding from the reduced state.

Table 1. The extents of R2 value versus each cluster region in wild-type, A9G (cluster 1), W62G (clusters 3), W111G (cluster 5), and W123G (cluster 6) lysozyme at pH 2, in which the free sulfhydryl groups are blocked by methylation [29].

Cluster Number	1	2	3	4	5	6
WT	+	+	+	+	+	+
W62G	–	–	–	–	±	±
A9G	+	+	+	+	+	+
W111G	±	±	±	–	–	–
W123G	±	±	±	–	±	–

Analysis of the Early Stage of the Folding Process of Reduced Lysozyme Using Variants Containing a Pair of Cysteines

The well-established method for analysis of the folding process of reduced proteins is to identify the formation of disulfide bonds, as done for bovine pancreatic trypsin inhibitor (BPTI) [30, 31], hirudin [32], potato carboxypeptidase inhibitor [33], epidermal growth factor [34], etc. These proteins have three disulfide bonds that can potentially adopt 75 different disulfide isomers. In contrast, the number of potential isomers in hen lysozyme, which has four disulfide bonds, is 762, indicating that the mechanism of disulfide bond formations is complicated [35]. Tachibana [36] constructed four species of lysozyme variants that contained only one disulfide bond, and evaluated the disulfide bond formation in each. This method can be used to clarify the interactions involved in the formation of disulfide bonds. Therefore, in order to elucidate which disulfide bond is prominently formed in the early stage of the folding of reduced lysozyme, we prepared all possible species of lysozyme variants containing a single pair of cysteines (1SS lysozyme) [37].

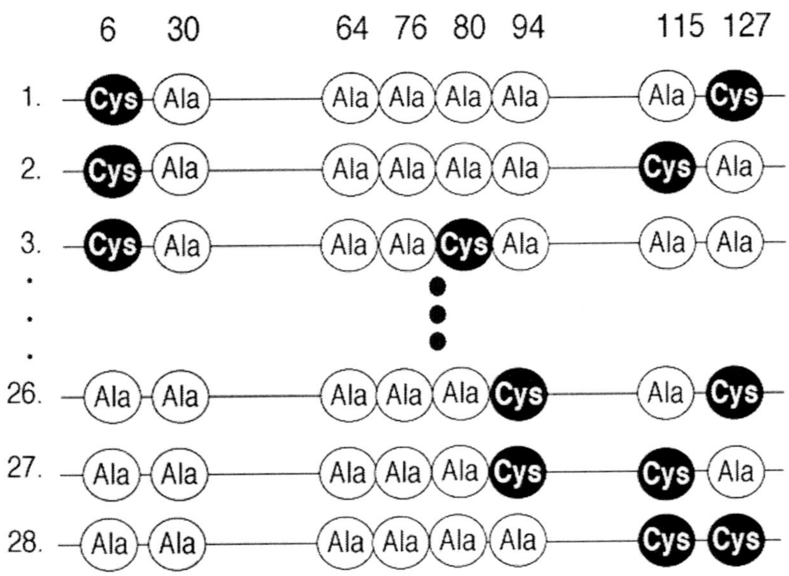

Figure 4. Primary structures of the 1SS lysozymes. All possible species of lysozyme variants containing a single pair of cysteines were prepared. The numbers show the residue positions.

The 1SS lysozymes were constructed by replacing Cys with Ala. For example, lysozyme variants containing a single pair of Cys6-Cys127 were constructed by changing Cys30 to Ala, Cys64 to Ala, Cys76 to Ala, Cys80 to Ala, Cys94 to Ala, and Cys 115 to Ala, resulting in lysozyme variants that retained only Cys6 and Cys127. We prepared all 28 species of 1SS lysozymes in the same way (Figure 4). These 1SS lysozymes were overexpressed in *E.coli* BL21 cells as inclusion bodies. As the N-terminal residue of hen lysozyme is lysine, a Met residue was attached to the N-terminal of lysozyme by an *E. coli* expression system. Since an extra Met residue attached to hen lysozyme has been reported to give a lower refolding yield and a reduced solubility of the lysozyme, we designed the 1SS lysozymes such that a Ser instead of a Met residue would be attached to the N-terminal of hen lysozyme, according to our previous report [38]. The purification of these variants from inclusion bodies was performed as described in our previous paper [37].

Evaluation of the Formation of Disulfide Bonds in 1SS Lysozymes

The equilibrium disulfide formation reaction was carried out at pH 8.0 in the presence of 0.1 mM GSSG and 1.0 mM GSH according to previous methods [37]. The extent of the formation of disulfide bonds was expressed as the ratio of the concentration of the oxidized form to that of the reduced form, which is obtained from the peak area on the chromatographic pattern of each lysozyme variant by reverse-phase HPLC. A typical chromatogram for Cys6-Cys30 1SS lysozyme after oxidation of the reduced lysozyme in the presence of 6M guanidine hydrochloride is shown in Figure 5. The oxidized variant (denoted Oxi) and the reduced variant (denoted Red) were separated from each other. The reduced lysozyme maintained some hydrophobic clusters even in the presence of 8 M urea at pH 2, which creates denaturing conditions [27]. Therefore, in order to determine whether there is some structure in lysozyme in the presence of 6 M guanidine hydrochloride, which creates highly denaturing conditions, we used a series of lysozyme variants as a probe, and measured the extent of disulfide bond formation in lysozyme variants in the presence of 6 M guanidine hydrochloride. The decrease in entropy in each lysozyme variant by formation of a disulfide bond is calculated as $0.75\nu R\ [\ln(N/\nu+3)]$, where N and ν correspond to the number of amino acid residues surrounded by a disulfide bond and twice the number of disulfide bonds, respectively [39]. As shown in Figure 6, the plot of free energy change for the formation of disulfide bonds in the 1SS lysozyme variant in the presence of 6 M guanidine hydrochloride against the theoretical free energy change derived from the decrease in entropy of the polypeptide chain showed a good correlation (open circles in Figure 6), indicating that the denatured state of hen lysozyme in the presence of 6 M guanidine hydrochloride adopts a randomly coiled structure. Wu *et al.* suggested that the formation of disulfide bonds in alpha-lactalbumin in the presence of 6 M guanidine hydrochloride was controlled by random polypeptide chain entropy [40]. However, the information on alpha-lactalbumin is limited to the formation of two native disulfide bonds. On the other hand, our results were obtained by analyses using 28 lysozyme variants. Thus, it was conclusively demonstrated that the formation of the disulfide bonds in the random structure of the protein is entropically driven.

Next, the free energy changes in the formations of the disulfide bonds for 1SS lysozyme in aqueous solution were evaluated. Figure 6 shows a plot of the free energy changes against the theoretical free energy changes derived from the decreases in entropies of the polypeptide chain of lysozyme (filled circles). Even in aqueous solution, the formations of disulfide bonds are governed by the chain entropies to some extent. However, all the disulfide bonds in aqueous solution formed more efficiently than those in the presence of 6 M guanidine hydrochloride. The scattering of the free energy changes for the formations of the disulfide bonds among all lysozyme variants implied that the non-random folding occurred in the extremely early stage of the folding of reduced lysozyme, as well as the existence of a somewhat compact structure in the reduced form [37]. Thus, this method is applicable to detect the interaction in the early stage of folding from the reduced protein.

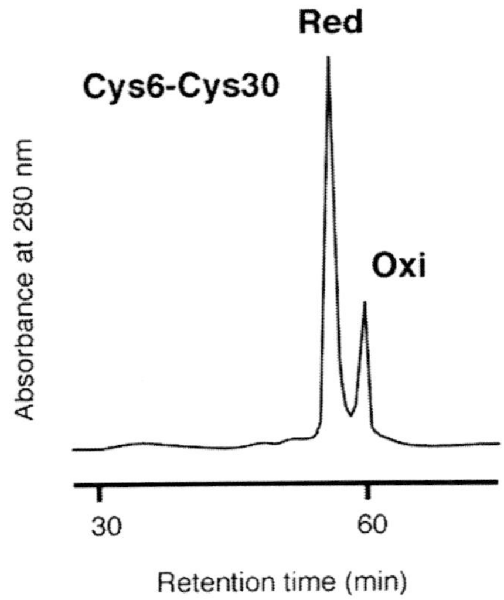

Figure 5. A typical pattern of the oxidized form and reduced form of the 1SS lysozyme variant in the presence of 6M guanidine hydrochloride in the reverse-phase HPLC. The column (μ-BONDASPHERE C4 150 x 3.9 mm) was eluted with a gradient of acetonitrile in 0.05% TFA from 30% to 40% in 100 min at a flow rate of 1 ml/ml.

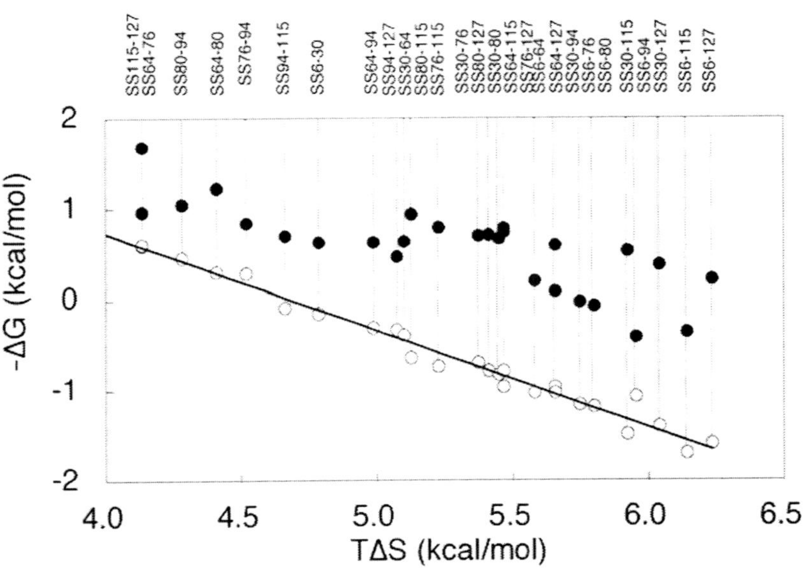

Figure 6. The free energy change for the formations of disulfide bonds in 1SS lysozyme variants in the presence of 6 M guanidine hydrochloride (open circles) and those in aqueous solution (closed circles) against the theoretical free energy changes derived from the decrease in entropy of the peptide chain of lysozyme at pH 8 and 22°C. The cysteines of 1SS lysozyme are indicated by dotted lines. (Redrawn from Figure 2 in ref 37.)

Evaluation of the Formation of Disulfide Bonds in W62G 1SS Lysozyme in 8M Urea Solution

In order to examine the effect of disrupting hydrophobic clusters by mutation of W62G on the early stages in the folding process, we constructed variants of W62G containing only one pair of cysteines (W62G 1SS lysozyme), and we then evaluated the extent of the formation of disulfide bonds [41]. From analysis of the disulfide bond formation in 1SS lysozyme, it was suggested that the denatured state of hen lysozyme in the presence of 6 M guanidine hydrochloride adopts a randomly coiled structure. On the other hand, denatured lysozyme in the presence of 8 M urea, which is a weaker denaturant than guanidine, possesses some hydrophobic clusters, as demonstrated by NMR measurements (Figure 2) [27]. The formation of disulfide bonds in 1SS lysozymes in the presence of 8M urea would not be expected to be the same as that in the presence of 6M guanidine hydrochloride. Therefore, at first, we investigated whether the residual structure affected the formation of disulfide bonds even in the presence of 8M urea.

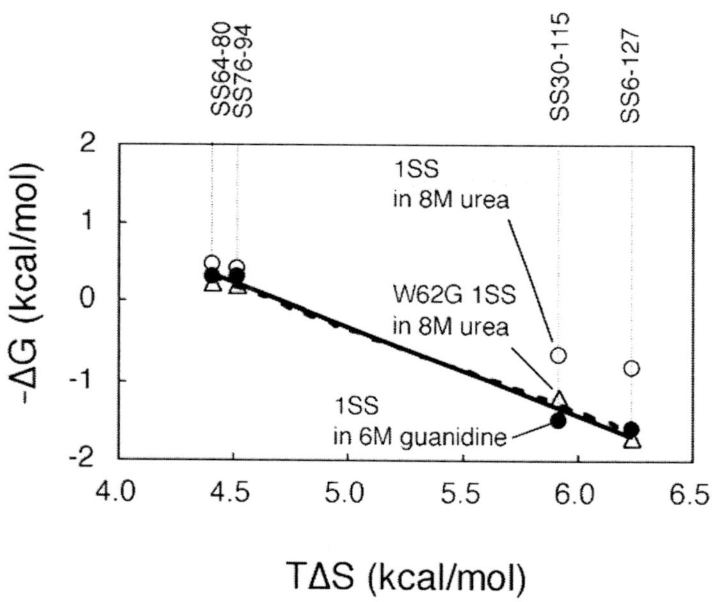

Figure 7. The free energy changes for the formation of disulfide bonds in 1SS lysozymes (open circles) and W62G 1SS lysozymes (open triangles) in the presence of 8 M urea and 1SS lysozyme variants in 6 M guanidine hydrochloride (filled circles) against the theoretical free energy changes derived from the decrease in entropy of the polypeptide chain of lysozyme. The data points correspond to cysteine formation of the 1SS lysozymes. (Redrawn from Figure 3 in ref 41.)

The disulfide exchange measurements for four 1SS lysozymes and four W62G 1SS lysozymes containing native disulfide bonds, Cys6-Cys127, Cys30-Cys115, Cys64-Cys80, or Cys76-Cys94, respectively, were performed in 8 M urea. The resulting products were analyzed by reverse-phase HPLC as described above. The extent of the formation of disulfide bonds was evaluated based on the ratio of the oxidized form to the reduced form of the protein, whereby each of these values was obtained from the peak area on the chromatographic pattern. The plots of the free energy changes, derived from the extent of the formation of disulfide bonds among the 1SS lysozyme variants in 8M urea against the entropy of the polypeptide chains, are shown as open circles in Figure 7. For comparison, the results for 1SS lysozymes in the presence of 6 M guanidine hydrochloride are indicated by filled circles. Although the free energy changes of W62G 1SS lysozymes (open triangles) in 8 M urea solution were found to be identical to those of randomly coiled structures (filled circles) under highly denaturing conditions, the free energy changes of the 1SS lysozymes (open circles) in 8 M urea were greater than those of the W62G 1SS lysozymes. This result indicated that the formation of the disulfide bonds in the 1SS lysozymes was more efficient than that in the W62G 1SS lysozymes in 8 M urea. Especially, the free energy change of the formation of Cys6-127 or Cys30-115 was affected more significantly than that of Cys64-80 or Cys76-94 by W62G mutation. As described above, it was found that, from the viewpoint of the difference in the free energy change of the formation of an SS bond between the cysteines in the random structure and that in the condensed structure, the cysteine pair between the remote residues was affected more than that between the close residues. Namely, in the condensed structure, the degree of approach between the remote residues is greater than that between the close residues in the cysteine pair, because the condensed structure is compact. These findings revealed that the formation of hydrophobic clusters influenced the formation of disulfide bonds even in 8 M urea solution. Therefore, it is likely that the disruption of the hydrophobic clusters led to the absence of a prominent interaction between the amino acid residues in 8 M urea solution.

Evaluation of the Formation of Disulfide Bonds in W62G 1SS Lysozyme in an Aqueous Solution

The folding of a protein from a denatured condition *in vitro* is initiated by rapid dilution of the protein in a concentrated denaturant solution in an aqueous solution lacking the denaturant. Therefore, in order to examine the interaction involved in the formation of disulfide bonds at the early stages in the process of folding, the disulfide exchanges on 1SS lysozymes in aqueous solution were measured, under conditions corresponding to those for the initiation of protein folding [41]. There are four cysteines, Cys64, Cys76, Cys80, and Cys94, near Trp62 in the wild-type lysozyme. In addition to the preparation of W62G 1SS lysozymes containing a native pair of cysteines, Cys64-Cys80 and Cys76-Cys94, we also prepared four W62G 1SS lysozymes containing a nonnative pair of cysteines, i.e., Cys64-Cys76, Cys64-Cys96, Cys76-Cys80 or Cys80-Cys94, respectively. The exchange measurements of the disulfide bonds of the 1SS lysozymes under aqueous conditions (0.1M Tris-acetate containing 0.1 mM EDTA, pH 8.0) were carried out according to the previously described methods [37]. The respective free energy changes required for the formation of disulfide bonds in these 1SS lysozymes were calculated based on the ratio of the reduced form to the oxidized form, as determined by reverse-phase HPLC analysis. The plots of the free energy changes on lysozyme variants against the entropy of the polypeptide chains are shown in Figure 8. The filled circles show the free energy changes of the 1SS lysozyme in 6 M guanidine solution, as described above. The points of free energy change of each W62G

1SS lysozyme (open triangles) were lower than those of the 1SS lysozyme (open circles). This result indicated that more interactions were required to form the disulfide bond in the W62G 1SS lysozyme than in the 1SS lysozyme. Moreover, the free energy changes in W62G 1SS lysozymes were linearly dependent on the chain entropies between cysteines, whereas those of the 1SS lysozymes showed scattering. The scattering data indicated that nonrandom folding occurred during the early stages in the process of folding of the reduced lysozyme. On the other hand, the free energy changes in the 1SS lysozymes in the presence of 6 M guanidine hydrochloride showed good correlation with the chain entropies between cysteine residues. The W62G 1SS lysozymes exhibited similar behavior, even when in aqueous solution. These results suggested that the reduced W62G lysozyme was almost randomly folded at the early stages of the folding, due to the large disruption of the hydrophobic clusters. The present results suggest that the residual structure of the denatured state does indeed exert an effect on the folding of lysozymes.

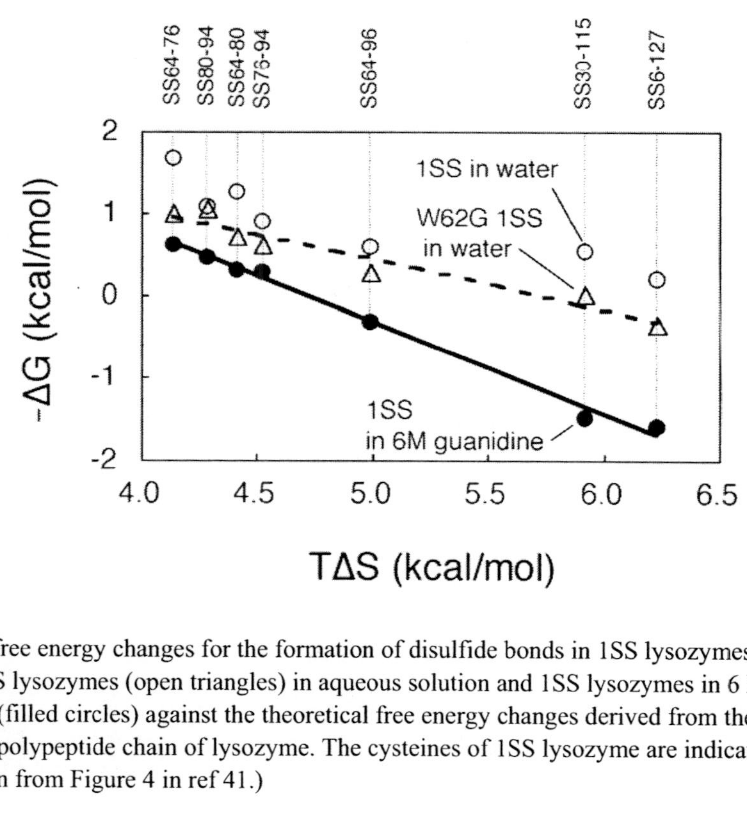

Figure 8. The free energy changes for the formation of disulfide bonds in 1SS lysozymes (open circles) and W62G 1SS lysozymes (open triangles) in aqueous solution and 1SS lysozymes in 6 M guanidine hydrochloride (filled circles) against the theoretical free energy changes derived from the decrease in entropy of the polypeptide chain of lysozyme. The cysteines of 1SS lysozyme are indicated by dotted lines. (Redrawn from Figure 4 in ref 41.)

The Effect of the Structure of the Denatured State of Lysozyme on Aggregation

Aggregation was found to take place during the early stages in the process of the folding of lysozyme from its reduced form, and the process of aggregation kinetically competes with the folding reaction [42]. Therefore, the effect of the structure of the denatured state of lysozyme on aggregation was examined by measuring the time-course of the recovery of activity from the reduced form of W62G lysozyme [41]. Refolding of the reduced lysozymes was conducted according to previous procedures [43] with a slight modification. The folding yield was determined by the ratio of activity at an appropriate time to the original total activity of each lysozyme. The final folding yield of the W62G lysozyme was approximately 50%, whereas that of the wild-type lysozyme was 85%. The reduced wild-type lysozyme in 8 M urea solution was renaturated by rapid dilution, and the yield was found to reach approximately 85% under reproducible conditions [43]. The residual material (15%) forms an aggregate following kinetic competition with the folding reaction [42]. In order to determine whether the aggregation of the W62G lysozyme occurred at the early stage or at the late stage after the formation of the disulfide bond, a reduced and carboxamidemethylated (CAM) W62G lysozyme and CAM wild-type lysozyme were prepared. CAM lysozymes were dissolved in 8 M urea solution (pH 8.6) and then diluted 100-fold with 0.1 M Tris-HCl buffer (pH 8.0) as under the renaturation condition. The extent of aggregation of both CAM lysozymes in the solution was evaluated by the increase in absorbance at 320 nm [44]. Figure 9 shows the increase in absorbance at 320 nm and 30 min after dissolving the CAM lysozymes. At a concentration of 20 μg/ml, which is identical to the protein concentration of the renaturation of the reduced lysozyme, the extent of aggregation of CAM W62G lysozyme was 3.4-fold more than that of the CAM wild-type lysozyme. This result was consistent with the difference in the folding yield upon the renaturation of both reduced lysozymes. At higher protein concentration, the difference in the extent of aggregation between the CAM W62G lysozyme and the CAM wild-type lysozyme increased. Thus, it was confirmed that the decrease of the folding yield of reduced W62G lysozyme was caused by the formation of aggregates during the early stages of the folding process. Since the structures of the CAM W62G lysozyme and the CAM wild-type lysozyme differ in the denatured state, these results indicated that the residual structure of lysozyme was involved in the aggregation. Therefore, it was concluded that the random folding that occurred during the early stages of the folding process of the reduced lysozyme facilitated the aggregation.

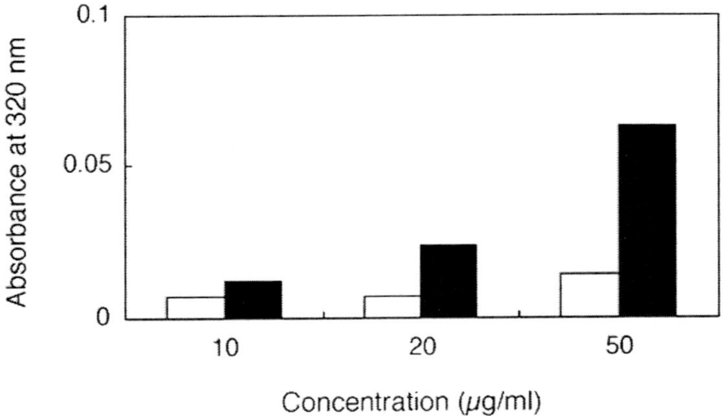

Figure 9. The aggregation measurement of the reduced CAM wild-type lysozyme (open bars) and the reduced CAM W62G lysozyme (filled bars). The reduced CAM lysozymes were dissolved in 8 M urea solution (pH 8.6) and then diluted 100-fold with 0.1 M Tris-HCl buffer (pH 8.0). The extent of aggregation of both CAM lysozymes in the solution was evaluated by the increase in absorbance at 320 nm at the concentration of 10, 20 or 50 μg/ml. (Redrawn from Figure 7 in ref 41.)

THE EFFECT OF THE STRUCTURE OF THE DENATURED STATE OF LYSOZYME ON EARLY EVENTS OF THE FOLDING PROCESS FROM REDUCED LYSOZYME

The time-course of the recovery of activity from the reduced form of the wild-type and W62G lysozyme is shown in Figure 10. The recovery of activity from the reduced wild-type lysozyme has been observed immediately after the initiation of renaturation, as described in our previous studies [43, 45], as well as in other studies [46, 47]. On the other hand, in the case of the reduced W62G lysozyme, a lag phase was observed in the time course, as determined by the recovery of activity. Under the same conditions, such a lag phase in the recovery of the activity of reduced lysozymes has never been observed in the refolding of many types of reduced mutant lysozyme with single-point mutations. It is possible that, during the lag phase, the reduced W62G lysozyme has not yet formed an active structure. In order to confirm the extent of the recovery of activity among the reduced lysozymes, the refolded species were compared with the corresponding intact species by ion-exchange HPLC. After stopping the refolding by adding aminoethylmethanethiosulfonate (AEMTS), which immediately alkylates the thiol groups [48], the pH of the renaturation mixture was lowered to 5 by adding acetic acid. Then, ion-exchange HPLC was performed at pH 5 for each sample solution. The refolded product in the wild-type lysozyme after 1 min of renaturation appeared as a peak on ion-exchange HPLC (Figure 11), and the folded yield was nearly identical to that obtained by the observation of lytic activity. In the case of the W62G lysozyme, there was no refolded W62G lysozyme peak detected by elution on ion-exchange HPLC after 1 min of renaturation (Figure 11). This result was consistent with the observation of a lag phase in the time course of the recovery of activity of the reduced W62G lysozyme, indicating that the reduced W62G lysozyme has not yet formed an active structure during the lag phase.

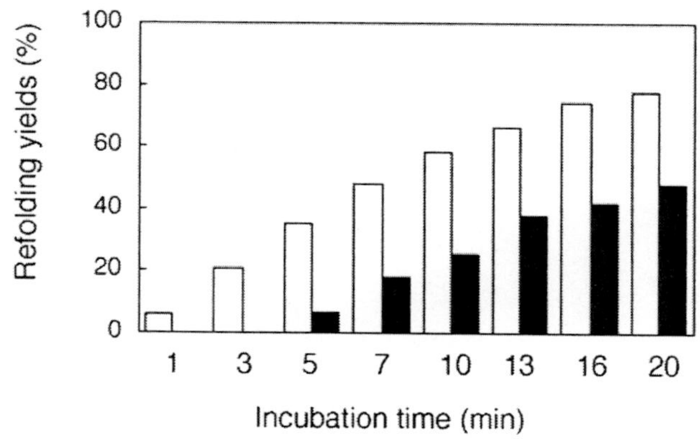

Figure 10. The time-course of the recovery of activity from the reduced form of the wild-type (open bars) and W62G lysozyme (filled bars). (Redrawn from Figure 5 in ref 41.)

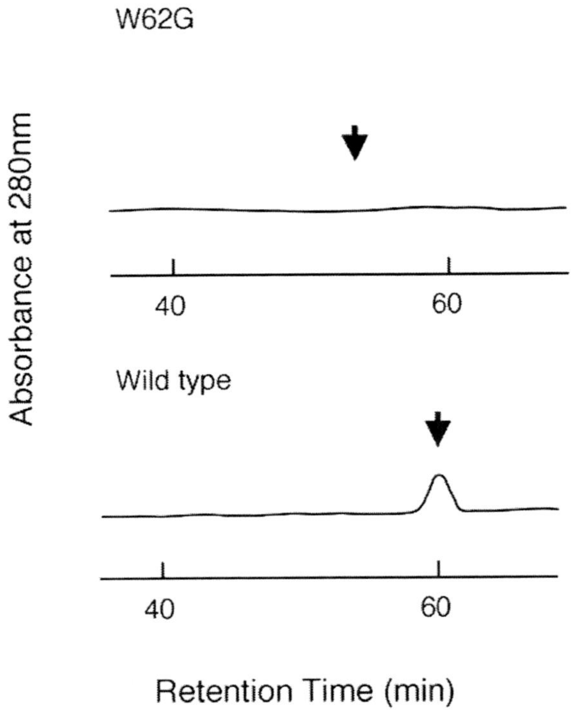

Figure 11. Ion-exchange chromatography HPLC of the renaturation mixture of the reduced wild-type lysozyme and W62G lysozyme for 1 min. The column (Asahipak ES-502C, 7.8 x 100 mm) was eluted with a gradient of 40 ml of 0.1 M acetate buffer at pH 5.0 and 40 ml of the same buffer containing 0.5 M NaCl at a flow rate of 1.0 ml/min. Arrowheads indicate the elution time of the respective intact lysozymes. (Redrawn from Figure 6 in ref 41.)

(A) $D \rightarrow N$

(B) $D \rightarrow I_1 \rightarrow I_2 \rightarrow I_3 \rightarrow\rightarrow\rightarrow N$

(C) $D \rightleftarrows I_1 \rightleftarrows I_2 \rightleftarrows \cdots \rightleftarrows I_i \rightleftarrows I_N \rightarrow\rightarrow\rightarrow N$

Figure 12. The folding process of the denatured and reduced lysozyme. (A) Two-state model analogous to the model of the wild-type lysozyme. (B) Multi-state model analogous to the results of refolding experiments of the reduced W62G lysozyme. (C) The kinetic mechanism of aggregation during the folding of the denatured and reduced lysozyme proposed by Goldberg *et al.* in 1991 [42].

Moreover, a simulation of the folding process of the reduced W62G lysozyme was attempted in order to confirm the presence of intermediates during the early stages in the refolding of the reduced W62G lysozyme. By using the higher-order Runge-Kutta methods [49], all of the rate constants for the following equations of the folding process of the W62G lysozyme from the denatured structure (D) to the native structure (N) were altered. When the folding process of the reduced W62G lysozyme was assumed as a two-state model analogous to the model of the wild-type lysozyme (equation in Figure 12A), it was not adjusted according to the results of the refolding experiments. However, the more the intermediates (I_1, I_2, and I_3 in Figure 12B) were inserted into the process of folding from the denatured form to the native form (Figure 12B), the more the results of the refolding of the reduced W62G lysozyme were fitted to the results of the refolding experiments. Based on these results, it appears that the process of refolding of the reduced W62G lysozyme includes extra intermediates during the early stages in the folding.

Goldberg *et al.* proposed kinetic mechanisms of aggregation during the folding of the denatured and reduced lysozyme [42]. They assumed that during the transition from the unfolded structure (U) to the intermediate (I_i), the protein can either irreversibly enter the aggregation pathway or proceed to the native structure (N), as none of the states following I_i can aggregate (Figure 12C). In this model, the processes between U and I_N occur very rapidly; thereafter, the transition from I_N to N occurs slowly. The present results indicated that in the process of folding of the reduced W62G lysozyme the aggregation increased more than it did in the case of the folding of the wild-type lysozyme. This finding indicates that the number of species leading to the aggregation increased more than the number leading to the I_N state. Furthermore, we found that the renaturation of the reduced W62G lysozyme included some intermediates at the early stages in the folding process. The accumulation of intermediates would be expected to cause a delay in the formation of species leading to the I_N state, resulting in an increase in aggregation. The accumulation of intermediates in the folding process is known to cause partial folding or misfolding [50]. The present results of the experiments using the W62G 1SS lysozymes indicated that the disruption of the structure of the denatured state caused random folding during the early stages of the folding of the reduced lysozyme. It is well known that random interactions with respect to refolding lead to nonnative scrambled species in the experiments on ribonuclease [51]. Therefore, during the early stages of the process of reduced W62G lysozyme folding, the occurrence of random folding would be expected to lead to misfolded species. Thus, the intermediates might have accumulated due to this random folding at the early stages in the folding of reduced W62G lysozyme.

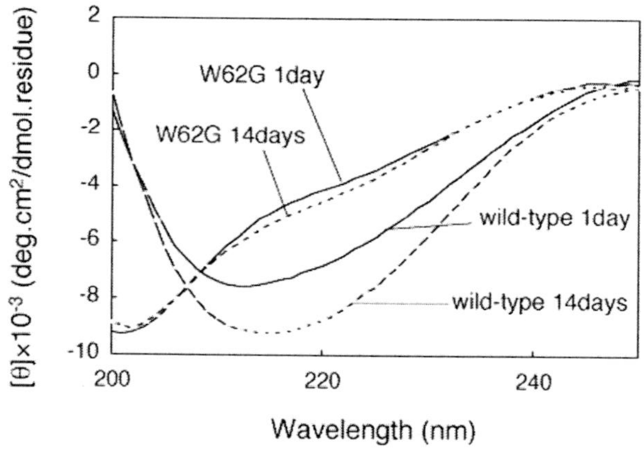

Figure 13. Time-dependence of the CD spectra of the CAM wild-type lysozyme or the CAM W62G lysozyme after 1 day or 14 days of incubation in 50 mM sodium maleate at pH 2.0 and 25 °C. (Redrawn from Figure 10 in ref 41.)

THE INFLUENCE OF RESIDUAL STRUCTURE OF LYSOZYME ON AMYLOID AGGREGATION

Under a strongly acidic condition, lysozyme without any disulfide bonds can form amyloid fibrils [52, 53]. Although such acidic conditions were extremely different from the physiological condition in which the refolding of reduced lysozyme was carried out, it was very important to determine whether the hydrophobic clusters—i.e., the residual structure—were involved in the amyloid aggregation. Therefore, in order to examine whether the hydrophobic clusters affect the formation of amyloidogenic fibrils, CAM W62G lysozyme and CAM wild-type lysozyme were incubated in 50 mM sodium maleate at pH 2.0, 25 °C, and protein at a concentration of 8 mg/ml, since it has been shown that lysozyme without any disulfide bonds could form amyloid fibrils at this concentration [41]. It was considered that a beta conformation is a common feature in the amyloid fibrillogenesis [54]. Figure 13 shows the CD spectra of the incubated CAM W62G lysozyme and CAM wild-type lysozyme. After 1-day incubation, the CAM wild-type lysozyme had already formed the beta structure (Figure 13), whereas the CD spectra of the CAM W62G lysozyme indicated a random structure even after 14 days of incubation (Figure 13). The diagnostic amyloid was evaluated in the presence of thioflavine T fluorescence (ThT), a fluorescent dye specific for amyloid structure [55]. Figure 14 shows the fluorescence emission of ThT at 485 nm in the presence of CAM lysozymes taken at intervals during the incubation at pH 2.0. The fluorescence intensity of ThT in the presence of CAM wild-type lysozyme increased after 1-day incubation, whereas that in the presence of CAM W62G lysozyme did not increase after 14 days of incubation (Figure 14). These results indicate that the CAM wild-type lysozyme forms amyloid fibrils after incubation under these conditions, but the CAM W62G lysozyme does not. The condensed structure in the denatured state of the wild-type lysozyme not only contributed to the efficient folding of the reduced lysozyme, but also was involved in the formation of amyloid fibrils. Thus, it was suggested that the disruption of the condensed structure in the denatured state by the W62G mutation promoted the aggregation during the early stages of folding, but deterred the formation of amyloid fibrils.

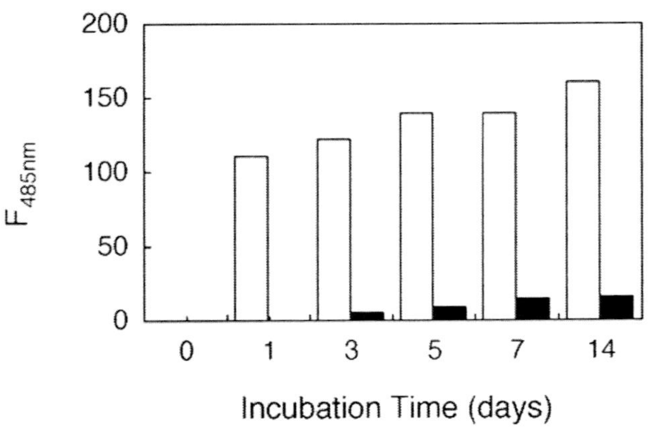

Figure 14. The fluorescence emission at 485 nm of ThT in the presence of the CAM wild-type lysozyme (open bars) or the CAM W62G lysozyme (filled bars) during the incubation at pH 2.0 and 25 °C. (Redrawn from Figure 11 in ref 41.)

Involvement of the Residual Structure of the Denatured State of Lysozyme on the Folding *in Vivo*

The protein folding *in vivo* is conducted with the help of molecular chaperones in order to achieve high efficiency. Although the folded stable protein has progressed to the secretion pathway, the misfolded intermediate or unstable proteins have been led to the degradation pathway by the quality control. However, the rupture of this system causes the accumulation of misfolded protein, leading to protein conformational diseases. As was shown above, we demonstrated that the residual structure of the denatured state was involved in the formation of amyloid fibrils *in vitro*. So far, there has been no report in which the denatured state structure of a protein had an influence on the protein folding *in vivo*. Therefore, in order to examine whether the disruption of the denatured state structure by W62G mutation has an influence on the folding of hen lysozyme *in vivo*, W62G lysozyme was secreted from yeast *Saccharomyces cerevisiae* [56]. The yeast *Saccharomyces cerevisiae* was cultivated at 30°C for 125 h to express and secrete W62G lysozyme as described in the literature [57]. The purification of W62G lysozyme was carried out according to the previous report [57]. The yield of W62G lysozyme was similar to that of the wild-type lysozyme (*ca.* 1 mg/L). From the results of gel chromatography and peptide analysis, it was found that the purified W62G lysozyme from yeast contained the unstable species which have free cysteines, with the exception of the native form. In order to examine the disulfide bond formations in these species, the trapping of cysteines in the species was carried out using AEMTS, which has high reactivity to cysteine residues [58]. It is possible that the cysteine modified with AEMTS could be converted to taurine by performic acid oxidation, and then the taurine could be detected by amino acid analysis. Purified W62G lysozyme from yeast was dissolved in 0.1M Tris-HCl pH 8.0 buffer containing 1 mM AEMTS. Since no amount of cysteine in W62G lysozyme could be modified by AEMTS after incubation at 40°C for 10 min, W62G lysozyme was dissolved in 0.1M Tris-HCl pH 8.0 buffer containing 8 M urea and 1 mM AEMTS to accelerate the access of the reagent to cysteine residues in the molecule. After incubation at 40°C for 10 min, the concentration of the urea was diluted to 2 M. TPCK-trypsin was added and the solution was incubated at 40°C for 2 h. The RP-HPLC patterns of the tryptic peptides derived from the wild-type lysozyme and W62G lysozyme are shown in Figure 15, respectively. There was no peak for the wild-type lysozyme except for the undigested wild-type lysozyme (peak I) in Figure 15, indicating that the lysozyme was not digested by trypsin under this condition due to its significant stability. On the other hand, partially digested peaks appeared for the W62G lysozyme, except for the undigested W62G lysozyme (peak II) in Figure 15. After digestion of the protein solution for 12 h, the RP-HPLC pattern in Figure 15 did not change, indicating that the unstable species contained in the W62G lysozyme were completely digested within 2 h. The amino acid compositions of the tryptic peptides in Figure 15 after acid hydrolyses of the performic acid-treated peptides were determined. Taurine was detected at the peptide in the peak marked with the asterisk in Figure 15, and the peptide corresponded to the tryptic peptides containing Cys64, Cys76, Cys80, and Cys94. To investigate the formation of the disulfide bonds among these cysteines further, the peptide in the peak with the asterisk was digested with alpha-chymotrypsin and prolylendopeptidase according to the previous method [59]. From analyses of the amino acid compositions, the peak in the peptide marked with an asterisk in Figure 15 possessed two cysteines, Cys80 and Cys94, and a nonnative disulfide bond, Cys64-Cys76 (data not shown). Thus, it was suggested that the purified W62G lysozyme from yeast partially contained the misfolded species including cysteine residues [56]. This result implied that the disruption of the residual structure in the denatured state also affected the folding of the lysozyme *in vivo*. The formation of the residual structure in the denatured state should lead to the correct folding pathway. However, in the present case, the random structure of the denatured state would cause the production of quasi-stable species in the folding process, resulting in the secretion of misfolded species. Thus, it was concluded that the residual structure in the denatured state of lysozyme *in vitro* was closely related with the folding process *in vivo*.

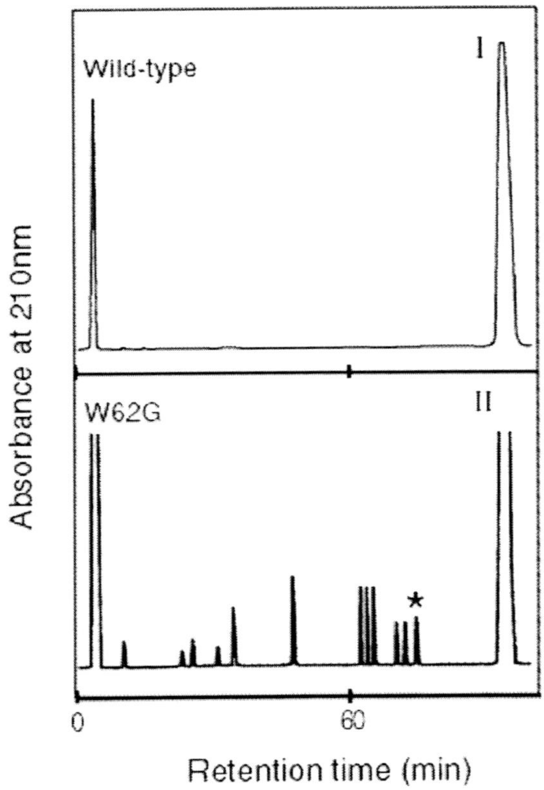

Figure 15. RP-HPLC of tryptic peptides derived from the wild-type HEL and W62G lysozyme treated with AEMTS. The column (Wacosil C18, 4.6 mm X 250 mm) was eluted with a gradient of 50 ml of 1% acetonitrile and 50 ml of 50% acetonitrile, both containing 0.1% HCl, at a flow rate of 0.6 ml/min. Taurine was detected in the peptides corresponding to the asterisked peak. (Redrawn from Figure 4 in ref 56.)

CONCLUSION

Although Trp62 is located on the protein surface and is thus exposed to solvent in the native structure, it has long been unknown how Trp 62 exerts such a substantial effect on the folding of lysozyme. Recently, it was found that the condensed structure in the denatured lysozyme was stabilized by the nonnative and long-range interactions involving Trp62. The various single mutations revealed different residual structures, indicating that the hydrophobic clusters in the residual structure were hierarchically built up. On the other hand, it has been shown that the residual structure of the denatured state of lysozyme affects the early events of the folding of the reduced lysozyme, thus indicating that disruption of the hydrophobic core led to random folding. The random folding at the early stages in the folding process facilitated the aggregation. The mutation of Trp62 to Gly in hen lysozyme led to the appearance of a lag phase at the early stages of folding from the reduced form. Simulation of the folding process revealed that intermediates were present during the early stages of the folding. These results suggest that the presence of randomly formed intermediates kinetically delayed the folding process, and led to the severe aggregation of the reduced lysozyme. Moreover, it was found that the disruption of the hydrophobic clusters deterred the formation of amyloid fibrils, meaning that the mechanism of amyloid aggregation was different from the conventional aggregation at the early stage of folding of the reduced lysozyme. Finally, it was found that the residual structure in the denatured state of HEL *in vitro* was closely related with the folding process *in vivo*. In any case, we demonstrated that the residual structure in the reduced lysozyme was tightly connected to the initial features of folding from the reduced form. It is hoped that these findings will lead to new insights into the folding of proteins.

REFERENCES

[1] Chothia, C. (1992). Proteins - 1000 families for the molecular biologist. *Nature 357*, 543–544.

[2] Orengo, C. A. Jones, D. T. & Thornton, J. M. (1994). Protein superfamilies and domain superfolds. *Nature 372*, 631–634.

[3] Coulson, A. F. & Moult, J. (2002). A unifold, mesofold, and superfold model of protein fold use. *Proteins 46*, 61–71.

[4] Hua, Q. X. Gozani, S. N. Chance, R. E. Hoffmann, J. A. Frank, B. H. & Weiss, M. A. (1995). Structure of a protein in a kinetic trap. *Nat Struct Biol.* 2, 129-138

[5] Chang, J. Y. Li, L. & Bulychev, A. (2000). The Underlying Mechanism for the Diversity of Disulfide Folding Pathways. *J. Biol. Chem. 275*, 8287-8289.

[6] Cemazar, M. Zahariev, S. Lopez, J. J. Carugo, O. Jones, J. A. Hore, P. J. & Pongor, S. (2003). Oxidative folding intermediates with nonnative disulfide bridges between adjacent cysteine residues. *Proc. Natl. Acad. Sci. USA. 13*, 5754-5759.

[7] Feng, H. Zhou, Z. & Bai, Y. (2005). A protein folding pathway with multiple folding intermediates at atomic resolution. *Proc. Natl. Acad. Sci. USA. 102*, 5026-5031.

[8] Imoto, T. Johnson, L. N. North, A. C. T. Philip, D. C. & Rupley, J. (1972). Vertebrate lysozyme. In The Enzyme (Boyer, P. D. ed.), 3rd edit., *7*, 666-868.

[9] Blake, C. C. F. Johnson, L. N. Mair, G. A. North, A. C. T. Philips, D. C. & Sarma, V. R. (1967). Crystallographicstudies of the activity of hen egg-white. *Proc. Roy. Soc. ser. B. 167*, 378-388.

[10] Radford, S. E. Dobson, C. M. & Evans, P. A. (1992). The folding of hen lysozyme involves partially structured intermediates and multiple pathways. *Nature 358*, 302-307.

[11] Miranker, A. Robinson, C. V. Radford, S. E. Aplin, R. T. & Dobson, C. M. (1993). Detection of transient protein folding populations by mass spectrometry. *Science 262*, 896-900.

[12] Itzhaki, L. S. Evans, P. A. Dobson, C. M. & Radford, S. E. (1994). Tertiary interactions in the folding pathway of hen lysozyme: kinetic studies using fluorescent probes. *Biochemistry 33*, 5212-5220.

[13] Chaffotte, A. F. Guillou, Y. & Goldberg, M. E. (1992). Kinetic resolution of peptide bond and side chain far-UV circular dichroism during the folding of hen egg white lysozyme. *Biochemistry 31*, 9694-9702.

[14] Anderson, W. L. & Wetlaufer, D. B. (1976). The refolding pathway of reduced lysozyme. *J. Biol. Chem. 251*, 3147–3153.

[15] van den Berg, B. Chung, E. W. Robinson, C. V. Dobson, C. M. (1999). Characterisation of the dominant oxidative folding intermediate of hen lysozyme. *J Mol Biol. 290*, 781-796.

[16] Jarrett, N. M. Djavadi-Ohaniance, L. Willson, R. C. Tachibana, H. Goldberg, M. E. (2002). Immunochemical pulsed-labeling characterization of intermediates during hen lysozyme oxidative folding. *Protein Sci. 11*, 2584-2595.

[17] Gething, M. J. & Sambrook, J. (1992). Protein folding in the cell. *Nature 355*, 33–44.

[18] Ueda, T. Ohkuri, T. & Imoto, T. (1996). Identification of the peptide region that folds native conformation in the early stage of the renaturation of reduced lysozyme. *Biochem. Biophys. Res. Commun. 228*, 203-208.

[19] Ueda, T. Abe, Y. Ohkuri, T. Kawano, K. Terada, Y. Imoto, T. (1995). Kinetically trapped structure in the renaturation of reduced oxindolealanine 62 lysozyme. *Biochemistry 34*, 16178-16185.

[20] Shortle, D. & Abeygunawardana, C. (1993). NMR analysis of the residual structure in the denatured state of an unusual mutant of staphylococcal nuclease. *Structure 1*, 121-134.

[21] Wong, K. B. Freund, S. M. Fersht, A. R. (1996). Cold denaturation of barstar: ^{1}H, ^{15}N and ^{13}C NMR assignment and characterisation of residual structure. *J. Mol. Biol.* 259, 805-818.

[22] Blanco, F. J. Serrano, L. & Forman-Kay, J. D. (1998). High populations of non-native structures in the denatured state are compatible with the formation of the native folded state. *J. Mol. Biol.* 284, 1153-1164.

[23] 23. Neri, D. Billeter, M. Wider, G. & Wuthrich, K. (1992). NMR determination of residual structure in a urea-denatured protein, the 434-repressor. *Science 257*, 1559-63.

[24] Saab-Rincon, G. Gualfetti, P. J. & Matthews, C. R. (1996). Mutagenic and thermodynamic analyses of residual structure in the alpha subunit of tryptophan synthase. *Biochemistry 35*, 1988-1994.

[25] Schwalbe, H. Fiebig, K. M. Buck, M. Jones, J. A. Grimshaw, S. B. Spencer, A. Glaser, S. J. Smith, L. J, Dobson, C. M. (1997). Structural and dynamical properties of a denatured protein. Heteronuclear 3D NMR experiments and theoretical simulations of lysozyme in 8 M urea. *Biochemistry 36*, 8977-8991.

[26] Wagner, G. NMR relaxation and protein mobility. (1993). *Curr. Opin. Struct. Biol. 3.* 748-754.

[27] Klein-Seetharaman, J. Oikawa, M. Grimshaw, S. B. Wirmer, J. Duchardt, E. Ueda, T. Imoto, T. Smith, L. J. Dobson, C. M. & Schwalbe, H. (2002). Long-range interactions within a nonnative protein. *Science 295*, 1719-1722.

[28] Wilkins, D. K. Grimshaw, S. B. Receveur, V. Dobson, C. M. Jones, J. A. Smith, L. J. Hydrodynamic radii of native and denatured proteins measured by pulse field gradient NMR techniques. *Biochemistry 38*, 16424-16431.

[29] Wirmer, J. Schlorb, C. Klein-Seetharaman, J. Hirano, R. Ueda, T. Imoto, T. & Schwalbe, H. (2004). Modulation of compactness and long-range interactions of unfolded lysozyme by single point mutations. *Angew Chem Int Ed Engl. 43*, 5780-5785.

[30] Creighton, T. E. Goldenberg, D. P. (1984). Kinetic role of a meta-stable native-like two-disulphide species in the folding transition of bovine pancreatic trypsin inhibitor. *J. Mol. Biol. 179*, 497-526.

[31] Weissman, J. S. & Kim, P. S. (1991). Reexamination of the folding of BPTI: predominance of native intermediates. *Science 253*, 1386-1393.

[32] Chatrenet, B, & Chang, J. Y. (1993). The disulfide folding pathway of hirudin elucidated by stop/go folding experiments. *J. Biol. Chem. 268*, 20988-20996.

[33] Venhudova, G. Canals, F. Querol, E. Aviles, F. X. (2001). Mutations in the N- and C-terminal tails of potato carboxypeptidase inhibitor influence its oxidative refolding process at the reshuffling stage. *J Biol Chem. 276*, 11683-11690.

[34] Chang, J. Y. Li, L. & Lai, P. H. (2001). A major kinetic trap for the oxidative folding of human epidermal growth factor. *J. Biol. Chem. 276*, 4845-4852.

[35] Chang, J. Y. & Li, L. (2002). Pathway of oxidative folding of alpha-lactalbumin: a model for illustrating the diversity of disulfide folding pathways. *Biochemistry 41*, 8405-8413.

[36] Tachibana, H. (2000). Propensities for the formation of individual disulfide bonds in hen lysozyme and in the size and stability of disulfide-associated submolecular structures. *FEBS. Lett.* 480, 175-178.

[37] Shioi, S. Imoto, T. Ueda, T. (2004). Analysis of the early stage of the folding process of reduced lysozyme using all lysozyme variants containing a pair of cysteines. *Biochemistry 43*, 5488-5493.

[38] Mine, S. Ueda, T. Hashimoto, Y. & Imoto, T. (1997). Improvement of the refolding yield and solubility of hen egg-white lysozyme by altering the Met residue attached to its N-terminus to Ser. *Protein Eng. 10*, 1333-1338.

[39] Flory, P. J. (1956). Theory of elastic mechanisms in fibrous proteins, *J. Am. Chem. Soc. 78*, 5222-5235.

[40] Wu, L. C. Peng, Z. Y. & Kim, P. S. (1995). Bipartite structure of the alpha-lactalbumin molten globule, *Nat. Struct. Biol. 2*, 281-286.

[41] Ohkuri, T. Shioi, S. Imoto, T. Ueda, T. (2005). Effect of the structure of the denatured state of lysozyme on the aggregation reaction at the early stages of folding from the reduced form. *J. Mol. Biol. 347*, 159-168.

[42] Goldberg, M. E. Rudolph, R. & Jaenicke, R. (1991). A kinetic study of the competition between renaturation and aggregation during the refolding of denatured-reduced egg white lysozyme. *Biochemistry. 30*, 2790-2797.

[43] Maeda, Y. Ueda, T. Yamada, H. & Imoto, T. (1994). The role of net charge on the renaturation of reduced lysozyme by the sulfhydryl-disulfide interchange reaction. *Protein Eng. 7*, 1249-1254.

[44] Kurganov, B. I. Rafikova, E. R. & Dobrov, E. N. (2002). Kinetics of thermal aggregation of tobacco mosaic virus coat protein. *Biochemistry*, *67*, 525-533.
[45] Ueda, T. Yamada, H. Aoki, H. & Imoto, T. (1990). Effect of chemical modifications of tryptophan residues on the folding of reduced hen egg-white lysozyme. *J. Biochem. 108*, 886-892.
[46] Wetlaufer, D. B. Branca, P. A. & Chen, G. X. (1987). The oxidative folding of proteins by disulfide plus thiol does not correlate with redox potential. *Protein Eng. 1,* 141-146.
[47] Fischer, B. Sumner, I. & Goodenough, P. (1992). Analysis of catalytic properties of hen egg white lysozyme during renaturation from denatured and reduced material. *Arch. Biochem. Biophys. 298*, 361-364.
[48] Rothwarf, D. M. & Scheraga, H. A. (1992). Equilibrium and kinetic constants for the thiol-disulfide interchange reaction between glutathione and dithiothreitol. *Proc. Natl. Acad. Sci. 89,* 7944-7948.
[49] Cartwright, J. H. E. & Piro, O. (1992). The Dynamics of Runge-Kutta Methods. *Int. J. Bifurcations Chaos 2*, 427-449.
[50] Eaton, W. A. Munoz, V. Thompson, P. A. Chan, C. K. & Hofrichter. J. (1997). Submillisecond kinetics of protein folding. *J. Curr. Opin. Struct. Biol. 7*, 10-14.
[51] Anfinsen, C. B. (1973). Principles that govern the folding of protein chains. *Science 181*, 223-230.
[52] Cao, A. Hu, D. & Lai, L. (2004). Formation of amyloid fibrils from fully reduced hen egg white lysozyme. *Protein Sci. 13*, 319-324.
[53] Niraula, T. N. Konno, T. Li, H. Yamada, H. Akasaka, K. & Tachibana, H. (2004). Pressure-dissociable reversible assembly of intrinsically denatured lysozyme is a precursor for amyloid fibrils. *Proc. Natl. Acad. Sci. 101*, 4089-4093.
[54] Fezoui, Y. Hartley, D. M. Walsh, D. M. Selkoe, D. J. Osterhout, J. J. Teplow, D. B. (2000). A de novo designed helix-turn-helix peptide forms nontoxic amyloid fibrils. *Nat Struct Biol.* 7, 1095-1099.
[55] LeVine, H. (1993). Thioflavine T interaction with synthetic Alzheimer's disease beta-amyloid peptides: detection of amyloid aggregation in solution. *Protein Sci. 2*, 404–410.
[56] Ohkuri, T. Imoto, T. & Ueda, T. (2005). Effect of W62G mutation of hen lysozyme on the folding *in vivo. Biophys. Biochem. Res. Commun. 338,* 820-824.
[57] Hashimoto, Y. Yamada, K. Motoshima, H. Omura, T. Yamada, H. Yasukochi, T. Miki, T. Ueda, T. & Imoto, T. (1996). A mutation study of catalytic residue Asp 52 in hen egg lysozyme. *J. Biochem. 119*, 145-150.
[58] Rothwarf, D. M. & Scheraga, H. A. (1991). Regeneration and reduction of native bovine pancreatic ribonuclease A with oxidized and reduced dithiothreitol. *J. Am .Chem. Soc. 113*, 2671-2698.
[59] Ueda, T. Abe, Y. Ohkuri, T. Kawano, K. Terada, Y. & Imoto, T. (1995). Kinetically trapped structure in the renaturation of reduced oxindolealanine 62 lysozyme. *Biochemistry. 34*, 16178-16185.

In: Protein Folding: New Research
Editor: Tony R. Obalinsky, pp. 195-223

ISBN 1-59454-835-8

Chapter 5

SECONDARY STRUCTURE OF PROTEINS: IMPLICATIONS FOR FOLDING, FUNCTION AND PROTEIN STRUCTURE PREDICTION

Ivan Y. Torshin
Bioinformatix Consulting, LLC, Moscow, Russia

ABSTRACT

The protein structure is considered to have at least three basic levels: the primary, secondary and tertiary/quaternary. One of the aims of the post-genomic biology is establishing the definitive links between these levels of protein structure. This is also the task of the classical biophysical research of the protein folding which involves experimental studies of a few model proteins in order to get closer to the principles linking together the these levels of the protein structure. The present article concentrates on the roles of the intermediate structural level: the secondary structure. On one hand, biophysical studies of the protein folding suggest that the secondary structure can appear prior or concurrently with the major folding event. On the other hand, bioinformatical analyses, along with the data from computational chemistry presented in the article suggest that the secondary structure might contain considerably more information on the protein's tertiary structure, folding, stability and function than it is currently assumed. In particular, predictions of the tertiary structure of the proteins made exclusively on the base of the secondary structure were unexpectedly successful. The results suggest that the information contained in the secondary structure alone might be sufficient to describe and to predict not only the tertiary structure but also the functional regions in a protein. The new ultra-fast techniques emerging in the modern *in vitro* studies of the protein folding also suggest a unique place for the secondary structure during folding.

INTRODUCTION

The principal aim of a "post-genomic" biology is elucidation of the structures, functions and of the biochemical properties of the gene products in a genome. More than often, a large proportion of the proteome has little, if any, functional annotation. Both the high-throughput methods of the structural proteomics ("genomics") and the functional genomics endeavour to decipher the various functions of the proteins in particular genomes. In parallel, computational techniques of bioinformatics are being developed to assist the task.

The functional annotation of a genome implies different levels of the function: the genetic, the physiologic, the cellular, the biochemical and the biophysical levels. In particular, without detailed biochemical and biophysical characterization of the gene product, of its function, folding and stability, the understanding of the gene function will remain too general for any practical task, such as mutagenesis, protein engineering and protein design, as well as drug design and many other biomedical and biotech applications.

At any level (with the exception of the genetic), the function(s) of a gene is largely determined by the functions(s) of the related gene product, the protein. The protein structure is considered to have at least three basic levels: the primary, the secondary and the tertiary/quaternary. These levels of the classification are intrinsically interrelated and a change at each level can influence the protein function to a great degree. One of the main assumptions in the computational analyses of the proteins is that the primary structure of a protein (the amino acid sequence, which one of the outputs of a genomic project) largely determines the tertiary structure which, in turn, determines the entire range of functions of any particular protein in an organism. However, the exact nature of the connexion between the levels of the protein structure is not known and one of the aims of the post-genomic biology is finding the definitive links between these levels of the protein structure. Having these links established will greatly assist the task of the genome annotation as well as elaboration of various practical applications in biomedicine (which, more than often, includes the studies of the folding and stability of some particular proteins).

Functional annotation of a genome is required or, at least, is greatly desirable prior to elaborating any practical applications. Such an annotation involves not only identifying genes and assigning functions to gene products but also establishing the key residues which determine important aspects of the protein structure and function. Many of the current annotation methods rely on the searches of the similarity of the protein in question to the primary and/or the tertiary structures of some other, previously known proteins [1].

Of course, the functional annotation of a genome is not limited to these two approaches. The rise of the comparative genomics in the era of complete genomes permits the use of protein-protein interaction patterns and correlations between occurrences of related proteins in different organisms for the purposes of the general genome annotation. Molecular function could also be predicted from the sequence but without involving sequence similarities: by using sequence-derived features such as predicted post translational modifications, protein sorting signals and amino acid composition [2, 3]. Another method of a post-genomic way of annotating is the gene neighbour method based on the observation that if the genes encoding two proteins are close on a chromosome, the proteins tend to be functionally related [3].

However, the bulk of the approaches to the computational analysis of the protein function, folding and/or stability involve the search for a known protein in some way similar to the target protein. Mostly, these similarity searches exploit the similarities in primary structure (the BLAST algorithm, perhaps, best represents this approach [4]), of specific sequence patterns (such as those collected in PROSITE [5]) and, in a very few cases when the tertiary structure is available, the similarities in the tertiary structures (for example, [6]). Combinations of the methods that involve analysis of the similarities both at the primary and tertiary levels are also being developed (for example, [7] and [8]). There are thousands of bioinformatics studies that describe implementations or particular applications of the similarity searches based on the primary and/or tertiary levels of the protein structure. However, there is a general lack of the studies that would attempt the similarity searches at the level of the secondary structure, though the analysis of the predicted secondary structure is occasionally used in the prediction of the protein structure and function [3,7,9]. It's also admitted that the local structural information (such as secondary structure) is particularly useful in protein structural and functional analyses. In order to get the idea of the potential value of the secondary structure analyses in the post-genomic era, let us consider the informational and energetical aspects of each of the levels of the protein structure.

The Levels of the Protein Structure

There are *four conventional levels* of looking at a structure of a protein: the primary (the amino acid sequence), the secondary (helices, strands, turns and loops), the tertiary (three-dimensional structure of a single subunit) and the quaternary (organization of two or more subunits into a macromolecular complex) level of the protein structure [10]. There are, of course, also intermediate levels between these four (such as so-called "super-secondary structure"). This basic classification can be of a great use for the present analysis of the relative informational contents and the structural factors contributing to the relative energies of the individual residues. Let's consider the relative informational contents, subsequent compacting of the information from level to level as well as the energetic aspects of each of these levels.

First of all, we can classify these four levels into *sequential* (primary and secondary) and *spatial* (tertiary and quaternary) level groups (Figure 1). This distinction is geometrically clear since the primary and secondary structure can be unequivocally represented as strings or sequences of letters, while the tertiary and quaternary levels of structure also imply definite connections between distant parts of the polypeptide chain and a peculiar 3D arrangement. *Primary structure* (*1D,* Figure 1a) is the most important determinant of the secondary and of the tertiary/quaternary structure of a protein. These successive levels of the structural information are encoded by the variety of the amino acids along the sequence of the protein so the information is of relatively low compactness (20 types of amino acids often without any obvious functional patterns). In bioinformatics, protein sequences can sometimes be categorized as belonging to one or other "family" or "super-family" of the protein sequences. Some functional regions, such as phosphorylation sites, catalytic sites of well-characterized types and other specific sites can be identified directly from sequence using previously established sequence patterns (such as those collected in PROSITE database). From the energetical point of view, the primary structure does not bring any other structural restraint except the precise sequence of the residues of the definite types. Therefore, depending on the particular conformation of the entire sequence, the energy values of individual residues can vary greatly.

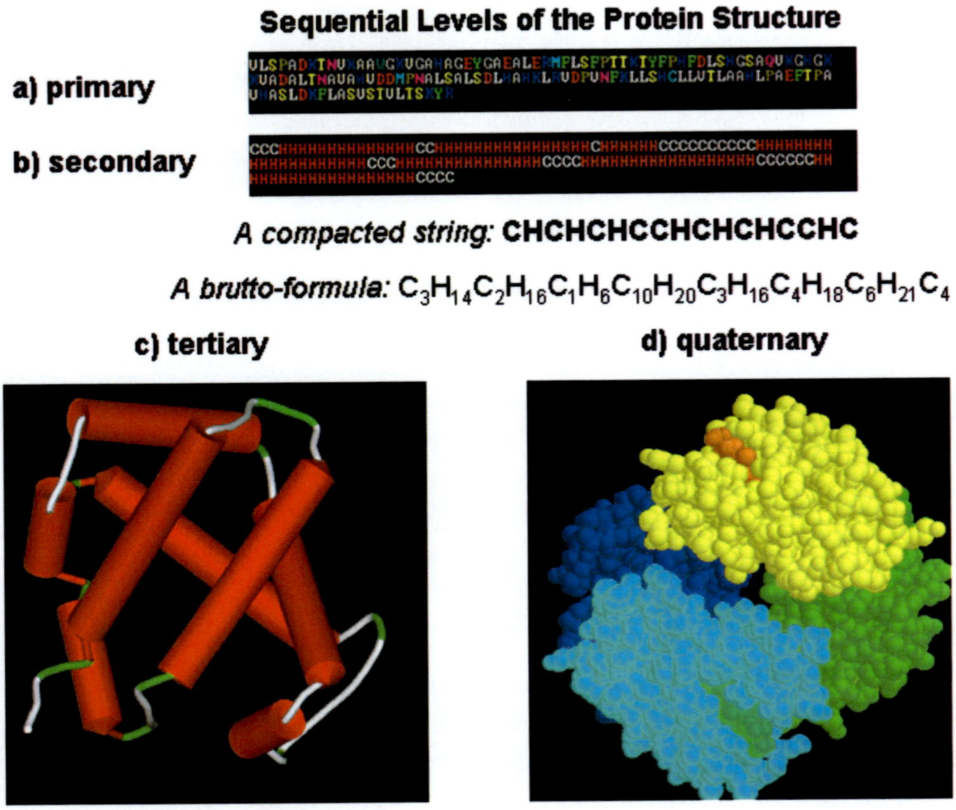

Figure 1. The structural information available at the different levels of the protein structure. The human haemoglobin was used as the example and the figure slides (a)-(c) correspond to alpha-subunit of haemoglobin (PDB 4hhb). a) *The primary structure (1D)*. The structural information is represented as the variety of the amino acids along the sequence of the protein (illustrated by the variety of the colours in the figure, red: negative residues; blue: positive residues etc). b) *The secondary structure (2D)*, "H" stands for alpha-helices and "C" (coil) stands for the loops/turns. The secondary structure was derived using STRIDE software. In this protein, only alpha-helices and loops are present and there are no beta-strands. The structural information at this level is the sequence of the three types of the elements of the secondary structure (illustrated by the overall quite uniform colouring) and can be represented as a string of the per-residue assignments or, alternatively, as the "compacted string" or as the "brutto-formula". c) *The tertiary structure (3D)*, the N-terminus is on the left. The structural information encoded at this level of the protein structure is the way in which the separate elements of the secondary structure are mutually arranged in 3D. The tertiary structure is usually classified as belonging to a certain general class of the protein architecture and the protein "fold" (particular architecture of the protein). In the case of the haemoglobin, the fold class is "all-alpha" while the "fold" type is "globin-like" (according to the SCOP classification [36]). d) *Quaternary structure* of haemoglobin (the orange spot corresponds to a heme molecule) consists of the two "alpha" and the two "beta" subunits organized in a tetramer of a "toroid" type. Protein tetramers, in more than 90% of the cases, tend to be either "toroid" or "pyramid" ([37] and unpublished data).

Considering the level of the *secondary structure* (*2D*, Figure 1b), some of the residues adjacent in the sequence are brought closer (for example, in a turn or in an alpha-helix) while some others are become further apart (the even/odd residues in the beta-strands). The structural information at this level of description becomes more compact: the secondary structure description of a protein contains, mostly, only three types of the elements (instead of the 20 types of the amino acids) and can be represented as a string of the per-residue assignments or, alternatively, as a compacted string (the super-pattern of the secondary structure types along the sequence, each letter representing an entire element of the secondary structure) or as a kind of a "brutto-formula" (figure 1b). This kind of information on the secondary structure is sometimes used as a secondary aid in protein structure prediction. As we'll see from the present article, the predicted secondary structure can also be used as the main and, practically, the sole criterion for the protein structure prediction. Geometrically, there are certain structural restraints (the postulated average geometry of the helices and of the strands). These structural restraints will reduce variability in the energies of the individual residues when conformation of the polypeptide with the fixed secondary structure changes. Applications of the method of the molecular energetic profiles, reviewed in the present article, indicate that the differences in energies of the individual residues, might reflect the biological functions of the residues in the native protein already at the level of the secondary structure.

The spatial levels of the protein structure include the tertiary and the quaternary structures. In the *tertiary structure* (*3D*, Figure 1c), the residues from different parts of the sequence are brought together forming the functional site(s) of the protein. Alternatively, the tertiary structure can be considered as a specific spatial arrangement of the elements of the secondary structure. As we know from biochemical studies, the tertiary structure is one of the main determinants of the protein's functional properties. The structural information at this level becomes highly compact: the protein has a distinct *general architecture* (fold class, "all-alpha" in the case of hemoglobin, Figure 1c) and distinct *specific architecture* (protein fold, "globin-like" in the case of the hemoglobin).

Thus, the variety of the amino acids fancifully as it were arranged along the sequence was compacted into the string of the secondary structure elements and, further, into a precise and specific fold. The tertiary conformations of the folded proteins are remarkably rigid, especially in the case of enzymes. The relative per-residue energies are determined, in part, by the spatial arrangement of the residues on the molecular surface of the folded protein.

Quaternary structure describes how two or more polypeptide chains associate to form a native protein structure. Some proteins function as a single subunit while biological function of others is possible only when several copies of the same subunit or several different subunits aggregate (Figure 1d). The quaternary level of protein structure can be considered as providing further fine tuning of the energies of the individual residues.

Looking again at this three/four-partite classification, we might notice that there seems to be an abrupt loss of the functional information while going back from the tertiary to the secondary structure. Indeed, to the tertiary structure corresponds almost a complete protein/domain of a definite biological function (for example, monomeric myoglobin is quite similar to the alpha-subunit of hemoglobin in 3D structure and also maintains the similar range of the physiological functions as the alpha-chain of the haemoglobin), while secondary structure mostly provides rather general a distinction between helices and strands. It was indeed an important discovery to establish the existence of such distinct elements as helices and strands in the overall protein design. However, this discovery was made in the middle of the past century and little has been added to our understanding of the fundamental, essential features of the protein design and the roles of the secondary structure since then.

In the present article, the term 'secondary structure' implies, before all, not so much the distinction between the helices and strands but rather the *super-pattern* that describes the mutual arrangement of the helices, strands and loops along the amino acid sequence of an entire polypeptide chain (Figure 1b). The description is more informationally compact and uniform than the primary structure (1D). The fold class can often be reliably guessed from the secondary structure (2D) though the exact fold type characterizing the tertiary structure (3D) is far from being obvious at the 2D level. The intermediary informational character of the secondary structure suggests that it can provide a valuable link that holds together the entire informational system of the primary, secondary and tertiary levels. Finding definitive links between these levels of protein structure is also the task of the classical biophysical research in the protein folding which employs detailed experimental studies of a few small proteins, usually called as 'model' proteins, in order to get closer to the principles linking together the three levels of the protein structure.

In this article, we will consider the data from the cellular and biophysical studies of the protein folding, as well as the results of molecular simulations and some bioinformatic studies (charge centers, molecular energetic profiling and protein structure prediction). This analysis represents an attempt to define the relation of the secondary structure to the protein folding, stability and function. The role of the secondary structure for the protein function is illustrated by the concept of the molecular energetic profiles which is inherently related to the notion of the levels of the protein structure. The concept of the molecular energetic profiles unites the various aspects of the protein structure, function, folding and stability. Prior to reading the main text of the article, it seems proper to keep in mind the two important discrepancies (or, rather, the points of attention) located at the edges between the biophysical, cellular and bioinformatic studies of the protein folding. The first one is a relative success of the numerous secondary structure prediction algorithms, which implicitly suggest that a local context (of about 20-40 residues) determines the secondary structure contrasted by the results of some biophysical experiments that seem to indicate no strong conformational preferences for the secondary structure elements. The second one is that recent biophysical studies suggest that the secondary structure of some proteins might form simultaneously with the tertiary structure while doing *in vitro* studies. At the same time, according to cell-related studies, the secondary structure of *any* protein can form already during the protein synthesis.

Cellular Aspects of the Protein Folding

A cell shows a variety of the proteins with very different folding mechanisms. Among them are structural proteins, transmembrane proteins and globular proteins. *Structural proteins* (like collagen or proteoglycans) hardly fold at all and maintain their biological functions in a largely extended state of the polypeptide chain. At best, one can mention the term 'folding' in relation only to the secondary structure of the structural proteins. *Transmembrane proteins,* due to the two-dimensional nature of the cellular membranes, are likely to show quite uniform folding mechanism which can be generally described as formation of the transmembrane helices followed by the helix-helix association. The *globular proteins*, which form the overwhelming majority of the cellular machinery, show the variety of functional shapes and, accordingly, the variety in the details of the folding mechanisms.

Most of the experimental studies of the protein folding are biophysical, which implies that they are done using *in vitro* model systems. The cellular studies are important as they emphasize the essential limitations of the *in vitro* experiments [11]. A protein, newly synthesized in cell, is certainly placed in an environment quite different from that of a test-tube. The three most important differences between the folding of the globular proteins in a test tube (*in vitro*) and in the cell (*in vivo*) are the presence of the sequential process of the chain synthesis, the macromolecular interactions in the cellular milieu and the initial chain conformation for the folding.

Firstly, the nascent protein chains in the cells are *synthesized sequentially* on ribosomes: that is, residue-by-residue. The ribosome channel is quite small and cannot contain more than 40-50 residues of a newly synthesized chain. Consequently, the already synthesized part of the protein sequence leaves the channel and can begin to fold while the rest of the protein is being synthesized. This process is known as co-translational folding and there is no likeness of it in the *in vitro* experiments (unless, of course, *in vitro* experiments use ribosome synthesis).

Secondly, the cellular milieu and, primary, cytosol, provide a highly crowded *macromolecular environment*, which is very unlike to the refolding buffer used in the *in vitro* refolding experiments. Non-specific interactions of the nascent chains are likely to increase the risk of the aggregation of the non-functional folding intermediates considerably inhibiting the folding in the cell in comparison to the *in vitro* folding. There are also macromolecular interactions that assist the cellular folding such as the interactions with various types of chaperons in the specific cellular compartments [11].

Thirdly, *the initial conformations* for the protein folding are likely to be very different between the *in vitro* folding experiments and in the cellular folding. In the case of the *in vitro* folding studies, the protein is firstly denaturated and then is refolded using some or other biochemical technique. However, it is well known that the standard techniques of the biochemical denaturation do not lead to a complete unfolding (that is, complete extension of the protein chain). Rather, the denaturation results in some semi-compact conformation, be it native-like or non-native. In distinction from the *in vitro* studies, in the cell (according to the ribosome structure [12]) the fragments of a single polypeptide chain are synthesized in the sequential fashion and are likely to be significantly extended at the earliest stages of the protein folding. This contention becomes entirely clear taking into account that the ribosome channel is only a few nanometers wide and cannot accommodate a structure wider than alpha-helix. Therefore, the secondary structure, which can form at the time scale of the tens of nanoseconds, can easily be formed in the ribosome channel long before the peptide leaves the channel. The significantly extended conformation of a protein in the ribosome channel, apart from its importance for the molecular energetic profiles, the potential for the post-genomic applications in bioinformatics [13] and for the realistic molecular simulations (considered further in this chapter), might also be important for the correct protein folding *in vivo*. Provided that these differences are kept in mind, let's proceed with the consideration of the *in vitro* studies of the protein folding and the respective roles of the secondary structure.

BIOPHYSICAL STUDIES OF THE PROTEIN FOLDING

Detailed biophysical studies have shown an amazing feature of the protein folding: the formation of intricate and regular architectures at extremely fast rates (sub-millisecond time scales). In comparison to many other of the related cellular processes (for example, synthesis of the polypeptides or formation of protein-protein interfaces), native-like structures emerge during the folding of a polypeptide chain almost instantaneously [14].

Protein folding is complex and multi-parallel process that leads to formation of highly specific protein architectures. For this process to be effective, the complexity should be somehow reduced or controlled. In the cell, co-translational folding and the chaperons may be effective ways to reduce the inherent complexity of the process. However, co-translational folding proceeds on the hundreds of milliseconds to second scale, while it might be possible for a protein to fold in a microsecond. In any case, proteins still can refold *in vitro*, without the assistance of the cellular folding machinery. The following brief review aims at elucidating the roles of the secondary structure in protein folding, from the point of view of the biophysical case studies of the folding of a few model proteins.

First of all, it should be remembered that most of the experimental studies on the dynamics of protein folding have been confined to time scales of 1 millisecond and longer. This limitation is due to the dead-time problem of the stopped-flow experiments, the most widely used technique which has become a standard for the folding studies. Consequently, the biophysical models of the protein folding (such as nucleation, framework and others, considered below) were based not only on this kind of experimental evidence but also using some kind of an *a priori* theoretical assumptions to explain the results obtained at the 1ms level of resolution.

The primary of these assumptions is that protein folding cannot occur through random search of all possible conformations, since any random 'mechanism' requires an astronomical amounts of time while we know from experiments that the actual folding proceeds on a submillisecond scale [15]. Due to the extreme (from the cellular point of view) rapidity of the folding process, there simply should be some strong determinism in the protein folding, there should be some sequential steps that simplify the informational complexity of the folding. These sequential steps can be considered at the level of individual atomic motions or, in a wider view, as distinct stages in a specific folding mechanism. Consideration of what these steps could be has lead to numerous proposals, thoroughly analyzed in an excellent review on the classical biophysical studies of the protein folding [16]. For example, *the nucleation-growth hypothesis* proposed that tertiary structure propagates rapidly from an initial nucleus of preformed secondary structure. The existence of such a secondary structure nucleus cannot be ascertained as yet due to the millisecond resolution of the most of the techniques, so other models were proposed: framework model, hydrophobic collapse model and a nucleation-condensation model. In *the framework model* secondary structure is, again, proposed to form first then the pre-formed secondary structural units interact to yield the native folded protein. At least, this assumption does not contradict to the newer ultra-fast experiments indicating that folding/re-folding of the individual elements of the secondary structure occurs on nanosecond scale and thus can occur many times long before the main folding event. The seeming problem with this model is that peptide studies show that isolated elements of secondary structure (helices and strands) seem to have relatively weak conformational preferences in the absence of the rest of the protein's 'framework' [16]. In *the hydrophobic collapse model* exclusion of the solvent by hydrophobic groups was proposed to 'drive' compaction of the protein thereby thus allegedly improving otherwise random conformational search. Detailed consideration of the problems with the hydrophobic collapse model is given in [14]. In short, the idea that the conformational search is facilitated within a nonspecific hydrophobic globule disregards non-specificity and non-directedness of the hydrophobic interactions, as well as the high specificity of the folding reaction and actual sub-millisecond time scales of the protein folding. Another grave problem with the two of the latter models is that the denatured state (the starting point of the folding studies) is rarely an entirely unstructured coil and the 'denatured' proteins appear to adopt some residual tertiary structure, be it native-like or non-native.

Consequently, biophysical researchers seek for other models based on the empirical data. For example, protein engineering studies of CI2 protein have shown that secondary and tertiary structure are formed in parallel as protein chain collapses. Largely, it's the work on the CI2 folding mechanism that led to formulation of *the nucleation-condensation mechanism*. Nucleation-condensation, albeit proposed as a result of study of a very few model proteins [16], suggests that a transition-state folding intermediate is formed during a condensation (collapse) of the protein chain around a diffuse nucleus. As the propensity for stable secondary structure increases, folding might follow the framework mechanism, according to which the transition state structure is assembled from pre-formed secondary structural elements. Apparently, the distinct informational advantage of this model is that it includes both the framework and hydrophobic collapse models as border cases. According to the nucleation-condensation model, the *stability* of the secondary structure is one of the main determinants of the precise folding mechanism of a particular protein. Thus, in the general folding scenario proposed by the nucleation-condensation mechanism the protein folding is schematically partitioned into the following three stages: specific and/or non-specific chain collapse; formation of the secondary and tertiary structure and repacking of the chain to lower energy conformations [17]. Each of the stages might be emphasized or reduced depending on the particular protein and the chosen experimental conditions. The three-step scheme allows classification and comparison of the folding mechanisms of different proteins with various topologies.

Thus, according to one of the most advanced empirical models of the protein folding, the secondary structure can appear either concurrently with the major folding event or, if folding of a protein is to occur through framework model, prior to the main folding event. Accordingly, pre-formation of the secondary structure appears to be a particular case of the nucleation-condensation model and the lack of inherent conformational preferences of the isolated elements of secondary structure from the peptide studies seem to provide additional support for the model. However, this relatively recent model from biophysics has also two points which need to be re-evaluated: the time resolution of the most of the biophysical techniques used for the folding studies and the problem of the size of the protein framework that supports the required secondary structure.

Different biophysical techniques, apparently, have different *time resolution* and a phenomenon observed using one technique can be 'invisible' for another. For example, kinetic studies that use stopped-flow circular dichroism and protein engineering, can detect the formation of secondary structure that are not always detected in hydrogen exchange experiments. Thus, in the case of lysozyme almost no protection from exchange was detected during the dead time of around 3 milliseconds, while dichroism data suggested formation of a native-like secondary structure despite that the circular dichroism measurements are also subject to the "dead time" instrumentation problem [18]. Using faster instrumentation with temporal resolutions down to picoseconds, it becomes increasingly clear that the formation of secondary structure can occur on the nanosecond time-scale. The studies using the ultra-fast techniques also suggest that the tertiary structure might form not on millisecond but rather on the microsecond scale [19]. The use of the novel biophysical techniques allowed to explore the elementary steps in protein folding, such as intrachain diffusion and formation of alpha-helices, beta-hairpins and loop structures. Kinetics of intrachain contact formation on the nanosecond time scale observed for a number of peptides suggest that while typical protein loops can form on a timescale of 30-50 ns, the helices and strands can form in 15-25ns. The minimum time constant for contact formation at the ends of tight turns was assessed to be in the range of 5-10 ns [20]. Consequently, the estimates concerning the secondary structure that are obtained from the studies in the scope of the nucleation-condensation model and the relevant instrumentation can reflect rather a gross average than details of an actual physical process of the protein folding of a particular protein molecule. In other words, the secondary structure still might, sort of, flicker at the nanosecond time scales and not be distinctly registered by most of the techniques commonly used for folding studies.

The problem of the *size of the protein framework* that supports the required secondary structure is another issue that is not well regarded in the present biophysical studies. Although cutting a protein into the peptides corresponding to the separate elements of secondary structure appears to suggest weak conformational preferences, it is still the question to be answered: how much of the protein framework of the native protein is needed to support the secondary structure which we observe in the native proteins. In particular, should this framework include some tertiary interactions or the local interactions along the chain would be the main determinant of the conformational preferences?

Answering the question through experimental studies is exceedingly important since in the available studies of the peptides' conformational preferences the peptides were cut from the native sequence according to the secondary structure definitions bluntly derived from the crystal structures. A few moments thinking will, however, suggest that the results of such studies will greatly depend on how much of a secondary structure element was excised from the native protein.

If, for example, there is helix 80-92 in the structure of the alpha-haemoglobin, then the corresponding peptide would be cut out and studied and 'weak conformational preference' would be probably found. However, for such a peptide study to be exhaustive, it is necessary to cut fragments of various sizes around the secondary structure elements known from the tertiary structure and only then investigate the conformational preferences of each of these peptides experimentally. In the case of the above mentioned helix, it would be necessary to study not only 80-92 peptide but also, say, 75-95, 80-100, 75-100 and, perhaps, tens of others. At present, to author's limited information, no such an exhaustive study was ever done even for a particular peptide, not to mention a single protein. So, the peptide studies might show weak conformational preferences, be that as it may. This result, however, seems to neglect the local sequence environment in the protein, which might alone be sufficient for much stronger conformational preferences. This statement remains a research hypothesis until the detailed experimental data will become available.

An indirect evidence for this hypothesis follows from the bioinformatics research: namely, the results of the prediction of the secondary structure of proteins. Although the current accuracies of the secondary structure predictions should be definitely improved, the secondary structure of most of the proteins can possibly be predicted with an average 80% accuracy (see, for example, the CASP5 and CASP6 results at the CASP site http://predictioncenter.llnl.gov/). A bioinformatic parameter (known as "sequence window"), that is usually adjusted to obtain the best predictions, reflects the local sequence context and is set, more often than not, to the value of 20-40, depending on a particular prediction algorithm. Apparently, these results of the bioinformatic studies can be used as a valulable indication in the the biophysical studies of the inherent conformational preferences of the individual peptides.

The actual time scales of the secondary structure formation, as well as the fact that carefully chosen peptides can have quite strong conformational preferences also suggested by the results of the realistic *molecular simulations of the protein folding*. Despite a number of claims and clamour around the millisecond molecular dynamics trajectories made on supercomputers, only one group of simulations, so far, was physically realistic enough to allow comparison with the results of the experimental studies. Known as "Folding@home" initiative [21], the idea was as plain as that: to use thousands of volunteer computers from all over the world as a super-cluster computational resource. The force field chosen for simulation was OPLS (Optimized Potentials for Liquid Simulations). In these unique simulations, two model *helical* systems: $Ac–A_5(A_3RA)_3A–NH_2$ ("Fs peptide") and $Ac–A_{20}–NH_2$ (poly-A peptide) were simulated and the folding rates were computed using the simulation results [21]. Each simulation was started from an extended chain conformation (with the main chain angles *phi*=-135°; *psi*=+135°) as the initial configuration. Qualitatively, both the Fs and poly-A helices folded by first undergoing rapid nucleation followed by propagation of the secondary structure toward the termini. Simulation of the model *beta-hairpin* (C-terminal hairpin of protein-G) suggested the following picture of the folding mechanism. Folding from the completely extended conformation begins with a rapid collapse to some compact structure. Temporary hydrogen bonds form condensing the peptide and decreasing the costly loop entropy that prevents formation of the hydrophobic core. These patterns of the hydrogen bonds have no resemblance to the final hydrogen-bonding pattern of the hairpin. The central event in the folding is when an interaction between the residues of the hydrophobic nucleus is established.

The technique also has allowed to simulate fast folding of an artificial mini-protein BBA5 [22] to compare the experimental and computational kinetics at the similar time scales. Helical structure in the unfolded state, fragment secondary structure propensity, rate of helix formation, rate of hairpin formation, and the rate for folding were all consistent with the available experimental evidence. Apart from giving correct order-of-magnitude estimates for the formation of the elements of the secondary structure, these simulation studies emphasize the transient but still persistent nature of the secondary structure.

In the following sections of the article, we'll use some of the implications from the cellular and biophysical studies of the protein folding while considering three novel bioinformatic models and corresponding techniques that employ, either directly or indirectly, the concept of the secondary structure. These bioinformatic models are the charge center model of the protein folding, the molecular energetic profiles of the protein function and the protein structure prediction using similarity searches at the level of the secondary structure.

THE CHARGE CENTER MODEL OF THE PROTEIN FOLDING

The current situation is, actually, ripe for the elaboration of universal bioinformatic methods for the protein folding analyses. On one hand, the constantly growing number of unique folds in PDB provides a great variety of the examples of the sequence-structure relationship. On the other hand, there are valuable biophysical studies of a number of the "model" proteins. For example, detailed data on the folding nuclei for a number of different proteins are becoming available (see, for example, a summary of the experimental data in [23]). The data on the hydrogen exchange cores for over 20 model proteins are also available (for example, in [24, 25]). The synthetic concept of the so-called "charge centers" was an attempt to bring into the bioinformatics of the protein folding very simple but, nevertheless, quite comprehensive concept that takes into account not only biophysical, but also cellular and biochemical aspects of the protein folding [14, 26, 27]. In brief, development of the two-charge-center concept begun from the idea of the hydrophobic collapse, took into account the time-scales of the actual protein folding rates, inherent properties of the electrostatic and hydrophobic interactions, data on the HSP chaperon motifs and resulted in a computational technique that predicts hydrogen exchange protein cores with an average 80% accuracy. Then, a general scenario for folding of the proteins was proposed which well corresponds to the scenarios established independently as the result of the experimental biophysical studies. Although the role of the secondary structure is, literally, secondary in the scope of the charge centers model, the secondary structure is still important for the charge center algorithm to work more accurately.

The charge centers model of the protein folding is takes into account both cellular and biophysical aspects of the protein folding. From *cellular point of view*, proteins are machines of definite function surrounded by specific electrostatic fields inherently involved in the protein function, folding and stability. In other words, we can consider the charge center model as a very low-resolution model of the protein electrostatics (which can be used to portray proteins inside a cell, for example). The charge center model takes electrostatic into account in the simplest way possible: by describing the general geometric distributions of the positively and negatively charged residues in a protein using the charge centers (averaged locations, sort of) of the charged residues in the entire subunit of a protein. At the same time, the location of highly identical hydrophobic sequences around the charge centers of the proteins suggests an important role of a local hydrophobic collapse (collapse of a 4-10 residue hydrophobic sequence) in initial stages of the protein folding.

The following two points illustrate the development of the charge center model of the protein folding from *biophysical point of view*. First of all, a "hydrophobic effect" is a purely thermodynamic theoretical description and does not take into account the time-scales of the folding kinetics. The hydrophobic effect, which includes multiple rearrangements of the protein chain and the solvent molecules, is a stochastic process. As such, equilibrium in such a system usually requires significant time. Secondly, the "hydrophobic interaction" is short-range: i.e., the changes in conformation cannot be coordinated over distances larger than 3–5 Å. Because so-called 'random search' during protein folding is a sheer nonsence (due to extremely fast time scales known from experiments), a much faster, long-range and more specific physical force is required to fit in with the sub-millisecond time scales. Electrostatic interactions are long-range (12–15 Å), are specific (the charges of one sign repulse while the charges of the opposite site attract) and, therefore, are most likely to be the main long-range and specific physical force in the protein folding [14].

For validation of this bioinformatic model in relation to the protein folding, the set of the hydrogen exchange cores was taken from [25]. It was found the charge center technique predicts the residues of the hydrogen exchange protein cores (which are the potential folding cores) with an average accuracy of 80% (50-100%, depending on the particular proteins, see the tables in [26]). The paper [26] is abundantly illustrated with examples of the charge centers in various proteins and the papers [14, 27] describe the precise sequence of steps for the CI2 protein folding deduced from the charge center model then comparing it with the experimental data. The following conclusions were reached as the result of the charge center analyses [26]: *1.* there is a semi-quantitative correlation linking the distribution of the charged residues in the sequence and their distribution in the native (tertiary) structure; *2.* The model allows the prediction of the residues of the hydrogen exchange core with relatively high accuracy by using protein-derived secondary structure; *3.* Short hydrophobic sequences participate in the local hydrophobic collapse; *4.* The general order of events in protein folding is as follows: local hydrophobic collapse (nucleation), electrostatic collapse of the core, global hydrophobic collapse, and slow annealing to the native state.

In experimental studies of the protein folding, as we remember, the drawbacks of the hydrophobic collapse models have lead to formulation of the nucleation-condensation mechanism. The results of the bioinformatic analysis of the charge centers appear to propose somewhat similar scheme. Thus, the steps 1-2 of the generic four-step charge center mechanism appear to detail the 1st step of the generic nucleation-condensation, whilst the steps 3 and 4 of the 4-step charge centers scheme well fit in with the 2nd and 3rd steps of the nucleation-condensation, correspondingly.

The charge centers analysis produces predictions compatible with other experimental data. For example, in accordance with the cellular studies, the small chaperones are likely to bind to the short hydrophobic sequences of ~6-7 residues in length, exposed on the nascent chains [11]. Sequence analysis of the protein set in [26] suggests that these sequences are likely to be the continuous hydrophobic sequences in the framework of the charge center model (step-1). By the way, these continuous hydrophobic sequences, proposed to be one of the early folding centers, are located preferably on the helices and beta-strands (in 90% of the cases, see Table V in [26]). This observation is in accordance with the results of the realistic folding simulation (above) showing very early formation of the secondary structure.

As the nucleation-condensation model, the charge center scenario itself also does not place any restrictions on the precise moment of formation of the secondary structure during protein folding. The secondary structure might form either on steps 1, 2 or even 3, depending on each particular protein. It should, though, be noticed that identification of the residues of the charge center clusters uses definitions of the secondary structure derived from the PDB files [26] and the accuracy of the prediction of the residues of the folding cores rises significantly if the secondary structure elements are accounted for (as described in [26]). In other words, the charge center analysis implies that the folding core is formed by a limited number of residues located at the specific elements of the secondary structure which might fully form prior to, during or after the main condensation event. In the scope of the charge center model, the secondary structure thus serves as means to regroup the identified residues in order to reduce the rate of the false positives. For the other two bioinformatic methods presented in this article (the molecular energetic profiles and the SSEFR protein structure prediction), the secondary structure of a protein is considerably more important and forms the essential basis of these novel bioinformatic techniques.

The Method of the Molecular Energetic Profiles

In the introduction to this article, we have considered the informational content as well as general energetic contributions that each level of the protein structure can provide. The matter of the energetic contributions is especially important for a relatively new area of bioinformatics: the physico-chemical methods. Thus, calculations of the relative energetic contributions of the residues in three-dimensional structures of the proteins [28] or using only the secondary structures [13] appear to produce functional information which is not obvious either from the visual inspection of the 3D structures [28], from some simplistic sequence pattern analyses [13] or from sequence identities [29]. The results of this type of calculations, termed as "the method of the molecular energetic profiles", suggest significant contribution of the stability of the secondary structure to the overall protein stability and also indicate that the secondary structure appears to be inherently related to the function of the native protein [13]. The list of the per-residue energies arranged along the amino acid sequence is termed as a "molecular energetic profile" while the same list ordered according to the energy values is a "molecular energetic histogram" (the examples of both are given in the Figures 2 and 3). In this section we consider the comparison of the molecular energetic profile calculations for the tertiary and secondary levels of the protein structure along with the possible implications for the protein function, stability and folding.

The method of the molecular energetic profiles allows identification of the potential functional residues. The method is based on the so-called *"relativity postulate"*, formulated as "relative physico-chemical properties of the functional residues of the enzymes are very distinct from the other residues in a molecule" [28-31]. This relativity postulate does not appear to be restricted to enzymes but is also applicable to proteins in general [28] as well as to other macromolecules such as various types of RNA: ribozymes [30] and tRNAs [31]. In brief, the functional residues in proteins tend to have extreme energy values and are often either "most destabilizing" (having the highest free energies among the residues of the protein, the right part of a molecular energetic histogram) or "most stabilizing" (having the lowest free energies, the left part of the histogram) [28]. What is of especial interest in the context of the present article is that this postulate appears to be applicable not only to the tertiary but also to the secondary structure of a protein. Recalling our consideration of the levels of protein structure in Introduction, we might notice that a residue can destabilize a tertiary structure either through unfavourable tertiary packing on the molecular surface and/or by destabilizing elements of the secondary structure. Consequently, removing the tertiary structure and by preserving the secondary structure, the relative contribution of each level can be assessed using the same calculation procedure based on the molecular mechanics.

The main features of the profiles and histograms, the roles of the secondary structure types and numerous method verification issues were considered previously [13, 28, 29, 32], here we'll just look at the example of the haemoglobin and then summarize the results of the other studies. Firstly, let's consider the results of the calculations when *applied to the tertiary structure* of the single alpha-chain (Figures 1c and 2ab). The most destabilizing residues (the right part of the histogram in the Figure 2b) are mostly involved in the *heme-binding site*: K61, H45, H87, H58; the residues H58 and H87 are the well-known 'proximal' histidines that bind the Fe-ion of the heme. These four amino acids were the top-most destabilizing (Figure 2b). *The protein-protein interfaces* of the three types (AB, AC and AD) in the ABCD tetramer were formed both by most destabilizing (AB: H103; AC: R141; AD: R141, R92) as well as most stabilizing (AB: E27, E30, D126; AC: D126; AD: D94) amino acid residues.

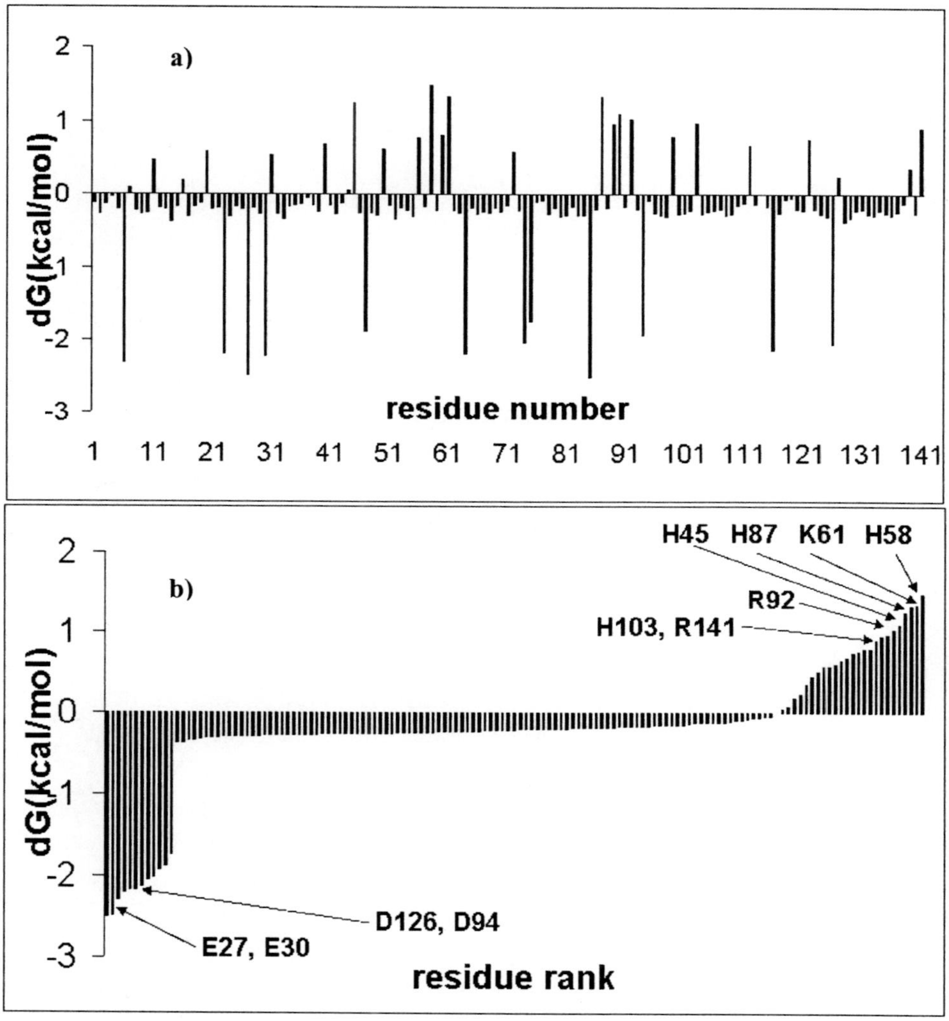

Figure 2. The molecular energetic profile and the molecular energetic histogram for the tertiary level of the protein structure (on the example of the alpha-chain of human haemoglobin). a) molecular energetic profile; b) molecular energetic histogram. The known functional residues are indicated, see the details in the text.

The calculation was *applied to the secondary structure* using the "most extended conformation" (see the paper [13] for the calculation details). Briefly, the most extended conformation (Figure 3a) complements the ways of describing the secondary structure shown in the Figure 1b. At a first glance, this conformation is only a legitimate computational artifice that allows to eliminate the native tertiary structure but to preserve the secondary structure. This is achived simply by putting into one line all of the elements of the secondary structure. However, such conformation of a protein is likely to be more than a computational artifice and might correspond to an intermediate stage during protein folding. For instance, in the case of the alpha-chain, the most extended conformation of the entire a-chain of haemoglobin is 15Å wide and 110 Å long (Figure 3a). As the ribosome channel is less than 2nm wide and ~10nm long [12], the most extended conformation of the alpha-chain wil fit the ribosome channel almost precisely. Accordingly, the most extended conformation of the proteins is likely to be a significant biological phenomenon related to the protein folding.

More detailed comparison of the molecular energetic profile for the most extended conformation (2D, Figure 3b) with the energetic profile for the native tertiary structure (3D, Figure 2a) shows a number of similarities (in particular, the groups of the destabilizing peaks in the middle of the sequence). Comparison of the respective histograms (2D in Figure 3c and 3D in Figure 2b) shows that the functionally important H58, K61, H103, H87 and R92 are among the most destabilizing both in 2D and 3D calculations. The same concerns the most stabilizing D94 and D126 (but not E27 and E30 that still were among the most stabilizing but not at the top of the list as in the case of the 3D calculations). The haemoglobin example suggests that the 2D calculations produce slightly less "sharp" histograms than the 3D ("sharp" in terms of determining the precise energetic ranks of the functional residues). This observation is not peculiar feature of the haemoglobin example but was also confirmed in calculations of about 40 protein [13] and in a subsequent study of more than 200 additional proteins [29]. Qualitatively, it corresponds to our logical deductions in introduction where we have considered potential roles of the levels of the secondary and tertiary structure in determining the energetic properties of the individual amino acid residues.

The above conclusions concerning the similarities between the molecular energetic profiles of the tertiary and the most extended conformations are not restricted to the example of alpha-chain of haemoglobin. In particular, the detailed comparison of the calculations on the tertiary structures and on the most extended conformations for more than 20 proteins presented in [13] have shown that at least 40% of the most destabilizing residues and 40% of the most stabilizing residues were the same in calculations using the tertiary structure (3D, which is fully folded and compact protein) and the most extended conformation (2D, which represents only the secondary structure). Consequently, the average contribution of the tertiary structure to the individual energetical differences between the residues would be 50%-60%. The results make clear that the secondary structure is likely to be an important factor in determining the relative energies of the individual residues in the native proteins.

Consequently, the information encoded already at the level of the secondary structure of a polypeptide chain can determine to a large extent, the stability, function and folding of the native protein. Of particular interest is the analysis of the sequence identities of the residues obtained in calculations that used only secondary structure. Of course, a sequence identity alone cannot serve as a criterion for any analysis, since often more 15-20% of the residues in each protein could be 'identical' while the key functional residues are considerably less numerous. Nevertheless, analysis of the test set of the 20 proteins in (described in [13]) and of the 216 proteins in [29] (the set of 216 proteins was previously described in [33]) have shown definite correlations between the sequence identities and destabilizing properties of the amino acid residues. Thus, odds ratio calculations show that the odds for the most destabilizing residues to be identical were considerably high (OR=1.8, 95% CI 1.5-2.2, $P<0.001$) while in the case of the most stabilizing residues, the odds were on the verge of the statistical significance (OR=1.2, 95% CI 0.96-1.4, $P<0.001$) [29]. When, however, both most stabilizing and the most destabilizing residues were taken, the odds were reasonable enough (OR=1.5, 95% CI 1.2-2.3, P<0.001).

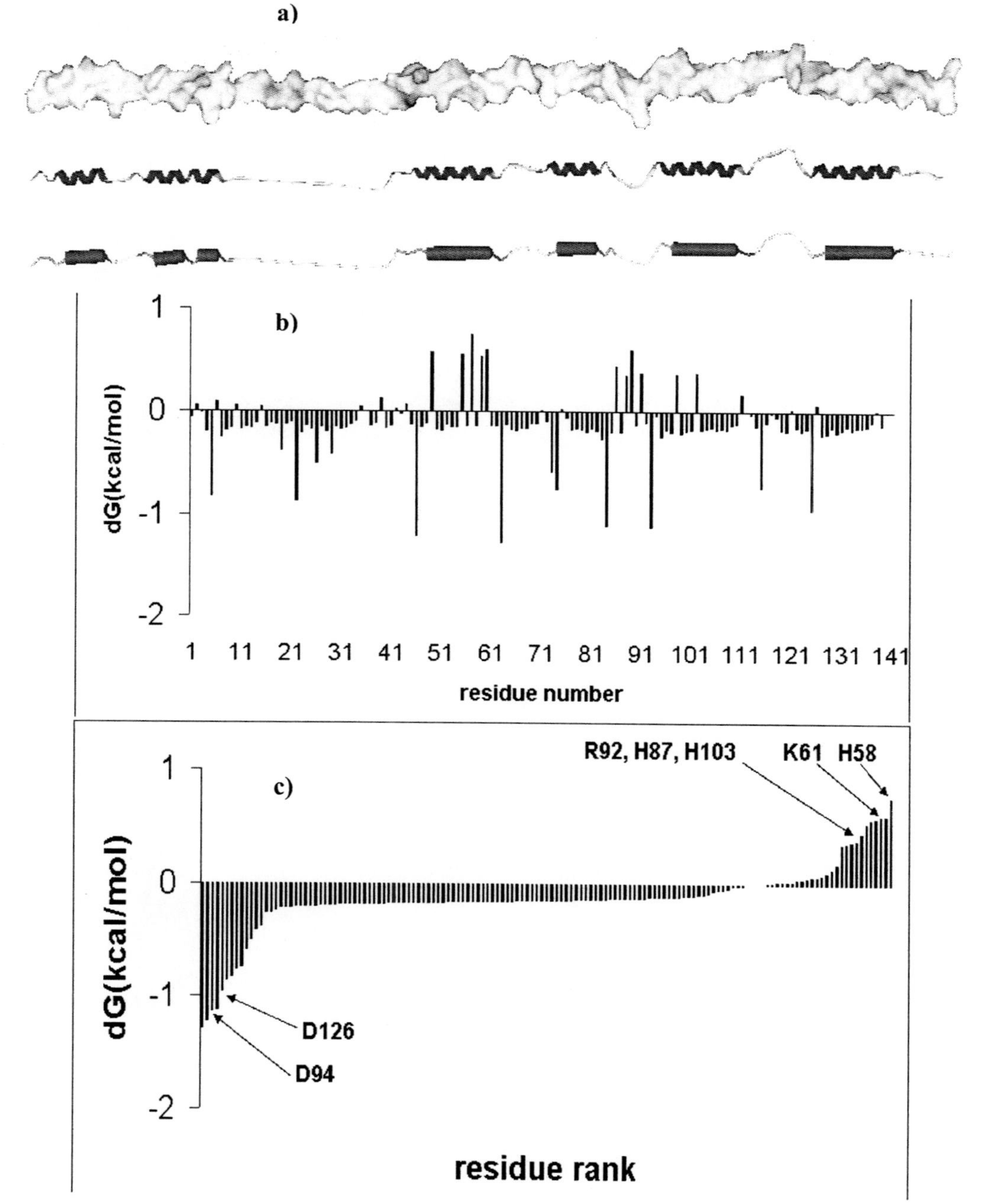

Figure 3. The most extended conformation and the molecular energetic profile/histogram for the level of the secondary structure of the human haemoglobin alpha-chain. a) the most extended conformation. From top to bottom: the molecular surface, the C-alpha trace and a schematic representation of the super-pattern of the secondary structure of the most extended conformation. The molecular surface illustrates the shape and a general distribution of the charged residues in the most extended conformation used in 2D calculations (dark grey: positive; grey: negative). b) the molecular energetic profile of the most extended conformation; c) the molecular energetic histogram.

Analysis of the larger set of the 216 proteins has shown that the most stabilizing and the most destabilizing residues identified in the 2D calculations did tend to have lower entropies (that is, the higher degrees of the sequence identities, $P<0.001$) than the rest of the residues. This result indirectly confirms the functional significance at least some of the residues identified in the 2D calculations [29]. Briefly, to establish the validity of the idea of the 2D calculations in a more uniform way requires a large-scale study of proteins. In a set of 216 proteins (given in full in [33]), the most destabilizing and the most stabilizing residues were identified using the 2D molecular energetic profile calculations. Sequence entropies were calculated using a similar procedure to that described in [33] and, subsequently, the sequence identities were obtained. The histogram that includes the energy ranking and the identity ranking (Figure 4) summarizes the results for various values of the energy cutoffs. As we see, the histogram clearly shows that the most stabilizing and the most destabilizing residues identified in the 2D calculations do tend to have higher degrees of the sequence identities (i.e., lower sequence entropies). The result thus statistically confirms the functional significance of at least some of the residues identified in the 2D calculations.

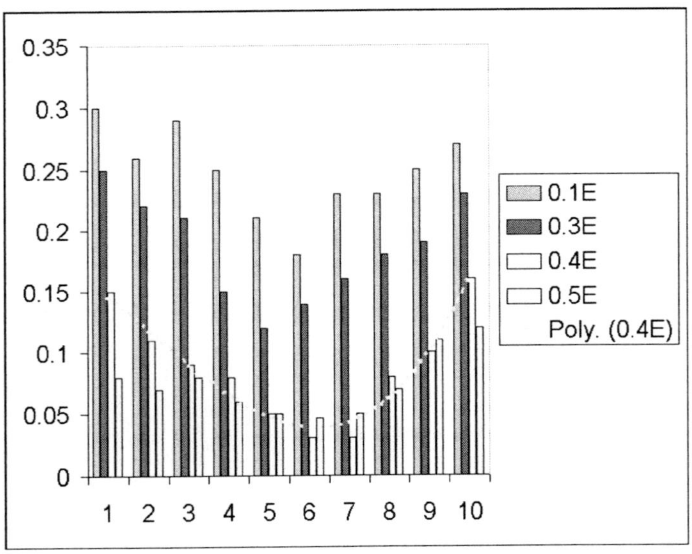

Figure 4. The sequence identity vs. per-residue-energy histogram. The histogram was compiled using the set of 216 proteins mentioned in the text. The most destabilizing amino acid residues are to the left, the most stabilizing residues are to the right side of the histogram. The dotted line denotes a polynomial approximation of the trend.

In the set of about 40 proteins [13], many of the residues known to be functional from biochemical and structural studies were identified in 2D calculations (the most extended conformation) [13]. Thus, ~55% of the destabilizing residues and ~55% of the most stabilizing residues in 2D calculations were either functional or were spatially clustered around the previously known functional sites within 6-8 angstrom distance. Although the corresponding figures for the calculations on the 3D structures were much higher (74% and 63%, respectively [28]), the 55% result is quite remarkable, taking into account that all of the tertiary interactions were neglected [32]. This opened possibility of predicting the functional residues from amino acid sequence and a secondary structure prediction [13]. A 70%

accuracy of the secondary structure prediction is, probably, the lowest level at which the method of the molecular energetic profiles would work most reliably [29] for prediction of the functional residues from amino acid sequence.

Summarizing, the main result of the calculations of the molecular energetic profiles at the level of secondary structure was that the secondary structure is an important determinant of the individual contributions of the amino acid residues to the protein stability. As shows the analyses of the sets of known functional residues, the most stabilizing and the most destabilizing residues identified in the 2D calculations tend to be related to the biological functions of the proteins. The analyses of the sequence identities of the most destabilizing residues show statistically significant correlation between the energetical properties of the residues and their sequence entropies. Both the molecular energetic profiles and the sequence identity analyses outline some peculiar spots in the protein sequence and structure without specializing what function these residues might have.

It is well known, for example, that a sequence identity analysis can be used not only for identification of the potential functional residues but also of the determinants of the protein folding and stability. Similarly, the molecular energetic profiles suggest that the secondary structure of a protein can also be an important determinant not only of the protein function, but also of the protein stability. Since the stability of the secondary structure seems to have direct implications for the protein folding (at least, in the scope of the nucleation-condensation model), the 2D calculations in the method of the molecular energetic profiles can be useful for folding studies. The implications of the *secondary structure super-pattern* (or the sequence of the elements of the secondary structure of the protein) for the protein structure prediction are considered in the last section of this article.

PROTEIN STRUCTURE PREDICTION

Multiple genomic projects produced vast amounts of protein sequences with little, if any, biological annotation. Attempting to obtain additional clues to protein's function, structural proteomics endeavours undertake the task of solving structures of as much proteins from an organism as possible. Structure not of every protein can be solved in this kind of large scale studies. Actually, structures of less than 20%-40% of the proteins expressed in a cell can be solved, not to mention the fact that in the expression studies usually cover much less than 40% of the actual cellular proteins. Therefore, in parallel to the structural proteomics/genomics endeavours, computerized methodologies for protein structure prediction are being developed. These computerized methodologies use the amino acid sequence as the input and are always based, explicitly or implicitly, on the databases of the experimentally established protein structures. At present, modeling 3D protein structure on the base of the amino acid sequence (the procedure known as "protein structure prediction") is generally divided into the three main basic groups of methods: comparative modeling, fold recognition and *ab initio* simulations.

Comparative modeling analyzes similarity of the sequence of the protein to be modeled (which is called as "target") to the sequences of proteins with known structures ("templates"). *Fold recognition* implies determining the "fold" (that is, general architecture or topology of the protein target) using the amino acid sequence. Although the border between the methods of comparative modeling and the fold recognition is not always distinct in practice, fold recognition does allow structure prediction for a wider range of targets than the comparative modeling. *Ab initio simulations* are, generally, supposed to use the sequence as the only input and a set of established physical laws (for example, in the scope of molecular mechanics) to produce the structure by simulating the actual process of folding.

These three approaches as well as many combinations thereof and the predictive value of the individual methods are covered at the controversial CASP conferences (http://predictioncenter.llnl.gov/) that still raise some interest in the general biological community. "CASP" decodes as a "***C***ritical ***A***ssessment of techniques for protein ***S***tructure ***P***rediction" and here we present the results from a recent CASP experiment, during which the author tested a novel methodology for the fold recognition [34]. Results of the automated analysis of the author's predictions for each of the CASP-6 targets are available at the CASP web-site (http://www2.predictioncenter.org/casp/casp6/public/cgi-bin/groups.cgi, group code P0061 or FRCC).

As the following analysis of these results suggests, the predictions of the tertiary structure of the proteins made exclusively on the base of the secondary structure were unexpectedly successful. In brief, the basis of this novel approach was a similarity search based on a predicted secondary structure and not so much on the analysis of the similarities of the amino acid sequences.

Technically, sequence similarity methods often stumble at the problem of "low sequence identity". Indeed, it is known that a number of structures can share common folds but, nevertheless, still have extremely low mutual sequence identity: below 10% and even 5% [6]. Apparently, there is a need for a new approach that would be based on principles other than on various sorts of stubborn attempts to reduce the fold recognition to well-known methods of sequence similarity searches.

If we look at our consideration of the levels of protein structure given in the Introduction, we'll see that there are not one but two *sequential levels* of the protein structure: the primary and the secondary structure. As decades-long practice shows that the reliability of the methods of sequence similarity search (that is, using the primary structure) tends to drop sharply at the sequence identities lower than 25%, the naturally arising question would be: could another sequential level (i.e., that of the secondary structure) be used for some kind of similarity searches?

Although the biophysical studies suggest that there are no strong conformational preferences for the sequences forming the individual elements of the secondary structure, the secondary structure can be predicted from amino acid sequence at an average accuracies of about 80% (in terms of $Q3_{total}$, one of the most stringent accuracy scores). Although this is a putative average and the data in recent CASPs give a comprehensive overview of the problem (see the web-pages at http://predictioncenter.llnl.gov, especially the data for CASP4, CASP5 and CASP6), the actual prediction of the secondary structure is based on the local sequence context. So, if there would be no strong conformational preferences that link the amino acid sequence and the corresponding secondary structure, the bioinformatic methods of the secondary structure prediction would never work. But they do work (though at various accuracies, of course).

One of the possible resolutions to this seeming paradox is that the secondary structure prediction algorithms use 20-40 sequence "windows" while in biophysical experiments much shorter fragments were studied. Therefore, it is likely that the local sequence context (that includes 2-3 consecutive elements of secondary structure) has conformational preferences that are much greater than those of the separated secondary structures usually investigated in the biophysical studies. As the research that links secondary and tertiary structure develops, it might turn out that the secondary structure of the sequence directly determines the tertiary. Accordingly, using the other sequential level of the protein structure (namely, the secondary structure) might produce more efficient and reliable methods of protein structure prediction that using the primary structure. It is quite apparent that such methods of this new plethora will be free, at least, from the problem of the low sequence identity.

One of such methods for fold recognition has been recently developed and was presented at CASP6 [34]. It's called EVM/SSEFR. E.V.M. ("Expert vs Machine") impliyng the necessity of an expert judgement of the most proper models, though the method itself is largely automated. SSEFR decodes as "Secondary Structure Elements for Fold Recognition". A block diagram of the method is presented in the Figure 5. The method has at least one principal drawback, which is clear *a priori* [34]: its accuracy will observably depend on the accuracy of the secondary structure prediction. The problem can be partially alleviated by using independent methods for the secondary structure prediction. It is also useful to check each 'suspicious' secondary structure element against the template and also to use predictions of the sequence borders of the SSEs (secondary structure elements). At lower accuracies of the secondary structure prediction the method will work reliably only if there is variety of the SSEs along the amino acid sequence. It means that procedure might not work well on sequences/structures containing only long loops and a few short beta-strands (which is the case of the kringle domain, for example). Let's consider here the CASP6 results for this method.

In the context of the CASPs, one of the widely used semi-automated measures of closeness of the model to the actual experimental structure is "global distance test" (GDT). GDT identifies the sets of residues in the predicted structure that deviate from the target by no more than a specified distance cut-off. The results of the test are usually plotted in coordinates r.m.s. vs %-of-residues and allow an instant visual comparison of the hundreds or thousands of predictions of one protein structure. An example of a GDT plot is given further in the Figure 6a. GDT plot is a powerful semi-automated measure of structure similarity useful for a quick visual assessment of the relative value of many predictions. However, even the CASP committee decided that GDT measure alone is not sufficient, at least as the CASP6 set of criteria shows. Among other criteria (of which there are about ten) there are r.m.s. (root-mean-square) deviation for the entire target structure, percent of residues correctly aligned in the model, percentages of residues that can be correctly aligned with allowance for residue shifts and rmsd-based clustering of predictions. It should be reminded that these criteria are rather rules-of-a-thumb and none of these criteria, including the GDT-related measures, does allow to judge with certainty whether the specific topology or "fold" (the peculiar mutual arrangement of strands and helices) of the prediction is similar to that of the target and to what extent similar. Nevertheless, the semi-automated GDT analysis seems to be one of the main arguments for the claimed objectivity of the CASP conferences.

Briefly, fold recognition predictions by the EVM/SSEFR method were submitted for 67 CASP6 targets. Evaluated by the CASP6 assessment group were predictions only for 49 out of these 67 targets (detailed assessments of the targets are available at the CASP web-site). Thus, 18 of the author's predictions (that is, 25%) were not assessed at all due to some obscure reason. Quite a few targets out of these 18 were cancelled due to premature release of the structural data by the impatient experimentalists and the other predictions were simply not evaluated without providing any official comments to the individual predictor groups nor to the entire CASP community. Still, despite this weird hassle with omitting $1/5^{th}$ of the predictions, the CASP6 still has provided a useful feedback.

Out of the predictions for the 49 targets, 11 can be classified as 'common failures'. This term means that none of the 200 prediction groups has produced a reliable prediction for the entire structure while some decent predictions were made for fragments of these targets. These targets were T0199, T0209, T0216, T0237, T0238, T0241, T0242, T0248, T0262, T0272 and T0273. Perhaps, these 'common failures' reflect the overall lack of understanding the fundamentals of the protein structure by the present-day science. It is remarkable, though, that most of these 11 'failures' (excluding T0238, T0242 and T0273) were multi-domain proteins. For more than a half of the 11 targets structures of the separated domains were predicted by some groups. Therefore, the main problem with these common failures seems to be the correct placement and/or assembly of the domains into the entire 3D structure.

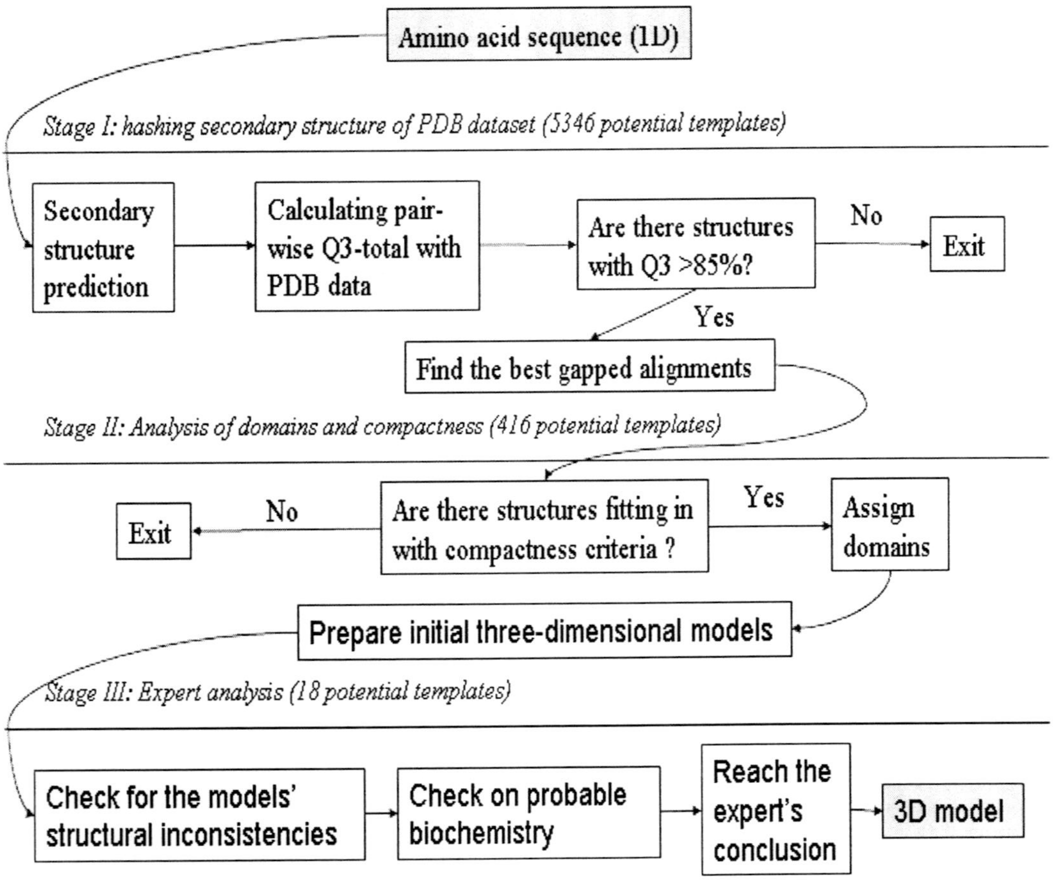

Figure 5. From 1D to 3D: the block diagram of the application of the EVM/SSEFR algorithm (on the example of the T0247 prediction).

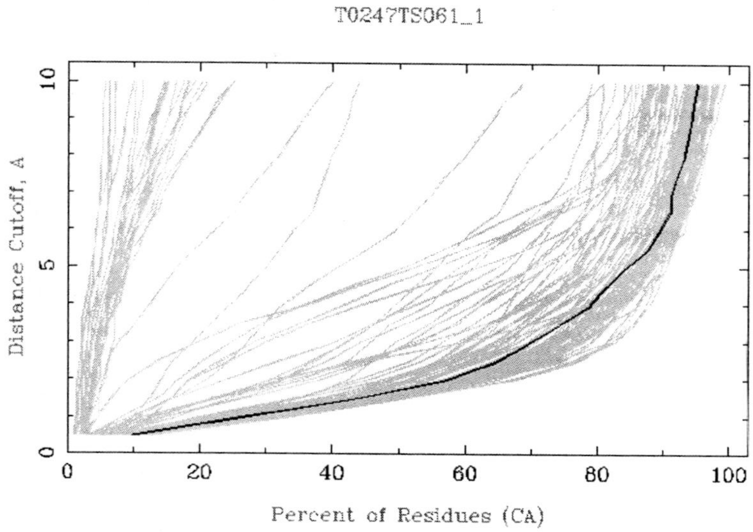

a)

b)

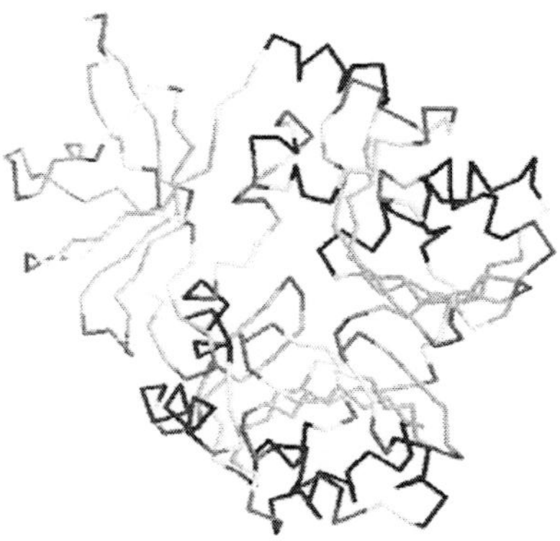

c)

Figure 6. A successful CASP6 prediction. Target T0247, a putative aminomethyltransferase from *E.coli,* has a three-domain structure of 364 residues in total. a) GDT plot. Each grey line represents GDT-assessment of a model provided by one predictor group participating in CASP6. The dark-grey line corresponds to the author's prediction. The figure was generated using the CASP6 server. b) T0247 (SSEFR model), a Rasmol rendering; c) T0247 (experimental structure).

Thus, the predictions for 38 targets remain to be analyzed. According to the GDT plots, EVM methodology predicted unequivocally correct models for 19 targets and produced largely incorrect predictions for 9 targets. Author's detailed inspection of each model has, however, shown that correct folds were actually predicted for 27 out of the 38 targets. Below, the results are considered mainly in accordance with the GDT criteria assisted by the results of the visual analysis. According to the GDT plots alone, the correct fold was undeniably recognized by EVM/SSFR for 19 targets (T0196, T0204, T0229, T0230, T0231, T0232, T0233, T0235, T0246, T0247, T0251, T0264, T0265, T0266, T0267, T0268, T0269, T0277 and T0282). In these predictions precise fold was correctly recognized and these models require only accurate side-chain and loop modeling. It also worth noting that only 7 out of these 19 targets had reliable BLAST hits, which shows that the method is quite independent on the sequence similarity searches. An example of GDT plot for a successful prediction is shown in the Figure 6.

Looking at the GDT plot for a particular prediction, we might have noticed that the models of the better quality tend to be associated with the right side of the GDT diagram, while worse models are to the left. There are some models that are in the relative 'middle' of the diagram (in these models typically 30%-50% percent of target's residues were predicted correctly). Despite all of its advantages, the GDT plot alone does not allow to conclude how accurate such intermediate models are. The author's method E.V.M. had produced 10 models of such 'intermediate' or 'average' GDT-assessed quality. Generally, in these predictions the overall fold was correctly recognized though some details of the fold were missing. The results are summarized in the Table 1.

In short, 6 out of the 10 models of the 'average' quality (a judgement based on GDT only) actually corresponded to the correct overall folds. GDT plots alone, therefore, are clearly not sufficient to recognize a correct fold prediction. Therefore, it is somewhat questionable that GDT plots are uniformly used for the assessment for the predictions not only for the comparative modeling but also of the fold recognition and *ab initio*-styled predictions by the CASP committee. Apparently, using the GDT plots for the fold recognition underestimates the quality of at least 10% of the predictions.

The results in the Table 1 also suggest that the correct fold predictions correlates with higher accuracy of the secondary structure prediction as judged by $Q3_{total}$ ($P < 0.03$). Although the correlation is statistically significant, there is no unequivocal association between the model quality and the accuracy of the secondary structure prediction. For example, $Q3_{total}$ for T0222 was 73% and the fold was correctly recognized while $Q3_{total}$ was 80%for T0279 and the prediction was grossly incorrect. It turns out that the problem is with inaccuracy of the secondary structure prediction lies in the incorrect prediction of *some* secondary structure elements rather than with the *average* accuracy. Nevertheless, the proposed 85% cutoff for $Q3_{total}$ [34] accuracy still appears to be a reasonable compromise.

According both to GDT and visual inspection, the EVM/SSEFR procedure has predicted largely incorrect folds for 11 out of the 38 targets (T0198, T0200, T0206, T0208, T0211, T0212, T0213, T0223, T0227, T0279 and T0280). In other words, the dark-grey lines (as in the Figure 6a) were much to the left of the GDT plot. These targets were mostly all-beta folds. Indeed, as it was expected [34], the procedure did not work well on most of the all-beta proteins which do not provide a variety of the secondary structure types along the sequence. Among these 11 targets, the percentage of the incorrectly predicted all-beta proteins was almost 6 times higher than correctly predicted so fold recognition of the all-beta folds definitely needs to be specifically dealt with in the framework of the EVM method.

It's interesting to note, nevertheless, that the failure of the method to predict the structures of the all-beta proteins might be not only because of the deficiencies in the algorithm or its implementation. As the biophysical studies and molecular simulations suggest, beta-structures firstly collapse into any compact structure and only then acquire the precise architecture and show more distinct secondary structure preferences. Therefore, the variety of the SSEs along the sequence, essential for the correct performance of the EVM/SSEFR method, implies certain biophysics: the folding mechanism of the mostly/all-beta proteins is likely to occur according to the hydrophobic collapse rather than to the framework scenario.

Thus, the novel fold recognition method that makes the primary accent on the similarity of the *secondary* and not of the *primary* structure, seems to work for 70% of the 'contestable' CASP6 targets (27 out of 38). The successful prediction of the bulk of the targets suggests that the secondary structure scanning can be an effective predictor of the specific topology of the protein structure (which is, quite obvious, is meant by the term 'fold recognition'). The relative success of the predictions implies, in particular, a very close link between the secondary and tertiary structure of the proteins. Research into the fundamentals of the connexion between the secondary and the tertiary levels of the protein structure is likely to be important for the protein folding studies.

Table 1. Analysis of the CASP-6 EVM/SSEFR predictions of average GDT-quality.

Target	Target description	Model description	Model rating	$Q3_{total}$
T0201	Mixed alpha/beta, 5 strands 2 helices	Mixed alpha/beta, 3 strands 3 helices, order of strands is similar	2	85%
T0222	Beta-barrel with a C-terminal domain.	Beta-barrel	2	73%
T0223	Two similar alpha/beta domains, each with 5 strands and 2 helices	One alpha/beta domain	0	56%
T0234	Beta-barrel	Beta-barrel	2..3	79%
T0235	Mixed alpha/beta, 2 sheets of 9 and 4 strands, 7 helices	Mixed alpha/beta, 2 sheets of 7 and 4 strands, 8 helices	2	75%
T0239	2 domains, mixed alpha/beta	1 domain, mixed alpha/beta	1	80%
T0263	Mixed alpha/beta, 4 strands, 2 helices and 1 helix	Mixed alpha/beta, 4 strands, 3 helices	3	82%
T0275	2 helices, 5 strands and 2 helices	3 helices, 4 strands and 1 helix	2	85%
T0276	2 betas, 3 and 8 strands each, 4 helices.	2 betas, 3 and 5 strands each, 4 helices. The order of the strands connection is not entirely correct	1..2	77%
T0279	Two mixed alpha/beta domains	Beta-barrel	0	80%

According to visual inspection, the models were rated as follows: 0- incorrect prediction; 1- some features of the folds predicted; 2-correct overall fold; 3-precise fold identified with all details in place. $Q3_{total}$ is the standard measure of the accuracy of the secondary structure prediction.

CONCLUSION

The secondary structure, which is a super-pattern of the helices, strands and loops along the entire polypeptide chain, is more informationally compact and uniform than the primary structure. Although it's possible that the secondary structure unequivocally determines the tertiary, the actual significance of information encoded in the secondary structure is being researched. Generally, the general fold class can be reliably guessed from the secondary structure (2D) [35] though the exact fold type is not always obvious at the 2D level. Nevertheless, a relative success of a protein structure prediction scheme based on the secondary structure does suggest that the secondary structure links together the primary, secondary and tertiary levels of the protein structure. The analyses of the 2D molecular energetic profiles suggest important implications for the protein function, stability and folding that are observably determined already at the level of the secondary structure. The classical biophysical studies of the protein folding do not suggest a universal role for the secondary structure formation (at least, in the scope of the most advance nucleation-condensation model). However, the seeming contradiction between the lack of distinct conformational preferences and a relative success of the secondary structure prediction schemes can be easily dissolved by considering a wider sequence context of each element of the secondary structure (as it was done in the calculations of the 2D molecular energetic profiles, for instance).

Considering the results of the cellular, biophysical and bioinformatic studies of the protein structure and folding that were reviewed in this article, let's reformulate here a summarizing picture of the protein folding after synthesis on ribosome. The bioinformatic model of the charge centers model provides a general biophysical scenario for folding of proteins. This scenario takes into account the roles of the long-range interactions as well as the actual time scales of the folding. According to this scenario, the secondary structure might form prior or after the main condensation event. This conclusion is compatible with the nucleation-condensation scenario from the experimental *in vitro* studies of the protein folding. However, the cellular environment can considerably alter the folding mechanism of any protein. Apart from the presence of the co-translational folding process, the elongated narrow channel observed in the ribosome structure directly suggests that a relatively small protein (100-200 amino acids) is likely to assume the most extended conformation (which is, roughly, a linear arrangement of the elements of the secondary structure) immediately after ribosomal synthesis. In the case of larger proteins, any fragment of the polypeptide chain was, at some time, in the most extended conformation- because of the geometrical restrictions of the rybozome channel. The ribosome channel can accommodate only an extended protein structure not wider than an alpha-helix, beta-strand or loop. Therefore, most extended conformation is likely to be the initial conformation for the *in vivo* folding process. According to the experimental data as well as the results of the realistic molecular simulations, the elements of the secondary structure can fold on nanosecond scale, which is more than enough for the formation of the most extended conformation in the channel of the ribosome.

Further, analyses of the most extended conformations (i.e., the spatial representation of the secondary structure) by means of the molecular energetic profiles suggests that that protein function can emerge already at the level of the secondary structure. Indeed, it is well known that the functional residues are often placed in large cavities with high surface accessibility rather than being densely packed in the protein interior. As the three-dimensional environment of these residues is not dense, the destabilizing effect of the secondary structure can indeed be observable. In fact, the comparisons of the 3D and 2D molecular energetic profiles have shown that the tertiary level of the protein structure more often leads to fine adjustments of the per-residue energies rather than to drastic changes in the stabilizing properties of the residues. From the point of view of the protein stability and function, as the secondary structure is formed, the individual energetical differences between the residues become more distinct than in a completely unfolded sequence. Then these differences are further adjusted at the later stages of the protein folding as the tertiary structure is being formed through the tertiary packing of the amino acid side-chains leading to the native and fully functional protein.

REFERENCES

[1] Whisstock JC, Lesk AM. Prediction of protein function from protein sequence and structure. *Q Rev Biophys* 2003;36(3):307-340.

[2] Jensen LJ, Gupta R, Staerfeldt HH, Brunak S. Prediction of human protein function according to Gene Ontology categories. *Bioinformatics* 2003;19(5):635-642.

[3] Dobson PD, Cai YD, Stapley BJ, Doig AJ. Prediction of protein function in the absence of significant sequence similarity.*Curr Med Chem* 2004;11(16):2135-2142.

[4] Altschul SF, Madden TL, Schaffer AA, Zhang J, Zhang Z, Miller W, Lipman DJ. Gapped BLAST and PSI-BLAST: a new generation of protein database search programs. *Nucleic Acids Res* 1997;25(17):3389-3402.

[5] Hulo N, Sigrist CJ, Le Saux V, Langendijk-Genevaux PS, Bordoli L, Gattiker A, De Castro E, Bucher P, Bairoch A. Recent improvements to the PROSITE database. *Nucleic Acids Res* 2004; 32:D134-D137.

[6] Holm L, Sander C. Protein folds and families: sequence and structure alignments. *Nucleic Acids Res* 1999;27(1):244-247.

[7] Kelley LA, MacCallum RM, Sternberg MJ. Enhanced genome annotation using structural profiles in the program 3D-PSSM. J Mol Biol 2000;299(2):499-520.

[8] Rychlewski L, Jaroszewski L, Li W, Godzik A. Comparison of sequence profiles. Strategies for structural predictions using sequence information. *Protein Sc*i 2000;9(2):232-241.

[9] Yang AS, Wang LY. Local structure prediction with local structure-based sequence profiles. *Bioinformatics* 2003;19(10):1267-1274.

[10] Shulz G, Schirmer R. *Principles of Protein Structure*. Springer, New York, 1979.

[11] Ellis RJ, Hartl FU. Principles of protein folding in the cellular environment. *Curr Opin Struct Biol* 1999;9(1):102-110.

[12] Nissen P, Hansen J, Ban N, Moore PB, Steitz TA. The structural basis of ribosome activity in peptide bond synthesis. *Science* 2000; 289(5481):920-930.

[13] Torshin IY. Computed energetics of macromolecules. Part II: functional residues- from amino acid sequence. In: *"Bioinformatics: new research"*, P. Van (Ed), Nova Science, New York 2005 (in press)

[14] Torshin IY, Harrison R. Protein folding: search for basic physical models. *ScientificWorldJournal* 2003;3:623-635.

[15] Eaton WA, Munoz V, Thompson PA, Chan CK, Hofrichter J. Submillisecond kinetics of protein folding. *Curr Opin Struct Biol* 1997;7(1):10-14.

[16] Daggett V, Fersht AR. Is there a unifying mechanism for protein folding? *Trends Biochem Sci* 2003;28(1):18-25.

[17] Ferguson N, Fersht AR. Early events in protein folding. *Curr Opin Struct Biol* 2003;13(1):75-81.

[18] Evans P, Radford S. Probing the structure of folding intermediates. *Curr Opin Struct Biol* 1994; 4(1):100-106.

[19] Callender RH, Dyer RB, Gilmanshin R, Woodruff WH. Fast events in protein folding: the time evolution of primary processes. *Annu Rev Phys Chem* 1998;49:173-202.

[20] Bieri O, Kiefhaber T. Elementary steps in protein folding. *Biol Chem* 1999;380(7-8):923-929.

[21] Pande VS, Baker I, Chapman J, Elmer SP, Khaliq S, Larson SM, Rhee YM, Shirts MR, Snow CD, Sorin EJ, Zagrovic B. Atomistic protein folding simulations on the submillisecond time scale using worldwide distributed computing. *Biopolymers* 2003;68(1):91-109.

[22] Snow CD, Nguyen H, Pande VS, Gruebele M. Absolute comparison of simulated and experimental protein-folding dynamics. *Nature* 2002;420(6911):102-6.

[23] Gromiha MM, Selvaraj S. Inter-residue interactions in protein folding and stability. *Prog Biophys Mol Biol* 2004;86(2):235-277.

[24] Woodward CK. Hydrogen exchange rates and protein folding. *Curr Opin Struct Biol* 1994; 4(1):112-116.

[25] Li R, Woodward C. The hydrogen exchange core and protein folding. *Protein Sci* 1999;8(8):1571-1590.

[26] Torshin IY, Harrison RW. Charge centers and formation of the protein folding core. *Proteins* 2001;43(4):353-364.

[27] Torshin IY, Harrison RW, Petock JM. Identification of protein folding cores using charge center model of protein structure. *ScientificWorldJournal* (MIAMI NATURE SYMPOSIUM) 2002;2(1):84-86.

[28] Torshin IY. Computed energetics of macromolecules. Part I: identification of the functional residues in spatial structures of proteins and RNA. In: "*Bioinformatics: new research*", P. Van (Ed), Nova Science, New York, 2005 (in press).

[29] Torshin IY. Computed energetics of proteins at the different levels of the protein structure. *Am Conf Theor Chem*, UCLA, California, 2005.

[30] Torshin IY. Computed energetics of nucleotides in spatial ribozyme structures: an accurate identification of functional regions from structure. *ScientificWorldJourna*l 2004;4:228-247.

[31] Torshin IY. The concept of molecular energetic profiles in application to tRNA structures. *Am Conf Theor Chem*, UCLA, California, 2005.

[32] Torshin IY. Computed energetics of macromolecules: identification of the functional residues in proteins and functional nucleotides in RNA. *Am Chem Soc*, 227th meeting, Anaheim, CA 2004.

[33] Elcock AH. Prediction of functionally important residues based solely on the computed energetics of protein structure. *J Mol Biol* 2001;312(4):885-896.

[34] Torshin IY. EVM (Expert vs Machine) strategy for fold recognition. *CASP6 meeting*, Gaeta, Italy, 2004.

[35] Li QZ, Lu ZQ. The prediction of the structural class of protein: application of the measure of diversity. *J Theor Biol* 2001;213(3):493-502.

[36] Murzin AG, Brenner SE, Hubbard T, Chothia C. SCOP: a structural classification of proteins database for the investigation of sequences and structures. *J Mol Biol* 1995;247(4):536-540.

[37] Torshin IY. Three-dimensional models of human 2'-5' oligoadenylate synthetases: a new computational method for reconstructing an enzyme assembly. *Med Sci Monit* (in press) 2005.

In: Protein Folding: New Research
Editor: Tony R. Obalinsky, pp. 225-248
ISBN 1-59454-835-8

Chapter 6

ELECTRONIC ASPECTS OF PROTEIN FOLDING: SUBSTITUENT EFFECTS OF AMINO ACIDS IN DIPEPTIDES

Donard S. Dwyer*

Departments of Psychiatry and Pharmacology, Toxicology and Neuroscience,
LSU Health Sciences Center, Shreveport, LA

ABSTRACT

Folding of proteins into their native conformation is determined by various extrinsic and intrinsic factors. The most important determinant in folding is the amino acid sequence, yet it is not known how this simple one-dimensional information specifies a complex three-dimensional (3-D) structure. In addition, hydrophobic effects play a major role in protein folding. However, these effects do not adequately explain secondary structural preferences of amino acids. Moreover, they represent the cooperative behavior of systems (protein plus solvent) and reflect the operation of more fundamental processes that are not well understood. This chapter will discuss how electronic effects play a major role in the fundamental aspects of protein folding. Previously, certain electronic properties of the 20 naturally-occurring amino acids have been characterized, including inductive and field effects, polarizability, and resonance effects. To follow up on this work, the hydrophilicity of amino acids has now been characterized in terms of electronic properties, specifically electron densities. In addition, various electronic properties of dipeptides have been related to secondary structural preferences and to NMR data. A model is presented here that views amino acid side chains as substituents along the peptide backbone, which affect electron density, and hence structure, as a function of the electronic features of the side chain groups. Interplay between the side chains and main chain atoms determines the degree of electron delocalization along the main chain and

---

* Contact Information: Departments of Psychiatry and Pharmacology, Toxicology and Neuroscience, LSU Health Sciences Center, 1501 Kings Highway, Shreveport, LA 71130. Email: ddwyer@lsuhsc.edu; Phone: 318 675-7612; Fax: 318 675-6148

the rotational flexibility of peptide segments. Greater flexibility is required for the adoption of α-helices and turns than for strand conformations. Thus, electronic properties of amino acid side chains may either promote or restrict conformational options in a protein in much the same way that substituent effects control reactivity and orientation in chemical reactions. The primary sequence of a protein specifies its final 3-D structure, in part through nearest-neighbor effects, which are also currently being characterized by quantum mechanics (QM) calculations. Ultimately, a better understanding of the electronic properties of amino acids and proteins will provide insight into protein folding at the atomic level and will allow more accurate prediction of 3-D structure starting from the amino acid sequence.

Key Words: Electronic properties, Quantum mechanics, Substituent effects, Protein folding.

INTRODUCTION

Significant progress has been made over the last 10 years in the prediction of the secondary and three-dimensional (3-D) structure of proteins starting from their amino acid sequence (Baker and Sali 2001; Rost 2001; Venclovas *et al.* 2003). Much of the progress has resulted from comparative modeling approaches, which include threading (Aszodi *et al.* 1997; Jones *et al.* 1999; Rost *et al.* 1997) and fold recognition (Simons *et al.* 1997, 1999). The best prediction algorithms currently achieve accuracy rates in the range of 70-80% (Karplus *et al.* 1999; Orengo *et al.* 1999; Rost 2001). Clearly, the amino acid sequence of a protein directs folding into the native 3-D conformation, but how? The most accurate homology-based methods have provided little insight into the actual mechanisms of protein folding at the molecular level. Moreover, most structure prediction methods do not address two important issues for protein folding that concern: (1) the speed of this process, and (2) the intrinsic factors that determine the folding trajectory. Many theoretical approaches focus on the process of folding (e.g., reaction intermediates [Kim and Baldwin 1990] or nucleation-condensation [Daggett and Fersht 2003]) without addressing mechanisms *per se*. Others focus on intrinsic factors (e.g., hydrophobic effects or entropic factors) that affect folding, but pay scant attention to the sequencing of folding events or the mechanics of the overall process (Kauzmann 1959; Creamer and Rose 1992). This paper will attempt to provide a comprehensive analysis of the folding problem from an electronic perspective in order to link mechanisms with processes.

I will start with the simplest formulation of the protein folding problem, namely prediction of secondary structure. While successful forecasting of secondary structure is not a prerequisite for the prediction of tertiary structure, it is difficult to imagine that a deeper understanding of protein folding can be attained without a better appreciation of the factors that determine secondary structure. The earliest strategies for predicting secondary structure were largely based on analysis of the preference of amino acids for particular conformations (α-helix, β-strand, and coil) derived from 3-D structural databases (Chou and Fasman 1978). Thus, Chou and Fasman (1978) and Williams *et al.* (1987) related the prediction of secondary structure to the probability that particular amino acids adopt a specific conformation (P_c). Threading approaches are essentially a variation on this theme and employ multiple sequence alignments, together with structural considerations, to predict the 3-D conformation of proteins (Aszodi *et al.* 1997; Jones *et al.* 1999; Rost *et al.* 1997). By contrast, other strategies for predicting secondary structure rely on the evaluation of intrinsic properties of amino acids, including thermodynamic factors (Munoz and Serrano 1995; O'Neil and DeGrado 1990), steric effects (Creamer and Rose 1992), and hydrophobicity (Gromiha and Ponnuswamy 1995).

Hydrophobicity is a major driving force for protein folding (Kauzmann 1959; Dill 1990). There is generally a good correlation between the hydropathy values for amino acids and their preference for β-strands and turns (Chou and Fasman 1978). However, these same intrinsic measures of hydrophobicity do not predict the propensity of amino acids to form α-helices. Moreover, hydrophobicity measures are empirically-derived and provide little real insight into the folding problem. One goal of this paper is to derive an expression for the hydrophobicity of amino acids from quantum mechanics (QM) calculations. This is part of a broader strategy to describe intrinsic factors that influence protein folding in purely electronic terms.

The electronic contributions to protein folding have largely been overlooked in most theoretical analyses to date. Molecular structure is ultimately determined by the precise distribution of electrons in the molecular orbitals (Bader 1990; Wiberg *et al.* 1991). Proteins are no different; they are simply larger than the usual quarry of QM approaches. There are many reasons to believe that folding will eventually be understood in terms of dynamic modulation of electron distributions. First, the speed of folding, including the Levinthal paradox (Levinthal 1968), appears to require nearly simultaneous adoption of structure over significant distances. Rapid charge transfer could account for some of the cooperativity in this process. Moreover, bond lengths and hydrogen bonding along the peptide backbone are determined by local electron densities, which are subject to modulation by solvent and side chain groups. Finally, bond rotation and backbone flexibility specify local protein conformations as a function of the degree of electron delocalization and hyperconjugation involving main chain atoms (Weinhold 2001).

Elsewhere, I have proposed that the electronic effects of amino acid side chains on protein folding are a special case of well-established substituent effects of chemical groups (Dwyer 2001, 2005). Substituent effects refer to the phenomena whereby chemical groups (substituents) attached to a larger molecule affect the chemical properties of the substituted molecule in a predictable manner (Hammett 1937; Taft 1952). As early as 1937, Hammett was systematically characterizing how various chemical groups affected the reactivity (ionization of substituted benzoic acids) of the host molecule. He defined the substituent constant, σ, to represent the collection of electronic properties of the substituent groups, which include inductive, field, and resonance effects. Numerous studies (reviewed in detail elsewhere [Charton 1981; Hansch *et al.* 1991; Topsom 1987]) demonstrated that substituent effects impact chemical reactivity, conformational stability, and rotational flexibility in substituted benzoic acids, phenols, and bicyclooctane carboxylic acids (Brinck *et al.* 1997; Charton 1981; Hansch *et al.* 1991; Pross and Radom 1981). Earlier work from my laboratory was the first to suggest that amino acid side chains should be considered as substituent groups on the peptide backbone that produce a similar array of electronic effects in proteins. There is clearly electron delocalization along the peptide backbone (Beratan *et al.* 1992; Eley and Spivey 1960; Marcus and Sutin 1985; Patten and Gordy 1960; Pruetz and Land 1979) and hyperconjugation as well. The degree of delocalization will be affected by side chain groups, which can either donate or withdraw electrons from the backbone (particularly the C_α atom) depending on the charge and electronegativity of atoms in the side chain (Dwyer 2005). Similarly, field effects of side chain groups affect the electron distribution along the peptide backbone acting through space. Previously, I showed that the electronic properties of amino acids are reflected in their pKa at the amino group and further that these properties correlated with propensity for secondary structure (Dwyer 2001). The 20 amino acids were divided into 5 groups on the basis of the strength of the side chain moieties as net electron donors or acceptors. A subsequent report described the partitioning of electronic (substituent) effects of amino acids into inductive, field, and resonance effects, and characterization of steric effects in terms of polarizability (Dwyer 2005). Here, I have refined the QM analysis of amino acids and derived an index for the hydrophilicity of the side chains based on semiempirical (PM3) calculations of electron density.

A final issue that will be addressed in this chapter concerns context effects in protein folding, specifically so-called nearest-neighbor effects, i.e., the reciprocal influence exerted by adjacent amino acids in a protein. A prior study from my laboratory revealed that the preference of pairs of amino acids for a particular secondary structure was related to the composition of the pairs with respect to the 5 groups of amino acids (Dwyer 2001). Thus for example, pairs of robust electron donors strongly favored α-helices or coil conformations over β-strands. These observations, along with NMR studies of the relationship between chemical shifts and secondary structure (Osapay and Case 1994; Wishart *et al.* 1991), highlight the potential significance of electronic factors in nearest-neighbor effects. Wu and Kabat (1973) were the first to fully appreciate that the preference of an amino acid for secondary structure is affected by the nature of the nearest residues in the N_{-1} and N_{+1} positions. Electronic features of the side chain groups appear to play a role in these effects (Dwyer 2001), although they have not been characterized in any detail. Additional support for this notion is provided by findings that the pKa of the amide and carboxyl groups of alanine tri- and tetra-peptides is affected by the location of lysine substitutions in the peptides (Ellenbogen 1952). Furthermore, α-proton chemical shifts in proteins detected by NMR are influenced by amino acids in the N_{-1} position (Wishart *et al.* 1991). A goal of the present work was to characterize the electronic contributions to nearest-neighbor effects in relation to secondary structure. In this report, QM calculations of electron densities, Mulliken populations, and bond lengths reveal relationships between the electronic properties of dipeptides and nearest-neighbor effects in secondary structural preferences. These studies provide the first insights into this relationship at the electronic level.

METHODS

Classification of Amino Acids

In order to facilitate analysis of nearest-neighbor effects in dipeptides, amino acids have been categorized into one of 5 classes on the basis of criteria outlined previously (Dwyer 2001). Assignments were based primarily on the pKa at the amino group with minor adjustments according to Charton's localized electronic effect constants. The 5 groups were categorized in terms of net electron donor or acceptor effects (stabilization or destabilization, respectively) at the amide proton bond. The groups were: O (strong donor - A, E, D, and P [single letter amino acid code]), U (weak donor – I, V, and L), Z (ambivalent – G, W, H, and S), B (weak acceptor – M, F, Q, Y, and T), and X (strong acceptor – R, K, and N). Cysteine was not included in any group and was analyzed separately.

Dipeptides

For most of these studies, dipeptides were created in the extended conformation with the Biopolymer program of the InsightII software package (Accelrys; San Diego, CA). This conformation was selected because it introduces the least initial bias into the system. The N- and C-termini of the peptides bore net positive and negative charges, respectively. One amino acid from each of the 5 groups was used in the first (N) position: A (O), V (U), G (Z), T (B), and K (X). All 20 amino acids were analyzed in the second (N_{+1}) position. The side chains of D and E carried a net charge of -1 e.u., whereas K and R carried net charges of +1 e.u. Dipeptides were minimized to convergence with the AMBER force field prior to the QM calculations. For comparison, 33 dipeptides were analyzed in both extended and helical conformations. In total, 141 dipeptides were analyzed.

QM Calculations

QM calculations of electron densities, Mulliken populations, bond lengths, etc. were carried out with a Silicon Graphics Indigo^2 workstation running AMPAC/MOPAC in the InsightII software package (Accelrys; San Diego, CA). The semiempirical PM3 method (Stewart 1989) was used with restricted Hartree-Fock conditions. SCF parameters included peptide correction and a geometry test. For comparison with the dipeptides, QM calculations were also performed on the individual 20 amino acids in their zwitterion form, with the exception of proline. The side chains of D, E, K, and R were charged as before.

Hydrophilicity Index

An initial attempt has been made to derive a purely electronic expression for the hydrophilicity of amino acid side chains. The concept of hydrophobic effects is somewhat of a misnomer (Hildebrand 1979). Hydrophobic effects arise mainly because water molecules are best-suited to interact with other water molecules rather than from repulsive interactions between water and non-polar solutes such as hydrocarbons. Therefore, I have focused here on the degree to which atoms in the side chains mimic or resemble the atoms of water to derive a hydrophilicity index. As a measure of the resemblance to water, the electron densities of atoms in the side chains (H_α in the case of glycine and H_β outward for other amino acids) were compared with the electron densities of the H and O atoms of water. The main chain atoms were ignored for this analysis and were considered to contribute equally to overall hydrophilicity across the set of amino acids. Equation 1 describes the derivation of the hydrophilicity index, Hyp,

$$\text{Hyp} = (\sum \rho_{aa}/\rho H_20 + \sum [1 - \rho_{aa}/\rho H_20])_{HB} - \sum (\rho_{aa}/\rho H_20)_{HC} \quad (1)$$

$\rho_{aa} \leq \rho H_20$ $\rho_{aa} > \rho H_20$

where ρ_{aa} and ρH_20 represent the electron density of individual atoms in the amino acid side chains (aa) and water, respectively, and HB and HC refer to potential hydrogen bonding atoms (O, N, S, and H bound to O or N) and hydrogen atoms bonded to carbon, respectively. The electron densities of H atoms of the amino acids were compared to the electron density of H atoms (0.8246) in water regardless of their HB or HC origin. The electron densities of O, N, or S atoms were compared to the electron density of the O atom (6.3508) of water. Solving equation 1 for water yields a Hyp value of 3.0, whereas cyclohexane yields -13.82. The correction in the HB term (if $\rho_{aa} > \rho H_20$) arises from the fact that a ratio greater than 1 is not possible, i.e., an atom in a molecule cannot mimic water better than water atoms themselves. Because the HC term is subtracted in equation 1, this adjustment is not necessary.

Statistical Analysis

For between-group comparisons, paired or unpaired Student's t-tests were used (as appropriate) to evaluate statistical significance of the data. In some cases, linear regression analysis was performed to determine possible correlations (Pearson's coefficient) between the various electronic properties and folding preferences. The preference of a given pair of amino acids for α-helix, β-strand, and coil conformations was taken from a large protein database analysis reported previously (Dwyer 2001).

RESULTS

QM Analysis of the 20 Amino Acids and Derivation of a Hydrophilicity (Hyp) Index

The starting point for this analysis was the characterization of the electronic properties of individual amino acids in order to: (1) have a standard for comparison with dipeptides, (2) begin secondary structure correlations, and (3) derive a hydrophilicity index on the basis of electron densities. A partial summary of these properties is shown in Table 1, which includes Mulliken population data and electron densities for the main chain atoms of the amino acids. It is clear that the electron distributions in the main chain atoms are influenced by the side chain groups. Side chain atoms may affect the main chain electron distributions via a combination of through-space and through-bond effects. As expected, there was an excellent correlation ($r > 0.96$) between the Mulliken population data and the calculated electron densities. Furthermore, as noted previously (Dwyer 2005) there was a significant correlation between the C_α Mulliken values ($C_{\alpha MULL}$) and the preference of amino acids for α-helices ($r = -0.6$, $p < 0.01$). This relationship will be examined in greater detail with the dipeptide QM calculations.

Table 1. QM calculations of electron populations and hydrophilicity of the 20 amino acids*

	Mulliken populations				Electron densities				Hyp
	N	C_α	C	O	N	C_α	C	O	
A	4.2250	4.5329	3.5210	6.5555	4.1460	4.3834	3.5848	6.5503	-3.42
I	4.2280	4.5243	3.5305	6.5545	4.1509	4.3783	3.5918	6.5495	-10.33
E	4.2300	4.5246	3.5083	6.5773	4.1519	4.3863	3.5706	6.5709	-2.65
V	4.2270	4.5231	3.5283	6.5549	4.1497	4.3771	3.5903	6.5499	-8.02
L	4.2268	4.5290	3.5229	6.5568	4.1498	4.3819	3.5861	6.5516	-10.31
D	4.2463	4.5099	3.4979	6.5821	4.1687	4.3566	3.5619	6.5752	-0.42
G	4.2273	4.6245	3.5164	6.5585	4.1456	4.4030	3.5799	6.5532	-1.02
W	4.2293	4.5194	3.5211	6.5590	4.1494	4.3728	3.5848	6.5537	-5.95
M	4.2292	4.5263	3.5234	6.5512	4.1517	4.3792	3.5873	6.5462	-6.90
H	4.2187	4.5375	3.5355	6.5560	4.1392	4.3835	3.5872	6.5509	-1.84
S	4.2211	4.5851	3.5020	6.5549	4.1429	4.4299	3.5681	6.5497	-0.32
F	4.2314	4.5197	3.5245	6.5549	4.1514	4.3721	3.5882	6.5497	-7.60
Q	4.2205	4.5326	3.5308	6.5521	4.1414	4.3847	3.5929	6.5472	-0.97
Y	4.2315	4.5185	3.5225	6.5559	4.1515	4.3716	3.5862	6.5507	-4.55
T	4.2212	4.5328	3.5280	6.5531	4.1398	4.3796	3.5907	6.5481	-2.63
R	4.2170	4.5313	3.5355	6.5409	4.1374	4.3849	3.5981	6.5367	0.14
K	4.2172	4.5308	3.5364	6.5409	4.1376	4.3844	3.5989	6.5367	-4.70
N	4.2445	4.5054	3.5235	6.5543	4.1619	4.3599	3.5874	6.5493	1.35
P	5.2224	4.1876	3.5261	6.6427	5.1481	4.1014	3.5821	6.6325	-6.22
C	4.2255	4.5410	3.5395	6.5452	4.1461	4.3931	3.6009	6.5409	-1.34

* QM values for the Mulliken populations and electron densities are shown for the main chain atoms indicated for each of the 20 naturally-occurring amino acids. The hydrophilicity index (Hyp) was derived as described in the Methods section.

From the electron density data, it was possible to derive a hydrophilicity index (Hyp) by solving equation 1. Each atom of the side chains (except for carbon atoms) was compared to its equivalent in water (hydrogen or oxygen) in terms of its electron density to estimate how closely a particular atom resembles its counterpart in water. Atoms capable of hydrogen bonding as donors or acceptors (HB) were assigned positive values, whereas hydrogens bonded to carbon (HC), regardless of the hybridization, were assigned negative values to account for the immiscibility of hydrocarbons in water as a function of size. The summation of the individual comparisons yielded the Hyp index shown in Table 1. The scale ranges from -10.33 (isoleucine) to 1.35 (asparagine). The Hyp index shows significant correlation to other hydrophobicity scales, including that of Kyte and Doolittle (1982) (r = -0.75), Jones (1975) (r = -0.78), and the water-vapor partition coefficient (r = 0.76). Interestingly, there was a high degree of correlation (r = 0.82) between the Hyp scale and the chemical shifts measured by NMR for amino acids in the coil conformation (Wishart *et al.* 1991). By comparison, the correlation between NMR chemical shifts and the Kyte-Doolittle scale was only r = 0.77. Similar to the Kyte-Doolittle scale, the Hyp index does a good job of predicting preference for coil (r = 0.7; $p < 0.01$) and strand (r = -0.6; $p < 0.01$) conformations in proteins. Thus, a measure of hydrophilicity based entirely on QM-derived electron densities appears to accurately reflect “hydrophobic effects,” including preference for secondary structure, of amino acids.

QM Analysis of Dipeptides

Results from the analysis of the electronic properties of individual amino acids encouraged similar investigation of dipeptides. Over 100 dipeptides were subjected to QM calculations and the extensive data from this analysis necessitated presentation in summary form. The data have been organized according to the 5 amino acids located in the first position of the dipeptides and the 18 amino acids (excluding proline) in the second position averaged with respect to the groups described earlier (O, U, Z, B, and X). Proline was not included in this final analysis because it adopts a non-extended conformation in the dipeptides, whereas cysteine was not a member of the 5 original groups. The data are summarized in Table 2 in terms of the Mulliken populations at the main chain atoms only. The row data represent the averages of the data for all members of a particular group. For example, the ala-O row (also OO) represents the average of the ala-ala, ala-asp, and ala-glu dipeptides, whereas the val-U row (UU) represents the average of the val-ile, val-leu, and val-val dipeptides, and so forth. The main chain atoms are represented from the N-terminal (N) residue to the C-terminal amino acid (N_{+1}) of the dipeptide.

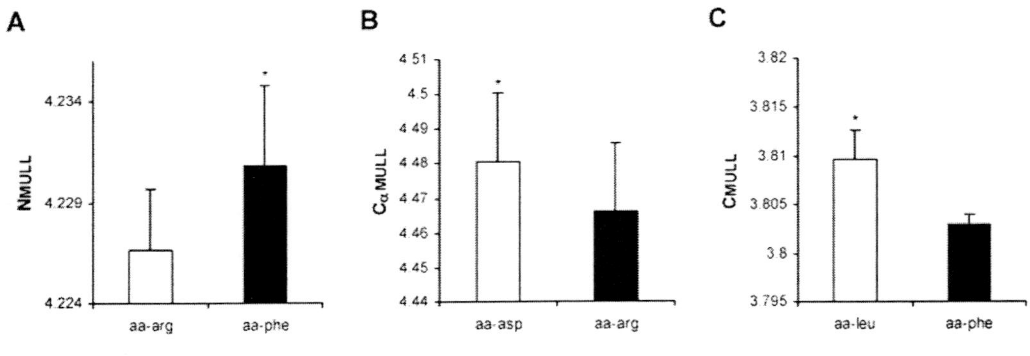

Figure 1. Nearest-neighbor effects of amino acids in the second position on Mulliken populations in the first residue. Mulliken population data from QM calculations were averaged for each of the 5 amino acids (aa) in the first position and arginine (arg), phenylalanine (phe), aspartic acid (asp), or leucine (leu) in the second position. The data presented here refer to average Mulliken populations at the N atom (A), Cα atom (B), and C atom (C) of the first amino acid in the pair. Error bars represent the standard errors and the asterisks denote significant differences between groups (*$p < 0.05$) determined by a paired Student's t-test.

Several conclusions can be drawn from these data. (1) The nature of the individual amino acid in the second position affects the electron distribution in the first residue. For example, the Mulliken/electron density values at the N and C_α atoms of glycine (N position) are 4.2135/4.1319 and 4.5597/4.3472, respectively with aspartic acid in the second (N_{+1}) position, whereas values for these same atoms of glycine are 4.2109/4.1280 and 4.5451/4.3321 with arginine in the N_{+1} position. Examples of amino acids in the second position producing significant differences in the first residue averaged over the 5 amino acids are shown in Figure 1. It is clear that arginine *vs.* phenylalanine in the second position results in different Mulliken population values at the N atom (N_{MULL}). The large error bars reflect inherent differences between amino acids in the first position rather than measurement or calculation errors. For example, The N_{MULL} value for glycine in the gly-arg dipeptide is

4.2109, whereas this value for valine in the val-phe dipeptide is 4.2438. Figure 1 includes a comparison of two other pairs of amino acids (N_{+1} position) with significant effects on the amino acid in the N position of the dipeptide: asp *vs.* arg (Figure 1B) and leu *vs.* phe (Figure 1C). In these cases, it is the Mulliken population at the C_α atom ($C_{\alpha MULL}$) or the C atom (C_{MULL}) of the first residue that is primarily affected. In general, the C_α and C atoms of the first residue were most sensitive to the nearest-neighbor effects of adjacent residues. (2) There were significant differences in the effects of the various groups of amino acids on electronic parameters in the first residue, i.e., the average of the C_{MULL} for gly-O was significantly different from that of gly-X (Figure 2A). Similarly, ala-O *vs.* ala-X, and ala-O *vs.* ala-B showed significant differences (Figure 2B,C). (3) Not surprisingly, the various groups of amino acids differ in their Mulliken populations for the N_{+1} main chain atoms (Table 2). For example, the average $C_{\alpha N+1MULL}$ for the O group is 4.3002, whereas it is 4.3315 for the Z group of amino acids. Thus, amino acids in the second position of the dipeptides exert significant effects on the electron distributions of amino acids in the first position, while retaining their distinct electronic properties.

Table 2. Mulliken population analysis of main chain atoms in dipeptides categorized according to 5 groups*

		N_N	$C_{\alpha N}$	C_N	O_N	N_{N+1}	HN_{N+1}	$C_{\alpha N+1}$	C_{N+1}	O_{N+1}
ala-O	OO	4.2274	4.4608	3.8216	6.4637	4.8840	0.8376	4.2993	3.5096	6.6090
val-O	OU	4.2359	4.4488	3.8281	6.4521	4.8956	0.8352	4.2991	3.5100	6.6091
gly-O	OZ	4.2127	4.5549	3.8236	6.4675	4.8805	0.8372	4.2992	3.5095	6.6087
thr-O	BO	4.2326	4.4610	3.8276	6.4520	4.8926	0.8348	4.3003	3.5105	6.6087
lys-O	OX	4.2279	4.4536	3.8290	6.4145	4.8721	0.8825	4.3031	3.5075	6.6251
	Avg.	4.2273	4.4758	3.8260	6.4500	4.8850	0.8455	4.3002	3.5094	6.6121
ala-U	OU	4.2275	4.4540	3.8034	6.4624	4.8886	0.8397	4.3043	3.5252	6.5973
val-U	UU	4.2370	4.4423	3.8091	6.4511	4.9010	0.8372	4.3040	3.5259	6.5974
gly-U	UZ	4.2119	4.5503	3.8060	6.4646	4.8841	0.8395	4.3045	3.5255	6.5969
thr-U	BU	4.2337	4.4556	3.8082	6.4503	4.8976	0.8374	4.3051	3.5264	6.5975
lys-U	UX	4.2269	4.4485	3.8149	6.4115	4.8911	0.8691	4.2999	3.5248	6.6137
	Avg.	4.2274	4.4701	3.8083	6.4480	4.8925	0.8446	4.3036	3.5256	6.6006
ala-Z	OZ	4.2275	4.4541	3.8080	6.4593	4.9088	0.8243	4.3308	3.5164	6.5960
val-Z	UZ	4.2367	4.4426	3.8139	6.4475	4.9205	0.8223	4.3301	3.5168	6.5962
gly-Z	ZZ	4.2118	4.5494	3.8101	6.4626	4.9048	0.8238	4.3311	3.5165	6.5955
thr-Z	BZ	4.2331	4.4559	3.8131	6.4473	4.9179	0.8216	4.3310	3.5170	6.5940
lys-Z	XZ	4.2249	4.4490	3.8120	6.4289	4.9140	0.8376	4.3343	3.5148	6.6087
	Avg.	4.2268	4.4702	3.8114	6.4491	4.9132	0.8259	4.3315	3.5163	6.5981
ala-B	BO	4.2290	4.4536	3.8004	6.4554	4.9029	0.8315	4.2974	3.5224	6.5941
val-B	BU	4.2393	4.4415	3.8061	6.4444	4.9149	0.8294	4.2969	3.5224	6.5941
gly-B	BZ	4.2130	4.5492	3.8021	6.4588	4.8988	0.8312	4.2976	3.5225	6.5936
thr-B	BB	4.2346	4.4552	3.8054	6.4441	4.9117	0.8288	4.2980	3.5229	6.5925
lys-Z	BX	4.2268	4.4479	3.8093	6.4166	4.9032	0.8541	4.2968	3.5205	6.6077
	Avg.	4.2285	4.4695	3.8047	6.4439	4.9063	0.8350	4.2973	3.5221	6.5964
ala-X	OX	4.2279	4.4498	3.7926	6.4659	4.9147	0.8204	4.2904	3.5274	6.5874
val-X	UX	4.2376	4.4382	3.7985	6.4540	4.9267	0.8185	4.2900	3.5274	6.5878
gly-X	XZ	4.2121	4.5447	3.7946	6.4688	4.9106	0.8201	4.2905	3.5276	6.5869
thr-X	BX	4.2334	4.4523	3.7974	6.4537	4.9242	0.8178	4.2910	3.5279	6.5874
lys-X	XX	4.2272	4.4436	3.7970	6.4066	4.9172	0.8582	4.2906	3.5280	6.6035
	Avg.	4.2276	4.4657	3.7960	6.4498	4.9187	0.8270	4.2905	3.5277	6.5906

*Mulliken population data are shown for the main chain atoms in the first (N) and second (N_{+1}) residues of the dipeptides. The results of QM analysis of 80 dipeptides have been summarized here according to the 5 groups of amino acids described previously (Dwyer 2001) and in the Methods section. The two-letter designation for the dipeptides is based on the group membership of the amino acids in the first and second positions.

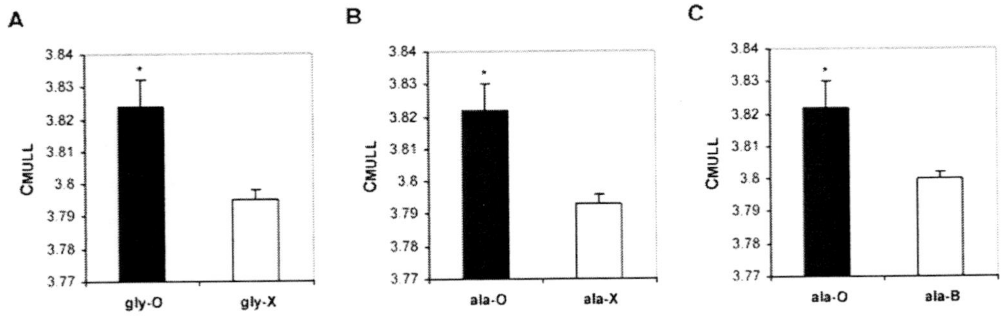

Figure 2. Nearest-neighbor effects in relation to the 5 groups of amino acids. For these comparisons, Mulliken population values for the C atom (C_{MULL}) were averaged according to the amino acid in the first position, gly (A) or ala (B, C) with each member of a group in the second position (e.g., O is gly-ala, gly-asp, and gly-glu, whereas X is gly-arg, gly-lys, and gly-asn). Student's t-test (unpaired) revealed significant differences between groups, $*p < 0.05$.

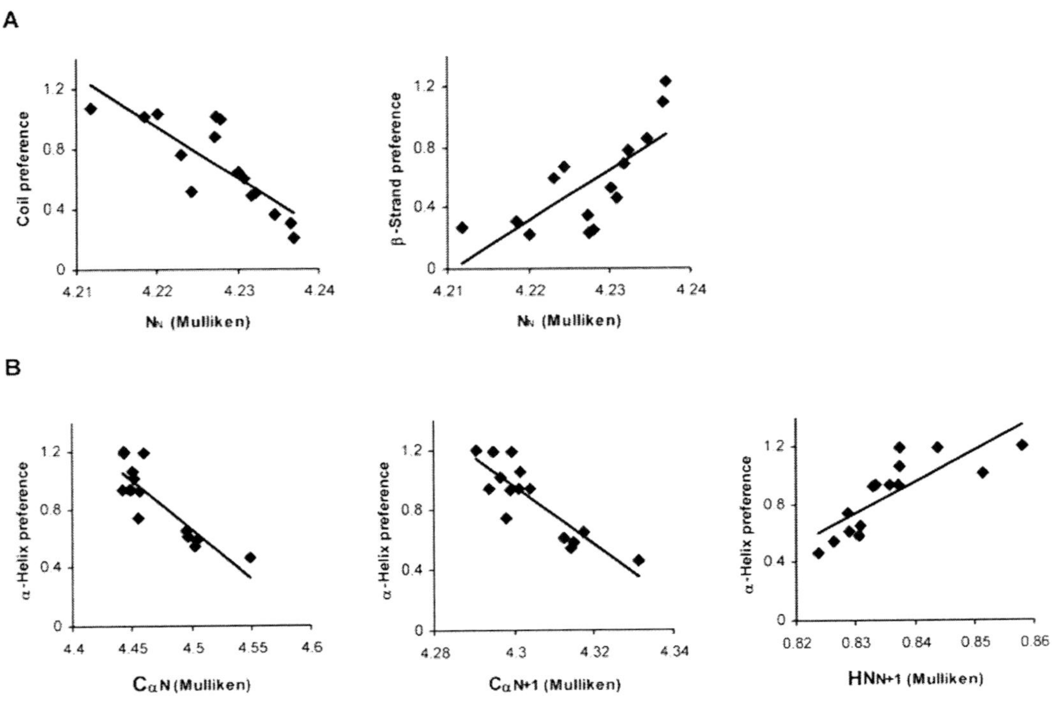

Figure 3. Linear regression analysis of the correlation between Mulliken populations at the atoms indicated and preference of dipeptides for secondary structure. (A) Correlation between N_N values and coil and strand conformations. (B) Correlations with preferences for α-helices.

Relationship to Secondary Structure

In view of the nearest-neighbor effects documented above and earlier reports of a relationship between electronic properties and secondary structure (Dwyer 2001), it seemed possible that the electron distributions in the dipeptides might be related to preference for secondary structure. Previously, I have analyzed 21,000 pairs of amino acids for their preferences for α-helix, β-strand, and coil conformations in relation to the 5 groups of amino acids. Thus, peptides comprised of OO pairs of amino acids tend to prefer α-helix ($P_c = 1.19$) and coil conformations (1.01) over β-strands (0.23), whereas BU pairs show a preference for β-strands (1.09) over α-helices (0.94) and coils (0.30). Because the original analysis did not distinguish the ordering of amino acids in the dipeptides, this same convention was used here. Thus, the Mulliken population values in Table 2 for the dipeptides OU and UO, BU and UB, etc. were averaged for the secondary structure comparisons. Linear regression analysis revealed striking correlations between Mulliken populations at certain atoms and preference of the dipeptides for secondary structure. Figure 3A shows that the N_{MULL} values significantly correlate with coil ($r = -0.82$) and strand ($r = 0.74$) conformations. Moreover, the $C_{\alpha MULL}$ data for both the first and second residues, and $HN_{N+1MULL}$ strongly predict preference of dipeptides for α-helices; the correlation coefficients are -0.86, -0.86 and 0.80, respectively (Figure 3B). For a single measure or index, these electronic properties represent some of the best predictors of secondary structure to date.

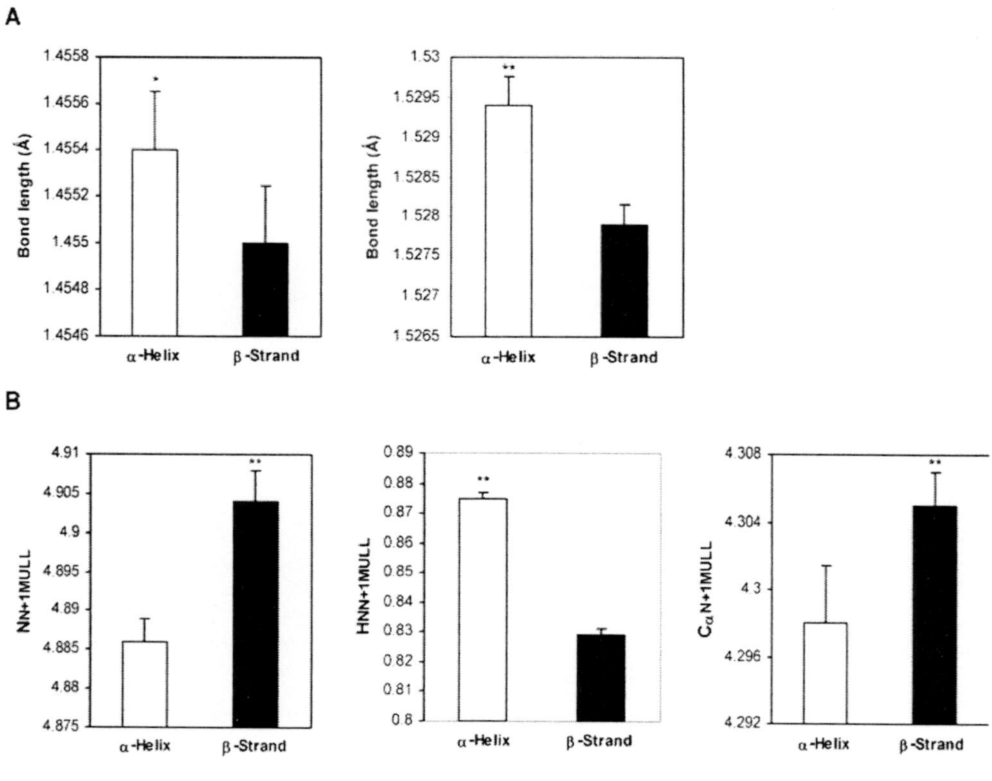

Figure 4. Comparison of electronic parameters for α-helices vs. β-strands. The same 33 dipeptides were analyzed by QM methods when configured in either an extended (β-strand) or helical conformation. (A) Bonds lengths between N_{N+1}-$C_{\alpha N+1}$ (left panel) and $C_{\alpha N+1}$-C_{N+1} (right panel) were averaged according to the structure. (B) Similarly, Mulliken population data (as indicated on the y-axes) were averaged for the dipeptides in α-helices vs. β-strands. The error bars represent standard errors and the asterisks indicate significant differences between groups (*$p < 0.05$; **$p < 0.01$).

These observations suggested that electron distributions at certain main chain atoms are in some way related to preference for secondary structure. To pursue this possibility more methodically, QM analysis was performed on 33 dipeptides in both extended and helical conformations. In these dipeptides, the structure was not an α-helix *per se*, but the second residue was appended with a dihedral angle consistent with the start of an α-helix. Several features were virtually diagnostic of the helical conformation including the bond lengths between $C_{\alpha N+1}$-C_{N+1}, and N_{N+1}-HN_{N+1}, and Mulliken populations of N_{N+1}, HN_{N+1} and $C_{\alpha N+1}$. Figure 4 illustrates the comparisons between Mulliken populations and bond lengths of main chain atoms in identical dipeptides arrayed in either an extended or helical conformation. The N_{N+1}-C_{N+1} and $C_{\alpha N+1}$-C_{N+1} bonds are considerably longer in helical dipeptides than in extended ones (Figure 4A). This agrees well with our analysis of C_{α}-C bond lengths in α-helices *vs*. β-strands of high resolution (< 0.93 Å) proteins (Dwyer 2005) from the Protein Database established by Bernstein *et al.* (1977). Finally, in the helical conformation, the $N_{N+1MULL}$ and $C_{\alpha N+1MULL}$ values are lower than in the extended (strand) conformation, whereas the $HN_{N+1MULL}$ values are significantly higher in helical dipeptides (Figure 4B).

DISCUSSION

Hydrophilicity as an Electronic Property

The data summarized here represent an attempt to quantify electronic effects related to protein folding, at least the adoption of secondary structure. I have described a new hydrophilicity index (Hyp) aimed at characterization of the hydrophobic properties of amino acids in purely electronic terms. This scale was based on electron densities calculated with the PM3 semiempirical QM method and comparisons between atoms in the side chains and the H and O atoms of water. This simple approach has yielded an all-electronic description of hydrophilicity that compares favorably to empirically-derived measures of hydrophobicity, including vapor-phase partition coefficients (Kyte and Doolittle 1982). Moreover, the new hydrophilicity index predicts secondary structural preferences of amino acids with the same accuracy as well-established hydrophobicity scales. Thus, it appears to reflect the same physicochemical properties as the empirical scales.

What does hydrophilicity mean at the electronic level? The O-H bonds in water are highly polarized and constitute permanent dipoles in comparison to C-H bonds, which although polarizable, represent transient dipoles. The hydrogen bond (H-bond) itself has partial covalent character (roughly 10% [Martin and Derewenda 1999]) due to hyperconjugation (Alabugin *et al.* 2003). Water molecules form a network of H-bonds that can be considered a "flickering cluster" (Frank and Wen 1957) where transient or fleeting contacts maximize the number of possible microstates (combinations of molecular arrangements) and thus the entropy of the system. The flickering in the network is due, in part, to the fact that H-bonding at one donor site (hydrogen atom) decreases the capacity for H-bonding by the other hydrogen atom (Huyskens 1977). Similarly, approach by a hydrogen atom to an oxygen atom already participating in an H-bond weakens this first H-bond. H-bonds of different strengths have been detected in water (Li and Ross 1993), which is consistent with this general interpretation. Thus, the degree to which a solute resembles the electronic properties of water will determine its ability to be accommodated in the flickering clusters with the least disruption. Hydrocarbon solutes in particular (also the methylene groups of amino acids) have several properties that diminish their miscibility in water. Because they do not resemble water, the hydrocarbons interact poorly via H-bonds. Consequently, they disturb the flickering cluster organization of water. In fact to accommodate the hydrocarbon groups, water polarizes the C-H bond, which tends to immobilize water molecules, while at the same time decreasing the microstates available to the solute due to polarization of the C-H groups. Ionic species produce such a reorganization of water (Kropman and Bakker 2001) despite their high degree of polarity. Finally, methylene groups prefer to interact with other methylene groups as part of a general tendency for "like to bind like" (Dwyer 1989, 1998).

Hydrophilicity in Protein Folding

Water molecules may affect protein folding in one of several ways. As outlined above, the electronic properties of water in comparison to hydrocarbons may encourage the association of side chains rich in methylene groups. Second, water molecules may form H-bonds with main chain carbonyl and amide groups. This is probably of secondary importance because the carbonyl and amide groups of other amino acids in the protein can effectively compete with water in the formation of intramolecular H-bonds. Third, field effects of water molecules in the solvent may serve to polarize atoms along the main chain and affect electron delocalization. Side chains that more closely mimic water will duplicate these field effects, whereas non-polar side chains would produce a different effect on the electron distributions. It is mainly solvent-induced self-association of methylene-containing side chains and polarization effects (or lack thereof) on main chain atoms that drive folding into coil and strand conformations. Therefore, it becomes an important goal to better understand the electronics of so-called hydrophobic effects. The Hyp index described here is a start in this direction. It may be possible to improve upon this index through the use of alternative QM methods, including density functional theory (DFT), or by incorporating additional electronic properties that provide a more comprehensive picture of what it takes to effectively mimic water.

Electronic Aspects of Nearest-Neighbor Effects in Dipeptides

The other major finding from this QM analysis concerns the demonstration of nearest-neighbor electronic effects in dipeptides. Thus, the nature of the amino acid in the second position affects the electron distribution in the first residue of the dipeptide and *vice versa*. When amino acids belonging to the strong electron donor group, O, were located in the N_{+1} position, they tended to raise the electron densities of the $C_{\alpha N}$ and C_N atoms, whereas amino acids that are strong electron acceptors (X group) had the opposite effect. Furthermore, the nature of the amino acids in the dipeptide affects bond lengths (hybridization) along the main chain, which governs rotational flexibility. Consequently, there are also ramifications for the structural preferences of the dipeptides. The electron distributions at certain atoms of the dipeptides strongly correlated with preference for α-helices ($C_{\alpha MULL}$) and coil/strand conformations (N_{MULL}). These observations were consistent with earlier studies that showed reciprocal structural influences of adjacent amino acids (Wu and Kabat 1973).

This work is predicated on two basic principles: (1) the electron distribution along the main chain affects the structure of a peptide/protein segment, and (2) this distribution is dynamic (there is electron delocalization and hyperconjugation along the backbone), and is affected by the amino acid side chains acting as substituent groups. Is there evidence that electron delocalization occurs along the peptide backbone of proteins? A wealth of data demonstrates that this must be the case. For a start, the planar nature of the peptide bond reflects resonance at this bond. In addition, charge transfer and movement of electrons in proteins are long-established phenomena that underlie protein redox reactions and migration of radicals (Hopfield 1974; Marcus and Sutin 1985). Electron tunneling in cytochrome c, myoglobin, and other proteins has been characterized in some detail (Cowan *et al.* 1988; Wuttke *et al.* 1992) and proceeds more efficiently through bond orbitals than through space (Beratan *et al.* 1992; Closs and Miller 1988; Moser *et al.* 1992). Migration of electron holes in irradiated proteins also occurs through bonds including the peptide bond depending upon the motion and orientation of the side chains (Patten and Gordy 1960; Pruetz and Land 1979). The movement of electrons along the peptide backbone is possible due to inherent delocalization and hyperconjugative effects (Patten and Gordy 1960). Electron transfer may extend over long distances in proteins and the rate of movement is very rapid, on the order of ps (Closs and Miller 1988). Finally, proteins behave as semiconductors under the right conditions (Eley and Spivey 1960), which is an extreme example of electron delocalization.

Studies of electron migration in proteins suggest that this phenomenon may contribute to nearest-neighbor effects. For example, electrons in irradiated proteins migrate across peptide bonds and even saturated bonds in side chains via hyperconjugation (Patten and Gordy 1960). Theoretical calculations of charge conductivity along the peptide backbone revealed that neighboring residues affect the underlying conductive energy band structure (Suhai 1974). Along similar lines, QM analysis of electronic effects in model collagen peptides showed that the dihedral angles in proline residues were affected by the "puckering" in adjacent prolines (Improta *et al.* 2002). Electronic effects of amino acids on pKa and chemical shifts in small peptides extend over several residues as measured by proton dissociation (Ellenbogen 1952) and NMR (Gmeiner and Facelli 1996). NMR studies have also revealed that the α-proton chemical shifts in proteins that distinguish secondary structures are influenced by the amino acid in the preceding position (Wishart *et al.* 1991). Taken together, these data provide initial insights into the possible mechanisms involved in nearest-neighbor electronic effects in proteins.

Mechanistic Aspects of Nearest-Neighbor Effects

How are nearest-neighbor effects produced? Adjacent amino acids may mutually influence each other through a variety of mechanisms. Theoretically, this may include inductive, resonance, and field effects, interaction of side chains with main chain atoms, steric effects, and hyperconjugation. It will first be useful to define the various effects that may be involved in nearest-neighbor interactions. Inductive effects refer to the ability of chemical groups to withdraw or donate electrons through bonds and are often equated with the electronegativity of the chemical or substituent group. Resonance effects refer to delocalization of electrons typically in π orbitals. Field effects are mediated through space and represent the ability of a chemical group to modulate the dipole of another group at a distance. Direct interaction of side chain groups with main chain atoms of adjacent residues is largely mediated via field and resonance effects. Here, I will argue for a reciprocal and interdependent relationship between polarizability and hyperconjugation that defines steric effects; this relationship is part of the same overall process at the electronic level. Previously, I derived polarizability constants for the 20 amino acid side chains (Dwyer 2005) and showed that there was an excellent correlation between these values and two measures of the steric effects of amino acids, namely the composite bulk index of Kidera *et al.* (1985) and the side chain gyration scale of Levitt (1976). Thus, polarizability is an electronic expression of steric effects, which makes sense from the perspective that polarizability is a measure of the deformability and reorientation of molecular orbitals. Polarizability and hyperconjugative effects are directly coupled as suggested by the work of Alabugin *et al.* (2003) who observed that "the rehybridization (and repolarization) itself can be considered an induced consequence of the hyperconjugative CT (charge transfer) interaction." Accordingly, steric effects can be viewed as the combination of polarizability and hyperconjugation, i.e., the balance between electron redistribution into bonding and antibonding orbitals as a consequence of external influences, including conformational changes. It is hyperconjugation which produces the partial covalent nature of H-bonds (Alabugin *et al.* 2003) and governs rotation about the σ bond in staggered *vs.* eclipsed ethane (Pophristic and Goodman 2001). In trying to relate these various factors to the substituent effects of side chains, it is worth mentioning that each chemical group produces a complex mixture of these effects. Which effect dominates is likely to depend on the context and orientation of the side chain group.

Previously, I have attempted to characterize inductive, field, resonance, and steric effects of the 20 amino acids. Scales for these electronic properties were derived from QM calculations and showed a good correspondence with existing scales that were either incomplete, or represented a combination of effects (e.g., inductive and resonance effects) (Dwyer 2005). According to this analysis, aspartic acid and glutamic acid have the highest inductive effects and act as strong electron donors, whereas the inductive effects of histidine and serine were weak. All four of these amino acids produced significant field effects, whereas alanine, isoleucine, leucine and valine exhibited very modest field effects, as expected. Interestingly, there was a good correlation between the inductive and field effects of an amino acid and $C_{\alpha MULL}$ populations (Dwyer 2005). Similarly, based on analysis of the data presented in Table 1 there was a significant correlation between field and resonance effects and the N_{MULL} data (r = -0.7 and 0.6, respectively). The polarizability index also showed a modest, but significant, relationship (r = -0.5) to the $C_{\alpha MULL}$ populations in Table 1. It appears that all of the electronic effects described here impact electron distributions at main chain atoms, however, some of these effects may be greater at particular atoms (due to geometry or other factors) or in relation to particular secondary structures. Previously, I have proposed a role for inductive effects in helix formation and hydrophobic effects in the promotion of strand and coil structures (Dwyer 2001). In view of the dipeptide data presented, this is surely an oversimplification of the processes at work.

Preference for Secondary Structure in Dipeptides

The net result of the various electronic effects acting on main chain atoms of a protein is redistribution of electrons among these atoms. Each amino acid will affect this redistribution differently leading to a distinct, sequence-dependent local structure, i.e., ϕ, ψ angles. The pattern of amino acid type (O, U, B, Z, and X) provides critical context information as judged by our earlier finding that certain dipeptides preferred particular secondary structures (Dwyer 2001). This finding has been replicated here in relation to the electronic properties of dipeptides (nearest-neighbor effects). Nearest-neighbor effects are an aspect of protein folding that is poorly characterized at the molecular level. Early work by Wu and Kabat (1973) led to the realization of a "distinct influence of neighboring amino acids on ϕ, ψ angles." The pairwise distribution of amino acids in proteins is non-random (Cserzo and Simon 1989), which suggests structural and/or functional significance for certain pairs of residues. In fact, Cserzo and Simon (1989) proposed that short-range interactions among amino acids give rise to the uniqueness of a protein fold.

As reported here, electronic features of the dipeptides show significant correlation with the tendency of the dipeptides to adopt secondary structure in proteins. This suggests that the composition of the dipeptides with respect to the 5 groups of amino acids influences protein folding via nearest-neighbor effects. Bond lengths in the second residue are a particularly good indicator of β-strand *vs.* α-helix conformations. Longer bond lengths derived from the QM calculations are associated with α-helices when the same dipeptides are compared in extended *vs.* helical conformations. This is consistent with our recent analysis of α-helices and β-strands in high resolution (< 0.93 Å) protein structures (Dwyer 2005). The slightly longer bonds in α-helices may reflect the greater rotational flexibility that is needed to achieve the twist in the peptide backbone. Viewed in another way, the shorter bonds observed in dipeptides that form β-strands may restrict rotation about these bonds relative to dipeptides that adopt helical structures. Other electronic features (Mulliken populations of main chain atoms) also predict preference for secondary structure. It is noteworthy that the $N_{N+1MULL}$ correlates with coil and strand conformations, whereas the $C_{\alpha MULL}$ in both the first and second residues strongly correlates with α-helix preference. The $C_{\alpha MULL}$ correlation with α-helices is also observed in individual amino acids (Dwyer 2005). The association of lower $C_{\alpha MULL}$ values with greater tendency towards α-helices is consistent with NMR studies that revealed a downfield shift (deshielding) in this same atom in α-helices in comparison to β-strands (Wishart *et al.* 1991). As argued above, a different combination of electronic effects may give rise to the Mulliken populations at N *vs.* C_α atoms. Folding into α-helices and strands may likewise require different electronic effects, which could explain the observed correlations with secondary structure. Generally, the data support the notion that different forces drive the formation of coils and strands *vs.* helices.

The other feature of the dipeptide that showed striking correlation to secondary structure was the Mulliken population at the HN_{N+1} atom. This is significant for two reasons. First, it demonstrates that nearest-neighbor electronic effects are not restricted to heavy atoms of peptides. Second, the increase in electron density (observed in QM calculations) at this atom in helical dipeptides as compared to extended dipeptides agrees remarkably well with NMR data showing increased shielding of HN atoms in helices *vs.* strands (Wishart *et al.* 1991). Careful inspection of the dipeptide structures from the QM analysis revealed that the decrease in electron density at the HN_{N+1} atom in extended conformations is due to interaction of this atom with the carbonyl group at the C-terminus. Presumably, a similar interaction in proteins explains the relative downfield shift observed in HN atoms in strand conformations.

Model of Electronic Effects in Protein Folding

In an effort to relate the findings in this paper to more general schemes of protein folding, a model is presented in Figure 5. At the heart of this model is the concept that amino acid side chains act as substituents on the peptide backbone and produce local changes in electron distributions based on their chemical properties. While this is a novel conceptualization of the protein polymer, Cornilescu *et al.* (2000) have previously noted that "the chemical nature of the amino acid side chain is expected to have some influence on spin-spin couplings" between C_α and C_β atoms. The question then becomes do substituent effects of amino acid side chains offer any advantages in the understanding of protein folding?

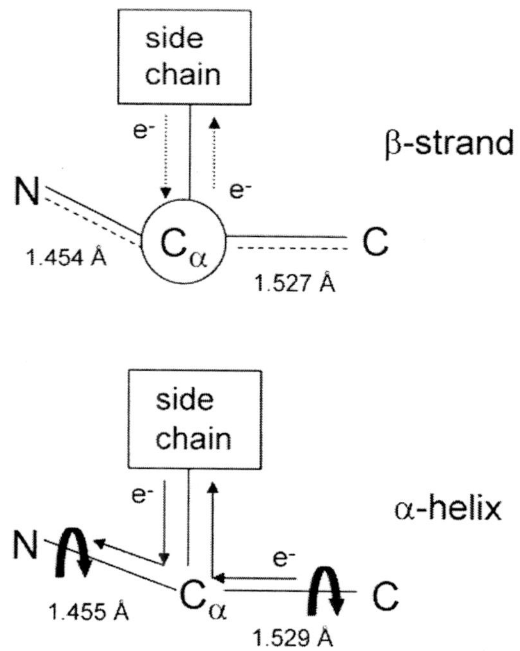

Figure 5. Model of electronic (substituent) effects on the peptide backbone in relation to secondary structure preference. Three main chain atoms are displayed and the amino acid side chain is represented by a box. Electron (e^-) donation or withdrawal is indicated by arrows. The dotted lines represent weak effects, whereas the solid lines represent strong effects that extend along the peptide backbone as indicated. The circle around the C_α atom in the β-strand denotes higher average electron density at this atom in dipeptides that prefer extended conformations. The dashed lines reflect greater π character (electron delocalization) in the β-strand, which leads to shortening of the bonds (average lengths in Å depicted below). In the α-helix, the local electron distributions permit or encourage greater rotation (solid curved arrows) about the main chain bonds.

It is the inherent chemical properties of amino acids that endow proteins with their unique features. The positive charge at the amino group and the negative charge at the carboxyl group separated only by the C_α atom insure the delocalization of electrons between the two charged moieties in an amino acid. This places the C_α atom at a critical junction and means that the substituent effects (electronic properties) of the side chain will impact the charge transfer between the amino and carboxyl groups. Theoretical studies have pointed out the critical nature of the main chain-side chain junction in conducting polymers and lattices (Avery 1964). Of course in a protein, the large separation between the amino and carboxyl groups nullifies direct interaction through bonds between these two charged species. However, as discussed here, there is significant electron delocalization along the peptide backbone. The degree to which side chain groups facilitate or interrupt this electron delocalization will change the electronic properties of the peptide backbone. This will include changes in bond length and rotational flexibility. Ease of rotation about the main chain bonds determines the likelihood that a residue will assume non-extended conformations.

According to the model, amino acid side chains serve as gates or valves regulating electron delocalization along the main chain. Net electron donors tend to exert their influence on upstream residues towards the N-terminus, whereas net electron acceptors have a greater impact towards the C-terminus. This is where nearest-neighbor effects become important because the substituent effects of adjacent residues may be additive, neutral, or in opposite directions. Moreover, as observed Hoffman and Ratner (1987) and Ayala *et al.* (2002), gating of electron transfer is conformationally sensitive, which in the model means that electron delocalization will be influenced by the relative rotation of adjacent peptide planes, in addition to side chain orientations. The net effects on main chain electron delocalization will result from the combination of inductive, field, resonance, and polarizability effects of the side chain groups. The precise pattern of side chain substituent effects for a particular segment of protein sequence will then determine the electron distributions along the main chain for that segment, and hence the local secondary structure. This scheme would explain the correlation between electronic properties and preference for secondary structure in relation to the composition of the dipeptides. For example, XX dipeptides have the highest preference for α-helices (1.20) and a low propensity for β-strand conformations (0.35), whereas BU dipeptides have a high preference for β-strands (1.09) and very low tendency for coils (0.30). Thus, an adjacent pair of strong electron acceptors will produce a very different local electron distribution than a pair that includes a weak electron acceptor and weak electron donor. Naturally, adoption of a particular secondary structure will be further affected by solvent effects and tertiary contacts in the protein as discussed below.

Speed of Protein Folding

Besides providing a cogent mechanistic basis for the emergence of secondary structure in proteins, the model also addresses the speed of the folding process. While it is not clear how hydrophobic effects or steric effects (as classically defined) explain the rapidity of folding, the electronic effects described here can quickly be propagated throughout the polypeptide chain on time scales consistent with the overall folding process. Thus, electron migration across saturated σ bonds of steroid spacers proceeds at a rate of about 20 Å per ns (Calcaterra *et al.* 1983). Moreover, the decay rate of electron tunneling through bonds is significantly lower than that through space (Beratan *et al.* 1992; Closs and Miller 1988). Langen *et al.* (1995) reported that electron transfer is more rapid in β-strands than α-helices. This is partly due to the difference in path lengths, but may also result from the different electronic properties of amino acids that prefer β-strands over α-helices. Greater resistance to electron transfer along the main chain may be generated via gating effects of side chains with strong electron donor or acceptor properties, which includes amino acids that prefer helical conformations. Of course, electron flow along the main chain may also direct the orientation of the side chains as gating occurs and produces redistribution of electrons in molecular orbitals. Thus, the electronics of protein folding is a two-way street. The side chains determine local electron distributions (and structural tendencies) as a function of their inherent electronic properties, and the emergence of secondary structure then impacts electron transfer and ultimately the orientation of the side chains. This leads to stabilization of a particular conformation. Consequently, the protein does not have to try out multiple conformations on its way to the native structure (the Levinthal paradox). Rather, initial structural features are generated nearly instantaneously in response to the electron distributions that are established as a function of the intrinsic properties (substituent effects) of the side chains. This limits the phase-space that is sampled by discrete segments, especially those with strong patterns of electronic and nearest-neighbor effects, i.e., preference for secondary structure. Furthermore, the sampling is not a stochastic process, but is driven by electronic effects (inductive, field effects, etc.) in the same way that substituents direct the orientation and reactivity of substitution reactions in aromatic compounds. In the language of the Levinthal paradox, the substitution reactions do not try out possible orientations; the possibilities are constrained by the electronics of the system. The early and rapid manifestation of the electronic effects described here may account for the initial "burst phase" of protein folding (Myers and Oas 2002).

Rate-Limiting Aspects of Folding

Electronic effects are fast enough to support the observed folding rates for proteins. Consequently, other aspects of protein folding appear to represent the rate-limiting steps, including solvent effects and the rearrangement of secondary structural elements into the final native 3-D conformation. Solvent effects in folding are slow to reach fruition because they require the coordinated rearrangement of water molecules and side chains that occupy significant volumes. In addition, the entropic effects of solvent are haphazard and do not guide the folding trajectory *per se*. Thus, valine and leucine should theoretically experience very similar solvent effects, yet in reality these amino acids display considerable differences in their preferences for secondary structure.

Tertiary interactions also play an important role in stabilizing the protein conformation, especially at the later stages of the folding process. The formation of these stabilizing tertiary contacts may occur through one of several related mechanisms, including diffusion-collision (Myers and Oas 2002), nucleation-condensation (Daggett and Fersht 2003), and topomer searching (Gillespie and Plaxco 2004). The diffusion-collision mechanism is highly compatible with the model outlined here. According to this mechanism, microdomains of local secondary structure form rapidly and these microdomains diffuse and collide with each other to produce stabilizing non-local (topology-dependent) interactions that give rise to the native conformation of the protein (Myers and Oas 2002). This is not to say that electronic effects are not involved in diffusion-collision, topomer searching, etc. When amino acid side chains form tertiary contacts, these interactions can either enhance or diminish the gating effects of those side chains on the main chain. This may in turn alter the electron distribution along the peptide backbone of the segments that interact. Consequently, tertiary interactions may either promote secondary structure formation or reorient structures already adopted in order to harmonize intramolecular consolidation. In this way, the same 5 amino acids may be observed in both α-helix and β-strand conformations as reported by Kabsch and Sander (1984). These mechanisms reflect context effects in folding akin to the nearest-neighbor effects, but expressed as a function of the topology of the protein rather than its sequence. Thus, in the collision/condensation phase of folding, additional non-local electronic effects are brought into play to refine and stabilize the protein structure.

CONCLUSION

Amino acid side chains behave as substituents on the peptide backbone that affect electron distributions along the main chain as a function of the electronic properties of the side chain groups. Important properties of the side chains include their inductive, field, and resonance effects and their hydrophilicity and polarizability. These electronic effects are rapidly propagated to and along the peptide backbone and appear to be largely responsible for the initial adoption of secondary structures in proteins – the burst phase of folding. In some simple proteins, these electronic effects may largely determine the final conformation with little involvement of folding intermediates. Interestingly, there was a close correspondence between the QM calculations of the electronic properties of dipeptides that related to secondary structural preferences and NMR findings concerning the degree of shielding at HN and C_α atoms in amino acids in β-strand *vs.* α-helical conformations. Thus, the electronic properties defined here appear to reflect intrinsic factors that determine preference for secondary structure. A novel concept introduced here is the notion that electron delocalization along the peptide backbone is subject to gating by amino acid side chains. The relative gating of electron flow along the backbone generates elements of secondary structure, which then coalesce to form the native tertiary conformation of the protein. The diffusion-collision model is an attractive mechanism for this rate-limiting step because stabilization of random collisions ultimately involves electronic effects, including electrostatic interactions, field effects, and association of similar species (e.g., hydrophobic side chains) through dispersion forces. Solvent plays a significant, yet complex role in protein folding. The hydrophilicity of amino acid side chains may serve as an internal image of these solvent effects. Thus, the degree to which a side chain mimics water will then determine the polarization effects of the side chain on main chain atoms and the preferred environment of that residue. Taken together, these studies provide encouragement to efforts aimed at the description of protein folding in purely electronic terms and mechanisms. Nevertheless, progress towards this goal will hinge on a more thorough characterization of the electronic properties of amino acids and short peptides.

REFERENCES

Alabugin, I. V., Manoharan M., Peabody, S. and Weinhold, F. (2001) Electronic basis of improper hydrogen bonding: A subtle balance of hyperconjugation and rehybridization. *J. Am. Chem. Soc.* 125, 5973-5987.

Aszodi, A., Munro, R. E. and Taylor, W. R. (1997) Protein modeling by multiple sequence threading and distance geometry. *Proteins* 29 S1, 38-42.

Avery, J. (1964) Excitation migration and biological systems. In B. Pullman (Ed.), *Electronic Aspects of Biochemistry* (pp. 29-41). New York, NY: Academic Press.

Ayala, I., Range, K., York, D. and Barry, B. A. (2002) Spectroscopic properties of tyrosyl radicals in dipeptides. *J. Am. Chem. Soc.* 124, 5496-5505.

Bader, R. F. W. (1990) *Atoms in Molecules: A Quantum Theory*. Oxford, UK: Clarendon Press.

Baker, D. and Sali, A. (2001) Protein structure prediction and structural genomics. *Science* 294, 93-96.

Beratan, D. N., Onuchic, J. N., Winkler, J. R. and Gray, H. B. (1992) Electron-tunneling pathways in proteins. *Science* 258, 1740-1741.

Bernstein, F. C., Koetzle, T. F., Williams, J. B., Meyer, E. F., Jr., Brice, M. D., Rodgers, J. R., Kennard, O., Shimanouchi, T. and Tasumi, M. (1977) The Protein Data Bank: A computer-based archival file for macromolecular structures. *J. Mol. Biol.* 112, 535-542.

Brinck, T., Haeberlein, M. and Jonsson, M. (1997) A computational analysis of substituent effects on the O-H bond dissociation energy in phenols: polar versus radical effects. *J. Am. Chem. Soc.* 119, 4239-4244.

Calcaterra, L. T., Closs, G. L. and Miller, J. R. (1983) Fast intramolecular electron transfer in radical ions over long distances across rigid saturated hydrocarbon spacers. *J. Am. Chem. Soc.* 105, 670-671.

Charton , M. (1981) Electrical effect of substituent constants for correlation analysis. In R. W. Taft (Ed.), *Physical Organic Chemistry* (Vol. 13, pp. 120-252). New York, NY: Wiley.

Chou, P. Y. and Fasman, G. D. (1978) Empirical predictions of protein conformation. *Annu. Rev. Biochem.* 47, 251-276.

Closs, G. L. and Miller, J. R. (1988) Intramolecular long-distance electron transfer in organic molecules. *Science* 240, 440-447.

Cornilescu, G., Bax, A. and Case, D. A. (2000) Large variations in one-bond $^{13}C^{\alpha}$-$^{13}C^{\beta}$ *J* couplings in polypeptides correlate with backbone conformation. *J. Am. Chem. Soc.* 122, 2168-2171.

Cowan, J. A., Upmacis, R. K., Beratan, D. N., Onuchic, J. N. and Gray, H. B. (1988) Long-range electron transfer in myoglobin. Ann. N. Y. *Acad. Sci.* 550, 68-84.

Creamer T. P. and Rose, G. D. (1992) Side-chain entropy opposes α-helix formation but rationalizes experimentally determined helix-forming propensities. *Proc. Natl. Acad. Sci. USA* 89, 5937-5941.

Cserzo, M. and Simon, I. (1989) Regularities in the primary structure of proteins. *Int. J. Pept. Prot. Res.* 34, 184-195.

Daggett, V. and Fersht A. R. (2003) Is there a unifying mechanism for protein folding? *Trends Biochem. Sci.* 28, 18-25.

Dill, K. A. (1990) Dominant forces in protein folding. *Biochemistry* 29, 7133-7155.

Dwyer, D. S. (1989) Amino acid sequence homology between ligands and their receptors: potential identification of binding sites. *Life Sci.* 45, 421-429.

Dwyer, D. S. (1998) Assembly of exons from unitary transposable genetic elements: Implications for the evolution of protein-protein interactions. *J. Theor. Biol.* 194, 11-27.

Dwyer, D. S. (2001) Electronic properties of the amino acid side chains contribute to the structural preferences in protein folding. *J. Biomol. Struct. Dynamics* 18, 881-892.

Dwyer, D. S. (2005) Electronic properties of amino acid side chains: quantum mechanics calculation of substituent effects. *BMC Chem Biol.* 5 (2), 1-11.

Eley, D. S. and Spivey, D. I. (1960) Semiconductivity in hydrated hemoglobin. *Nature* 188, 725.

Ellenbogen, E. (1952) Dissociation constants of peptides. I. A survey of the effect of optical configuration. *J. Am. Chem. Soc.* 74, 5198-5201.

Frank, H. S. and Wen, W.-Y. (1957) Ion-solvent interaction. Structural aspects of ion-solvent interaction in aqueous solutions: A suggested picture of water structure. *Discuss. Farad. Soc.* 24, 133-140.

Gillespie, B. and Plaxco, K. W. (2004) Using protein folding rates to test protein folding theories. *Annu. Rev. Biochem.* 73, 837-859.

Gmeiner, W. H. and Facelli, J. C. (1996) Quantum mechanical and experimental measurement of N-terminal charge effects on ^{1}HN and ^{1}HC$_\alpha$ chemical shifts in peptides. *Biopolymers* 38, 573-581.

Gromiha, M. M. and Ponnuswamy, P. K. (1995) Prediction of protein secondary structures from their hydrophobic characteristics. *Int. J. Pept. Prot. Res.* 45, 225-240.

Hammett, L. P. (1937) The effect of structure upon the reactions of organic compounds. Benzene derivatives. *J. Am. Chem. Soc.* 59, 96-103.

Hansch, C., Leo, A. and Taft, R. W. (1991) A survey of Hammett substituent constants and resonance and field parameters. *Chem. Rev.* 91, 165-195.

Hildebrand J. H. (1979) Is there a "hydrophobic effect"? Proc. Natl. Acad. Sci. USA 76, 194.

Hoffman, B. M. and Ratner, M. A. (1987) Gated electron transfer: When are observed rates controlled by conformational interconversion? *J. Am. Chem. Soc.* 109, 6237-6243.

Hopfield, J. J. (1974) Electron transfer between biological molecules by thermally activated tunneling. *Proc. Natl. Acad. Sci. USA* 71, 3640-3644.

Huyskens, P. L. (1977) Factors governing the influence of a first hydrogen bond on the formation of a second one by the same molecule or ion. *J. Am. Chem. Soc.* 99, 2578-2582.

Improta, R., Mele, F., Crescenzi, O., Benzi, C. and Barone, V. (2002) Understanding the role of stereoelectronic effects in determining collagen stability. 2. A quantum mechanical/molecular mechanical study of (proline-proline-glycine)$_n$ polypeptides. *J. Am. Chem. Soc.* 124, 7857-7865.

Jones, D. D. (1975) Amino acid properties and side-chain orientation in proteins: A cross correlation approach. *J. Theor. Biol.* 50, 167-183.

Jones, D. T., Tress, M., Bryson, H. and Hadley, C. (1999) Successful recognition of protein folds using threading methods biased by sequence similarity and predicted secondary structure. *Proteins Suppl.* 3, 104-111.

Kabsch, W. and Sander, C. (1984) On the use of sequence homologies to predict protein structure: Identical pentapeptides can have completely different conformations. *Proc. Natl. Acad. Sci. USA* 81, 1075-1078.

Karplus, K., Barrett, C., Cline, M., Diekhans, M., Grate, L. and Hughey, R. (1999) Predicting protein structure using only sequence information. *Proteins Suppl.* 3, 121-125.

Kauzmann, W. (1959) Factors in interpretation of protein denaturation. *Adv. Prot. Chem.* 14, 1-63.

Kidera, A., Konishi, Y., Oka, M., Ooi, T. and Scheraga, H. A. (1985) Statistical analysis of the physical properties of the 20 naturally occurring amino acids. *J. Prot. Chem.* 4, 23-55.

Kim, P. S. and Baldwin, R. L. (1990) Intermediates in the folding reactions of small proteins. *Annu. Rev. Biochem.* 59, 631-660.

Kropman, M. F. and Bakker, H. J. (2001) Dynamics of water molecules in aqueous solvation shells. *Science* 291, 2118-2120.

Kyte, J. and Doolittle, R. F. (1982) A simple method for displaying the hydropathic character of a protein. *J. Mol. Biol.* 157, 105-132.

Langen, R., Chang, I.-J., Germanas, J. P., Richards, J. H., Winkler, J. R. and Gray, H. B. (1995) Electron tunneling in proteins: Coupling through a β strand. *Science* 268, 1733-1735.

Levinthal, C. (1968) Are there pathways for protein folding? J. Chim. Phys. PCB 65, 44-45.

Levitt, M. A. (1976) Simplified representation of protein conformations for rapid simulation of protein folding. *J. Mol. Biol.* 104, 59-107.

Li, J. and Ross, D. K. (1993) Evidence for two kinds of hydrogen bond in ice. *Nature* 365, 327-329.

Marcus, R. A. and Sutin, N. (1985) Electron transfers in chemistry and biology. *Biochim. Biophys. Acta* 811, 265-322.

Martin, T. W. and Derewenda, Z. S. (1999) The name is bond – H bond. *Nature Struct. Biol.* 6, 403-406.

Moser, C. C., Keske, J. M., Warncke, K., Farid, R. S. and Dutton, P. L. (1992) Nature of biological electron transfer. *Nature* 355, 796-802.

Munoz, V. and Serrano, L. (1995) Elucidating the folding problem of helical peptides using empirical parameters. II. Helix macrodipole effects and rational modification of the helical content of natural peptides. *J. Mol. Biol.* 245, 275-296.

Myers, J. K. and Oas, T. G. (2002) Mechanisms of fast protein folding. *Annu. Rev. Biochem.* 71, 783-815.

O'Neil, K. T. and DeGrado, W. F. (1990) A thermodynamic scale for the helix-forming tendencies of the commonly occurring amino acids. *Science* 250, 646-651.

Orengo, C. A., Bray, J. E., Hubbard, T., LoConte, L. and Sillitoe, I. (1999) Analysis and assessment of ab initio three-dimensional prediction, secondary structure, and contacts prediction. *Proteins Suppl.* 3, 149-170.

Osapay, K. and Case D. A. (1994) Analysis of proton chemical shifts in regular secondary structure of proteins. *J. Biomol. NMR* 4, 215-230.

Patten, F. and Gordy, W. (1960) Temperature effects on free radical formation and electron migration in irradiated proteins. *Proc. Natl. Acad. Sci. USA* 46, 1137-1144.

Pophristic, V. and Goodman, L. (2001) Hyperconjugation not steric repulsion leads to the staggered structure of ethane. *Nature* 411, 565-568.

Pross, A. and Radom, L. (1981) A theoretical approach to substituent interactions in substituted benzenes. In R. W. Taft (Ed.), *Physical Organic Chemistry* (Vol. 13, pp. 1-60). New York, NY: Wiley.

Pruetz, W. A. and Land, E. J. (1979) Charge transfer in peptides. Pulse radiolysis investigation of one-electron reactions in dipeptides of tryptophan and tyrosine. *Int. J. Radiat. Biol.* 36, 513-520.

Rost, B. (2001) Review: protein secondary structure prediction continues to rise. *J. Struct. Biol.* 134, 204-218.

Rost, B., Schneider, R. and Sander, C. (1997) Protein fold recognition by prediction-based threading. *J. Mol. Biol.* 270, 471-480.

Simons, K. T., Kooperberg, C., Huang, E. and Baker, D. (1997) Assembly of protein tertiary structures from fragments with similar local sequences using simulated annealing and Bayesian scoring functions. *J. Mol. Biol.* 268, 209-225.

Simons, K. T., Bonneau, R., Ruczinski, I. and Baker, D. (1999) Ab initio protein structure prediction of CASPIII targets using ROSETTA. *Proteins Suppl.* 3, 171-176.

Stewart, J. J. P. (1989) Optimization of parameters for semiempirical methods. *I. Method. J. Comput. Chem.* 10, 209-220.

Suhai, S. (1974) Theoretical investigation of semiconductive properties in proteins. I. Electrical conductivity, charge carrier mobilities, and free paths in β-polyglycine. *Biopolymers* 13, 1731-1737.

Taft, R. W., Jr. (1952) Polar and steric substituent constants for aliphatic and o-benzoate groups from rates of esterification and hydrolysis of esters. *J. Am. Chem. Soc.* 74, 3120-3128.

Topsom, R. D. (1987) Some theoretical studies of electronic substituent effects in organic chemistry. *Prog. Phys. Org. Chem.* 16, 125-191.

Venclovas, C., Zemla, A., Fidelis, K. and Moult, J. (2003) Assessment of progress over the CASP experiments. *Proteins 53 Suppl* 6, 585-595.

Weinhold, F. (2001) A new twist on molecular shape. Nature 411, 539-541.

Wiberg, K. B., Hadad, C. M., Breneman, C. M., Laidig, K. E., Murcko, M. A. and LePage, T. J. (1991) The response of electrons to structural changes. *Science* 252, 1266-1272.

Williams, R. W., Chang, A., Juretic, D. and Loughran, S. (1987) *Secondary structure predictions and medium range interactions.*

Wishart, D. S., Sykes, B. D. and Richards, F. M. (1991) Relationship between nuclear magnetic resonance chemical shift and protein secondary structure. *J. Mol. Biol.* 222, 311-333.

Wu, T. T. and Kabat, E. A. (1973) An attempt to evaluate the influence of neighboring amino acids (*n*-1) and (*n*+1) on the backbone conformation of amino acid (*n*) in proteins. Use in predicting the three-dimensional structure of the polypeptide backbone of other proteins. *J. Mol. Biol.* 75, 13-31.

Wuttke, D. S., Bjerrum, M. J., Winkler, J. R. and Gray, H. B. (1992) Electron-tunneling pathways in cytochrome c. *Science* 256, 1007-1009.

In: Protein Folding: New Research
Editor: Tony R. Obalinsky, pp. 249-265

ISBN 1-59454-835-8

Chapter 7

SALIENT FEATURES OF RESIDUE CONTACTS IN PROTEIN STRUCTURES FOR DETERMINING THEIR FOLDING AND STABILITY

M. Michael Gromiha[1*] and S. Selvaraj[2]
[1]Computational Biology Research Center,
National Institute of Advanced Industrial Science and Technology (AIST),
AIST Tokyo Waterfront Bio-IT Research Building, Tokyo, Japan
[2]Department of Bioinformatics, Bharathidasan University, Tamil Nadu, India

ABSTRACT

During the process of protein folding, the amino acid residues along the polypeptide chain interact with each other in a cooperative manner to form the stable native structure. The knowledge about inter-residue interactions in protein structures is very helpful to understand the mechanism of protein folding and stability. We classified the inter-residue interactions into short, medium and long range based on a simple geometric approach. The features of these interactions in different structural classes of globular and membrane proteins have been delineated. The application of inter-residue contacts for predicting protein structural class and secondary structure prediction has been evaluated. Further, the relationship between inter-residue contacts and protein folding rates has been highlighted. Moreover, the importance of inter-residue interactions in protein folding kinetics and for understanding the stability of proteins has been discussed. In essence, the information gained from the studies on inter-residue interactions provides valuable insights for understanding protein folding and de novo protein design.

Key words: inter-residue interactions; protein folding; stability; folding rate; kinetics

---

* Corresponding author: Tel: +81-3-3599-8046; Fax: +81-3-3599-8081; E-mail: michael-gromiha@aist.go.jp

INTRODUCTION

The formation of stable secondary structures and a unique tertiary structure of proteins are dictated by intra molecular interactions between the constituent amino acid residues along the polypeptide chain as well as their interaction with the surrounding medium. During the process of protein folding, the hydrophobic force drives the polypeptide chain to the folded state overcoming the entropic factors, while hydrogen bonds, ion pairs, disulfide bonds and van der Waals interactions, define the shape and keep it from falling apart (Ponnuswamy and Gromiha, 1994). These non-covalent forces that arise from inter-residue interactions among sequential neighbors as well as those far away in the sequence cooperatively form and stabilize the native structure.

Tanaka and Scheraga (1975) categorized the inter-residue interactions into short, medium and long-range and proposed a hypothesis for protein folding by a three-step mechanism based on these interactions. For the past three decades, the concept of inter-residue interactions has been the main focus to understand the mechanism of protein folding and stability (Gromiha and Selvaraj, 2002a; 2004). Further, the short, medium and long-range interactions have been classified according to the distance of separation between the residues along the polypeptide chain. This classification has been used successfully to address the problem of protein folding and sequence recognition (Gromiha and Selvaraj, 1997; Miyazawa and Jernigan, 1999). Recently, inter-residue interactions have been characterized by the parameters, contact order and long-range order, which show a very strong correlation with the folding rate of small proteins (Plaxco et al. 1998; Gromiha and Selvaraj, 2001a).

DEFINITION OF SHORT, MEDIUM AND LONG-RANGE INTERACTIONS

The definition of short, medium and long-range interactions in a protein is based on the amino acid residues, which are in contact with each other (i) in the native structure and (ii) their respective locations in the sequence. For a given residue, the composition of surrounding residues, within a sphere of 8Å radius, is analyzed in terms of their location at the sequence level. The residues that are within a distance of two residues from the central residue are considered to contribute to short-range interactions, those within a distance of ±3 or ±4 residues to medium range and those more than four residues away to long-range interactions (Gromiha and Selvaraj, 1997, 2004).

The definitions of the short, medium and long-range interactions in protein structures are illustrated in Figure 1. In this figure, we show the surrounding residues of T152 (indicated by an arrow) in T4 Lysozyme (2LZM) within the sphere of radius 8Å. The residues, I150, T151, F153 and R154 (marked as s) are close to the residue T152 (central residue) along N and C-directions and these residues contribute to short-range interactions; the residues, R148, V149, T155 and G156 (marked as m) are separated by 3 or 4 residues from the central residue (T152) in the amino acid sequence and these residues contribute to medium-range interactions; other residues T157, W158, D159, A160, are separated by more than 4 residues and V94, R95 and A98 are far in the sequence level from T152. Accordingly, these residues (marked as l) contribute to long-range interactions.

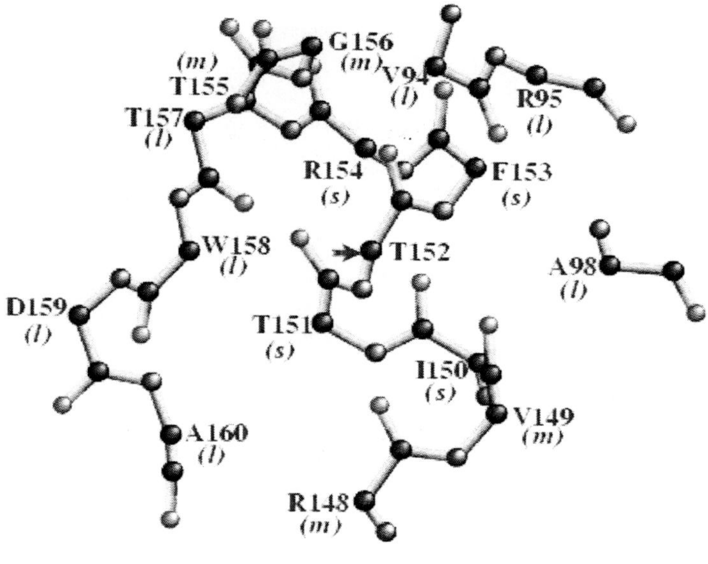

Figure 1: Representation of short, medium and long-range contacts in protein structures. A typical example of surrounding residues around T152 of T4 lysozyme within 8Å is shown (Gromiha and Selvaraj, 2004): s: short-range contacts, m: medium-range contacts and l: long-range contacts.

INTER-RESIDUE INTERACTIONS IN PROTEIN STRUCTURES

The nature of inter-residue interactions varies for each class of proteins and specifically in secondary structures. Proteins are categorized into four structural classes, namely, all-α, all-β, α+β and α/β. The average short, medium and long-range contacts for the residues in each of the four structural classes shows that the short-range contacts are similar in all classes and the role of medium and long-range contacts are distinct in each class. The average medium-range contacts are higher for all-α class proteins than all-β proteins, indicating the vital influence of medium-range contacts in the formation of α helices. Conversely long-range contacts are remarkably higher in the all-β proteins than all-α proteins, implying the importance of long-range effects in β-strands (Gromiha and Selvaraj, 1997). In the α+β and α/β classes the medium and long-range contacts lie in the range between all-α and all-β class proteins.

Preference of Amino Acid Residues in Medium and Long-Range Contacts

The preference of each amino acid to form medium and long-range contact has been analyzed and the results are presented in Table 1. The residue Met has the highest medium-range contact followed by Leu, Ala, Glu and Gln (Gromiha and Selvaraj, 1997) and all of them are found to be helix forming residues (Fasman, 1989; Gromiha and Ponnuswamy, 1995). This implies that these residues at the level of medium range, influence the formation, propagation and stabilization of helices. On the other hand, Pro has the lowest medium-range contact, indicating the fact that it is not a favored residue in α-helical conformation (Fasman, 1989; MacArthur and Thronton, 1991; Gromiha and Ponnuswamy, 1995).

The residue Ile has the highest long-range contact followed by Cys, Val, Tyr, Trp, Phe and Leu. This shows that hydrophobic residues mainly influence the long-range contacts, and these residues can serve as nucleation centers during the process of protein folding and get buried in the interior. The lowest value is observed for Glu and other residues having lowest long-range contacts are Lys and Asp. This result indicates that the ion-pairs may be formed between neighboring residues (Barlow and Thornton, 1983; Matthews, 1993).

Table 1. Average medium and long-range contacts for the 20 amino acid residues in globular proteins

Residue	Medium	Long
Ala	2.11	3.92
Asp	1.80	*2.85*
Cys	1.88	5.55
Glu	2.09	*2.72*
Phe	1.98	4.53
Gly	1.53	4.31
His	1.98	3.77
Ile	1.77	5.58
Lys	1.96	*2.79*
Leu	2.19	4.59
Met	2.27	4.14
Asn	1.84	3.64
Pro	*1.32*	3.57
Gln	2.03	3.06
Arg	1.94	3.78
Ser	1.57	3.75
Thr	1.57	4.09
Val	1.63	5.43
Trp	1.90	4.83
Tyr	1.67	4.93

The lowest medium-range contact and bottommost three long-range contacts are italic (Gromiha and Selvaraj, 1997).

Long-Range Contacts in Different Residue Intervals

Further, we have analyzed the long-range contacts in different residue intervals, 4-10; 11-20; 21-30; 31-40; 41-50 and >50. The observed average long-range contacts in four structural classes for these intervals are presented in Figure 2 (Gromiha and Selvaraj, 1999). This figure reveals the opposite trends in the formation of long-range contacts between all-α and all-β proteins. The all-α class proteins have more long- range contacts in the 4-10 range and the all-β class proteins have more long-range contacts in the 11-20 range. This may be due to the specific hydrogen-bonding pattern of α-helices and β-strands in these classes of proteins.

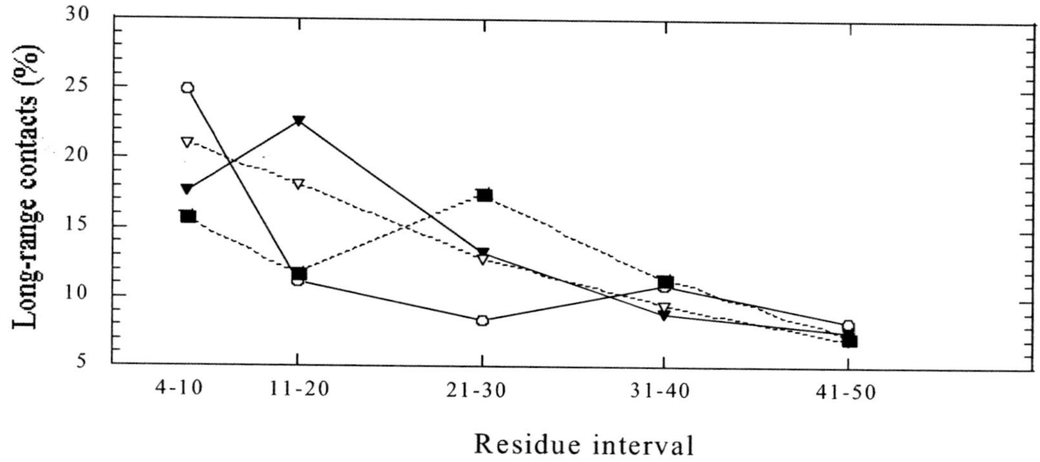

Figure 2: Average percentage of long-range contacts in different intervals for the four structural classes of globular proteins (Gromiha and Selvaraj, 1999).
○: all-α; ▼: all-β; ∇: α+β; ■: α/β

The behavior of proteins in α+β and α/β classes is interesting. The α+β class of proteins favors the range 4-10 while the α/β class of proteins prefers the 21-30 range. The helical and strand segments are segregated into separate domains in α+β proteins and the proteins in this class behave like either all-α or all-β type. We observed that the features of α+β proteins are similar to that of all-α proteins. In α/β class, the α-helices and β-strands occur alternatively and some residue distances are necessary to form β-strand, which leads to having higher contacts in 21-30 range. These results indicate that the long-range contacts from different intervals play a considerable role in the folding of proteins belonging to different structural classes.

Residue Contacts in Membrane Proteins

Membrane proteins generally have two folding types, α-helices or β-strands in the membrane. These proteins are termed as transmembrane helical (TMH) and transmembrane strand (TMS) proteins and the residue-residue contacts in these proteins are distinct to each other.

Transmembrane Helical Proteins

The average medium-range contact in TMH proteins is similar to all-α globular proteins, indicating a common behavior of helix packing in these two groups of proteins. Residue-wise analysis showed that Cys, Leu, Ile, Met, Val, Phe, Trp and Ala are the topmost residues with high medium-range contacts in TMH proteins (Gromiha and Selvaraj, 2001b). Strikingly, these residues are highly preferred in the membrane environment (Gromiha, 1999). All the charged residues (Asp, Glu, His, Lys and Arg) in TMH proteins have less medium-range contacts than all-α proteins. In coincidence with globular proteins, Pro has the lowest medium-range contacts due to the fact that it is a helix breaker (Fasman, 1989) and Pro is not a favored residue in membrane environment (Deber et al. 1990; Ponnuswamy and Gromiha, 1993).

Further, all the residues except Met and Pro in all-α proteins have higher medium-range contacts than long-range contacts, whereas in TMH proteins, residues Cys, Gly, Asn, Pro, Gln, Ser and Tyr have higher long-range contacts than medium-range contacts. It is noteworthy that the ratio between long and medium-range contacts for all charged residues is higher in TMH proteins than all-α proteins. This may be due to the presence of these residues near the termini of membrane spanning helices (Andersson et al. 1992).

Transmembrane Strand Proteins

TMS proteins have appreciably higher long-range contacts and lower medium- range contacts than all-β proteins (Gromiha and Selvaraj, 1997; 2001b). Considering the total contacts, one additional contact (11 contacts per residue) is observed for all residues in TMS proteins compared to all-β proteins, indicating the closer packing of β-strands in TMS proteins.

Residue-wise analysis showed that the residue Cys has the highest long-range contact followed by Met and Pro has the lowest long-range contact (Gromiha and Selvaraj, 2001b). Indeed it has been shown that Met and Pro are, respectively, high and low preferred residues in membrane spanning β-strands (Gromiha and Ponnuswamy, 1993; Gromiha et al. 1997). The ratio between the number of long-range and medium-range contacts for the positively charged residues is approximately 8 to 12 in TMS proteins, while it is 5 to 7 in all-β proteins. In the membrane spanning β-strand segments, the positive charged residues, Lys and Arg make significant contacts with other residues in the membrane (Gromiha and Suwa, 2003). This might be due to the formation of ion-pairs and/or cation-π interactions (Gromiha, 2003a).

The comparison of total medium and long-range contacts in TMS proteins revealed that on an average, all the residues have more long-range contacts that are remarkably 18 times higher than medium-range contacts. This might be due to the complex architecture of TMS proteins interspersed with polar residues in membrane, which make hydrogen bonding networks and electrostatic contacts with residues in neighboring β-strands that are far in sequence level.

Application of Residue Contacts in Protein Structure Prediction, Folding and Stability

Secondary Structure of Prediction

The information about the inter-residue interactions in different structural classes showed that secondary structure formation is mainly influenced by medium-range interactions in all-α proteins whereas it is influenced by long-range interactions in all-β proteins. As most of the secondary structure prediction algorithms take into account only the effect of neighboring residues along the sequence which include short and medium-range interactions, we hypothesized that secondary structure prediction of all-α proteins would be better than the other classes of proteins (Gromiha and Selvaraj, 1998).

Table 2. Accuracy of prediction in different structural classes by eight methods

Method	All-α	All-β	Mixed	Reference
Statistical analysis	*62.2*	49.5	55.3	Chou and Fasman (1974)
Information theory	*61.9*	58.2	58.1	Garnier et al. (1978)
Neural network	*67.0*	64.0	64.9	Qian and Sejnowski (1988)
Enhanced neural network	*79.0*	70.0	64.0	Kneller et al. (1990)
Neural network, PHD	*80.8*	68.8	72.4	Rost and Sandor (1994)
Hydrophobicity profile	*84.1*	83.6	79.8	Gromiha and Ponnuswamy (1995)
Neural network	*71.1*	66.3	66.9	Chandonia and Karplus (1996)
3D-1D compatibility	*74.5*	70.6	67.3	Ito et al. (1997)

The highest accuracy among the three structural classes is indicated italic (Gromiha and Selvaraj, 1998).

We have computed the average predicted accuracy levels of all the structural classes by eight different methods and the results are presented in Table 2. We observed that all the methods predict the secondary structures of all-α class better than other classes (Gromiha and Selvaraj, 1998). A plausible reason for this tendency can be ascribed to the predominant role of short and medium-range interactions in all-α proteins. Similarly, lower accuracy in the prediction of secondary structures in other classes of proteins implies the dominance of long-range interactions in them. Further, inter-residue interactions have been successfully used to predict the structural class of globular proteins (Kumarevel et al. 2000) and discriminate outer membrane proteins (Gromiha et al. 2005).

Protein Folding Rates

The residue contacts in protein structures have been used to understand the folding rates of two-state proteins. Recently, two parameters, contact order (CO) and long-range order (LRO) have been proposed to relate the total number of contacts and long-range contacts, respectively, with protein folding rates (Plaxco et al. 1998; Gromiha and Selvaraj, 2001a).

We defined a parameter, LRO for a protein from the knowledge of long-range contacts in protein structure (Gromiha and Selvaraj, 2001a). It is defined as,

$$LRO = \Sigma n_{ij}/N; \; n_{ij}=1 \text{ if } |i-j| > 12; \qquad (1)$$
$$= 0 \text{ otherwise,}$$

where i and j are two contacting residues in space within a distance of 8Å and N is the total number of residues in a protein.

Relationship between LRO and Folding Rates of Proteins

We have computed LRO using Eqn. 1 for a set of 23 small, two-state proteins and we found a good inverse relationship (r = -0.78) between LRO and experimental folding rate, ln(k) for all the considered proteins. Figure 3 indicates that the minimum distance of 12 residues in defining LRO has the best correlation between LRO and folding rates and significant correlation is obtained for the minimum residue separation of 10 to 15 residues (Gromiha and Selvaraj, 2001a). We set up regression equations for all-α, all-β and mixed class proteins by relating the folding rate and long-range order and we found an excellent agreement between the predicted folding rates and experimental observations (Gromiha and Selvaraj, 2001a). Recently, Punta and Rost (2005) used the concept of LRO for predicting protein folding rates from amino acid sequences.

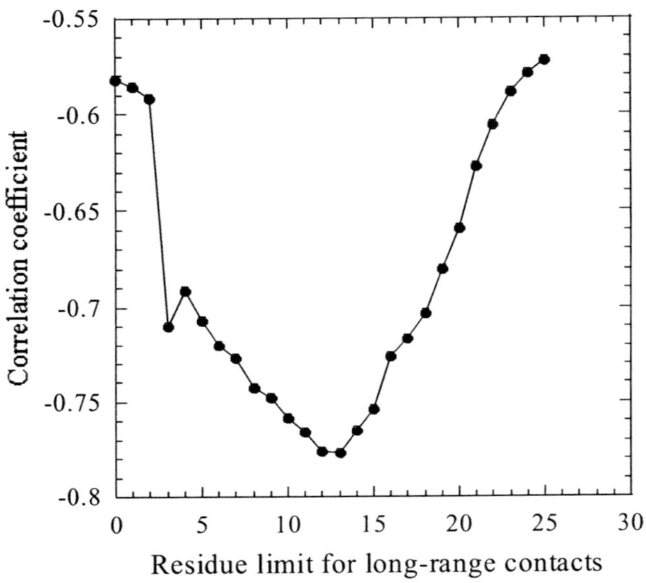

Figure 3: Plot connecting the correlation coefficient obtained between long-range contacts and folding rate of proteins, and the minimum limit to define long-range contacts.

Protein Folding Kinetics and Φ Value Analysis

Understanding the protein-folding pathways and kinetics is a challenging task. The Φ value approach provides a detailed understanding of transition state structures of folded proteins. We have computed the hydrophobicity associated with each residue in the folded state of two-state proteins and compared it with the Φ values of each mutant residue. We found that most of the residues with high Φ value coincide with local maximum in surrounding hydrophobicity, indicating the importance of hydrophobic interactions in the transition state.

Long-range Hydrophobic Contact Networks in Two-state Proteins

The analysis on the number of contacts for each residue that has high Φ value showed that more than 60 % of residues with high Φ values have long-range contributions to the extent of ≥ 50 % in the folded state. Particularly residues in β strands are stabilized by such long-range interactions; however residues in α helices are also stabilized by such interactions to a lesser extent. This highlights the vital role of long-range interactions in the formation of folding nucleus residues.

Further, we have identified a hydrophobic contact network pattern to relate the Φ values with long-range contacts, which will be helpful to understand the transition state structures of folded proteins (Selvaraj and Gromiha, 2004). As an example, we show the long-range contact network pattern for few proteins belonging to different structural classes.

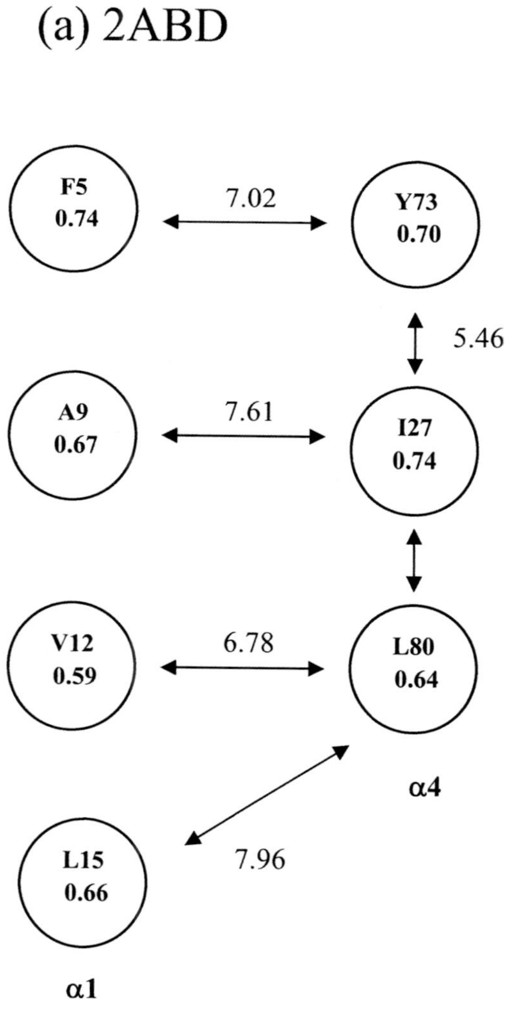

Figure 4 Continued on the next page

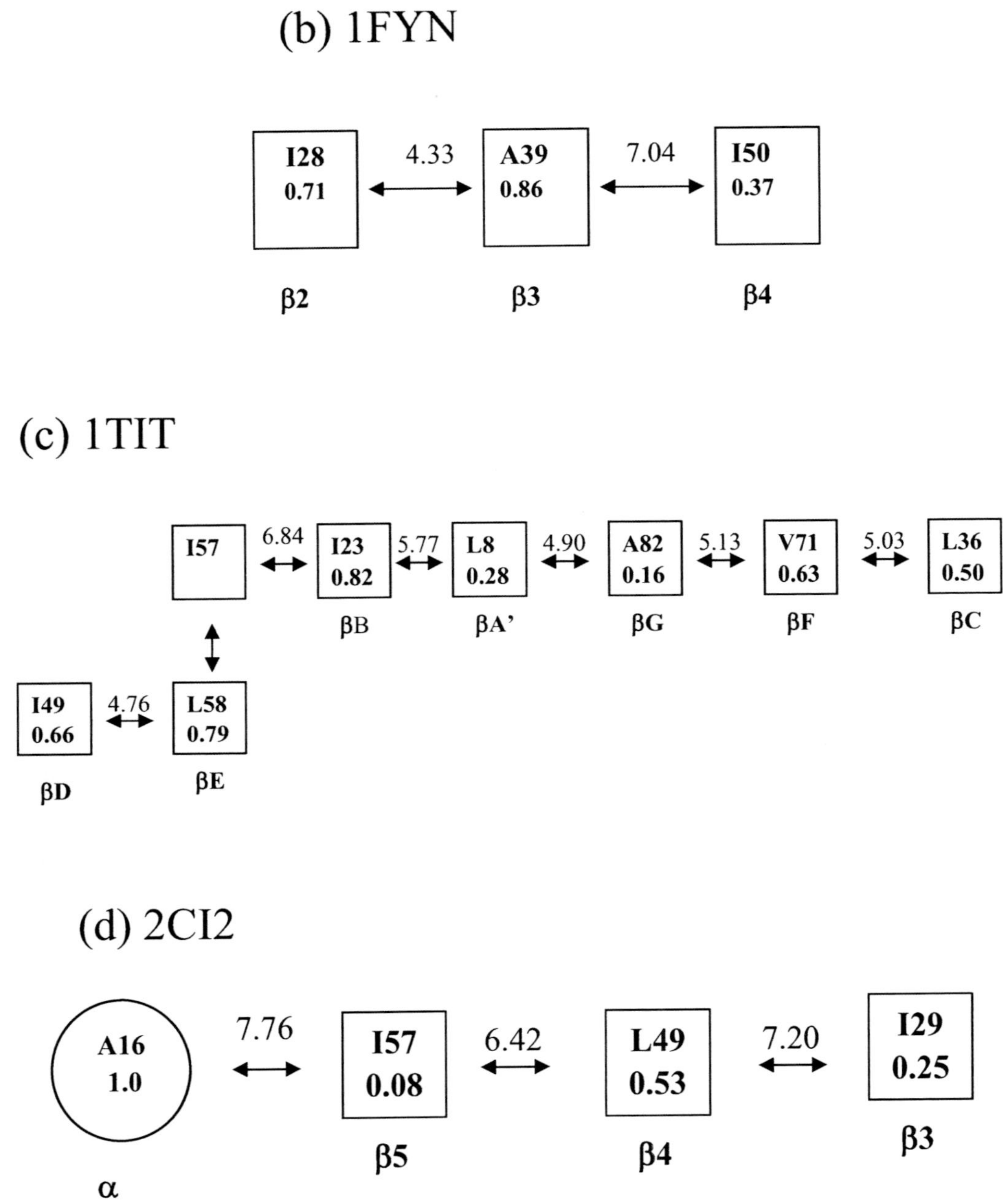

Figure 4: The long-range contact network pattern for four typical proteins: (a) acyl coenzyme protein (2ABD), (b) Fyn SH3 domain (1FYN), (c) titin (1TIT) and (d) chymotrypsin inhibitor (2CI2). Circles and squares indicate helices and strands, respectively. The residue information (name and number) and respective Φ values are given within the circles/ squares. The inter-residue distance (Cα-Cα) has been shown above the double head arrows. The secondary structural element to which a given residue belongs is indicated.

Figure 4a shows the long-range contact network pattern for a α-helical protein, acyl coenzyme binding protein. We observed that the residues in helix 1 (F5, A9, V12 and Leu15) form long-range contacts with residues in helix 4 (Y73 and L80). All these residues are thought to form productive interactions in the rate-limiting native like structure in this protein (Kragelund et al. 1999). In Im9, F15 of helix 1 has long-range contact with V68 of helix 4; also L18 of helix 1 has such contacts with L36 of helix 2. From Φ-value analysis, it has been suggested that the interface between helix 1 and helix 4 is the most structured region in the transition state (Friel et al. 2003).

In SH3 domains, especially in Fyn SH3 (Figure 4b), residues I28, A39 and I50 constitute a long-range residue contact network. These residues have been shown to be tightly packed in the transition state and are designated as the key residues in the folding nucleus (Northey et al. 2002). A similar pattern of interaction has also been seen among the folding nucleus residues of other SH3 domains such as Src, α-spectrin and SSo7D. The WW domain (1PIN) consists of three anti-parallel strands β1 (E12-M15), β2 (V22-N26) and β3 (A31-W34). The Φ-value analysis reveals that the residue with highest value (S19) is in the loop connecting β1 and β2, suggesting the formation of all transition-state interactions at this loop. Long-range hydrophobic contact is observed between M15 (β1) and V22 (β2). V22 makes contact with W34.

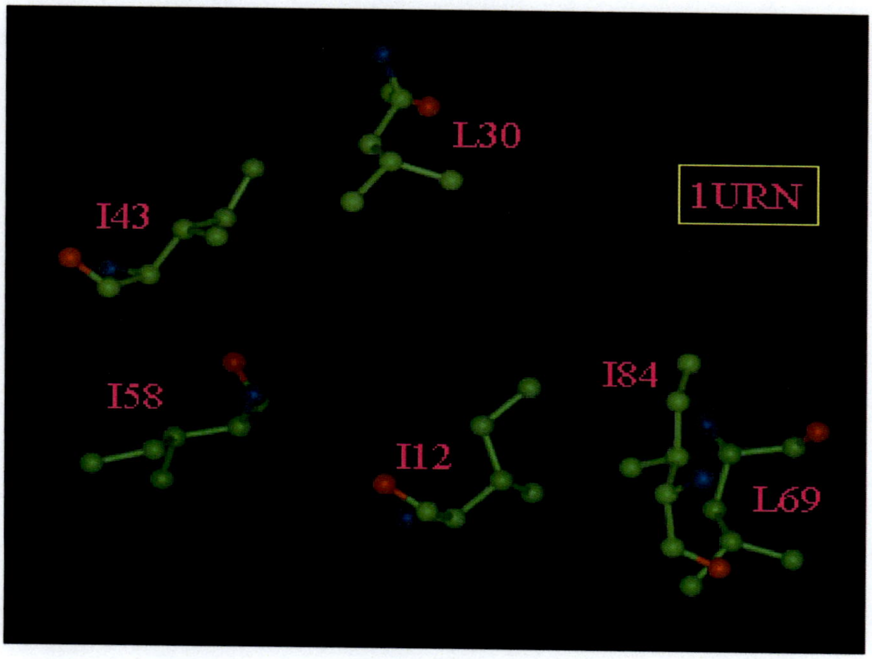

Figure 5: Hydrophobic clusters formed through long-range contacts in 1URN.

The long-range contact network for a β-sandwich protein (titin, 1TIT) is shown in Figure 4c. In this protein, I23 (strand B) makes long-range hydrophobic contact with L8 (strand A') and I57 (strand E). I49 (strand D) has contact with L58 (strand E). Further, F73 (strand F) makes contact with W34 (strand C) and A81 (strand G). Though W34 has not been mutated, it is flanked by residues G32 and L36 with high Φ values, and hence has been postulated to have the highest Φ value. As residues I23, W34, L58 and F73 form a diagonal layer of intra-sheet and inter-sheet interactions at the center of its hydrophobic core, these residues are thought to form the nucleation site for folding (Fowler and Clarke, 2001). The present analysis also shows the existence of long-range hydrophobic contact networks among residues participating in the folding nucleus and others with high Φ vales in each strand.

The contact network for chymotrypsin inhibitor (2CI2) belonging to α/β class is shown in Fig 4d. In this protein, A16 in the single helix and has a Φ value of 1, makes contact with I57 that in turn makes contact with L49. These residues are part of the hydrophobic core of CI2. In FK506 binding protein (1FKB) V2 in β1 makes long-range contacts with L74 and I76 in β4 and with some residues in α-helix. I76 in turn makes contact with V98 of β5. V24 in β2 makes contact with F46 in β3 and V101 in β5. Among these residues V2, V24, V63, I76 and V101 show Φ-values around 0.5. Thus a long-range hydrophobic contact network spans the entire folded structure. This shows that tertiary (long-range) contacts are established during the transition state (Fulton et al. 1999). Many of these residues also acquire maximum surrounding hydrophobicity in the folded state.

The formation of hydrophobic clusters through long-range contacts in a typical protein, 1URN is shown in Figure 5. We observed that the residues I12, L30, I43, I58, L69 and I84 are close to each other in space through long-range contacts. Interestingly, the residues L30 and I43 have high Φ values. It is envisaged that formation of such hydrophobic network of residues, through long-range interactions during the transition state will facilitate the further downhill movement in the folding free energy landscape.

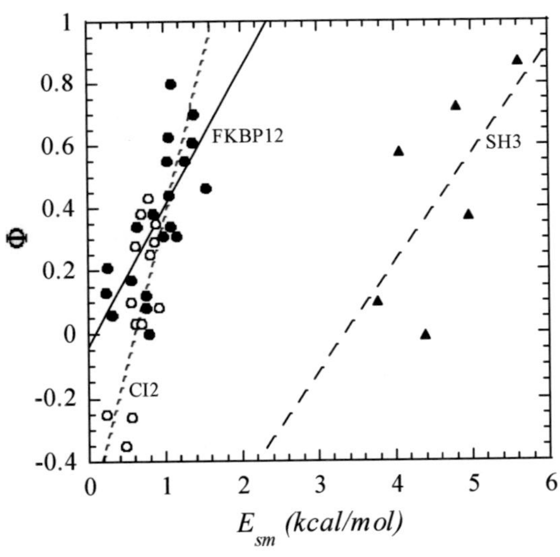

Figure 6: Relationship between experimental Φ values and E_{sm} in partially buried mutations of two-state proteins. The symbols, • , ○ and ▲ represent, FKBP12, CI2 and SH3 mutants and their respective r-values are 0.72, 0.72 and 0.66.

Relationship between Inter-Residue Contacts and Φ Values upon Mutations

We have analyzed the relationship between amino acid properties reflecting inter-residue interactions and Φ values upon partially buried and surface mutations (Gromiha and Selvaraj, 2002b). We found that the short and medium-range energy (E_{sm}) strongly correlated with Φ values, expressing the influence of medium-range interactions in the transition state structures of partially buried mutants. In Figure 6, we show the direct relationship between

E_{sm} and Φ for three proteins, FK506 binding protein (FKBP12), chymotrypsin inhibitor (CI2) and src SH3 domain (SH3). In exposed mutations, properties reflecting long-range interactions have a strong correlation with Φ values.

Protein Stability

We have analyzed the importance of inter-residue interactions to the stability of $(\alpha/\beta)_8$ (TIM) barrel proteins. We have proposed a method for locating the stabilizing residues in TIM barrel proteins based on long-range interactions (LRO and stabilization center) along with surrounding hydrophobicity and conservation score (Gromiha et al. 2004). We have identified 957 stabilizing residues in a non-redundant set of 71 $(\alpha/\beta)_8$ barrel domains. These 957 residues are placed in 434 stabilizing segments of various sizes and each domain contains one to 10 of these segments. We found that 8 segments per domain is the most abundant one and the residues in each stabilizing segments are connected with a long-range contact network as seen in Figure 7 (Selvaraj and Gromiha, 2003; Gromiha et al. 2004). The predicted stabilizing residues in triose phosphate isomerase are shown in Figure 8. Interestingly, the stabilizing residues Cys126 and Gly229, identified by our approach, have been reported as stabilizing ones from thermodynamic and kinetic experiments (Kursula et al. 2002; Gonzalez-Mondragon et al. 2004).

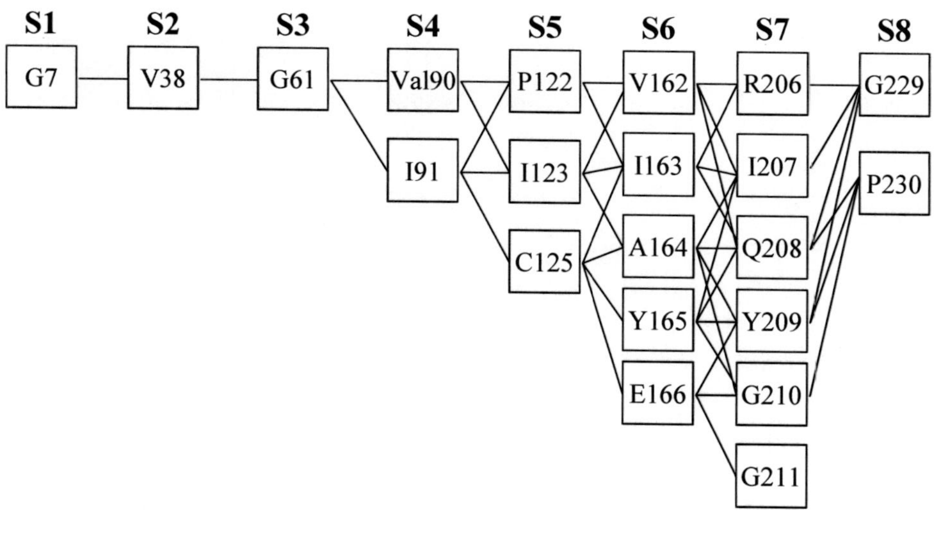

Figure 7: Long-range contact network between residues in each stabilizing segment of 1btm. The strand numbers are indicated as S1, S2 etc.

Protein Stability upon Buried, Partially Buried and Exposed Mutations

The properties reflecting inter-residue interactions, long-range non-bonded energy (E_l) and number of surrounding residues (N_s) have significant correlation with stability in buried and partially buried mutants, respectively (Gromiha et al. 1999). In the coil region of surface mutations, N_l (number of long-range contacts) has the second topmost negative correlation with $\Delta\Delta G$. Hence, the properties reflecting inter-residue interactions play an essential role to the stability of buried, partially buried and exposed protein mutants (Gromiha et al. 1999; 2002; Gromiha, 2003). Further, we observed the inclusion of sequence (neighboring residue information) and structural information (residues which are close to each other within the limit of 8 Å) improved the correlation between amino acid properties and protein stability upon partially buried and exposed mutations (Gromiha et al. 2002; 2004).

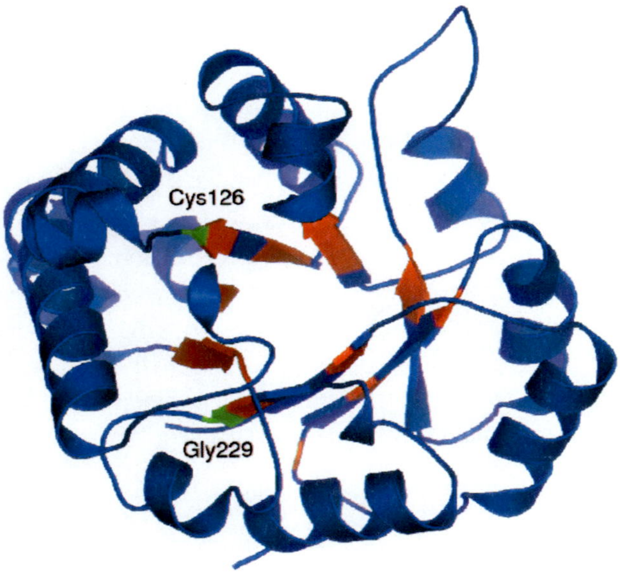

Figure 8. Stabilizing segments in triose phosphate isomerase. The experimentally observed residues Cys126 and Gly229 are shown in green.

Conclusion

The environment around each residue in a globular protein as defined in a sphere of 8Å radius has been effectively partitioned as comprising of residues that contribute to short, medium and long-range interactions. The medium-range interactions predominate in all-α class and the long-range interactions predominate in all-β class proteins. Accordingly, the performance of several structure prediction methods in different structural classes showed that all the methods predict the secondary structures of all-α proteins more accurately than other classes. The concept of contact order and long-range order, reflecting the importance of local and non-local interactions correlates well with folding rate of small proteins. Further, inter-residue interactions play an essential role for determining the transition state structures of two-state proteins. The long-range interactions have been used to locate the stabilizing residues in TIM barrel proteins and the properties reflecting inter-residue interactions have good correlation with protein mutant stability.

In essence, the three dimensional structures of proteins are dictated by short, medium and long-range interactions, and the information about inter-residue interactions in proteins will be very helpful to predict the secondary and tertiary structures of proteins and to understand their folding and stability.

REFERENCES

Andersson H, Bakker E, von Heijne G. 1992. Different positively charged amino acids have similar effects on the topology of a polytopic transmembrane protein in Escherichia coli. *J. Biol. Chem.* 267, 1491-1495.

Barlow, D.J, Thornton, J.M. 1983. Ion-pairs in proteins. J. Mol. Biol. 168, 867-885.

Chandonia, J-M, Karplus, M. 1996. The importance of larger data sets for protein secondary structure prediction with neural networks. *Protein Sci.* 5, 768-774.

Chou, P.Y, Fasman, G.D. 1974. Prediction of protein conformation. *Biochemistry*. 13, 222-245.

Deber, C.M., Glibowicka, M, Woolley, G.A. 1990. Conformations of proline residues in membrane environments. *Biopolymers* 29, 149-157.

Fasman, G.D. 1989. The development of the prediction of protein structure. In "*Prediction of Protein Structure and Principles of Protein Conformation* (Fasman, G.D., Ed.,) pp 193-316, Plenum Press, New York.

Fowler SB, Clarke J. Mapping the folding pathway of an immunoglobulin domain: structural detail from Phi value analysis and movement of the transition state. *Structure* 2001;9:355-366.

Friel CT, Capaldi AP and Radford SE. Structural analysis of the rate-limiting transition states in the folding of Im7 and Im9: similarities and differences in the folding of homologous proteins. *J Mol Biol* 2003;326:293-305

Fulton KF, Main ER, Daggett V, Jackson SE. Mapping the interactions present in the transition state for unfolding/folding of FKBP12. *J Mol Biol* 1999;291:445-461.

Garnier, J., Osguthorpe, D.J, Robson, B. 1978. Analysis of the accuracy and implications of simple methods for predicting the secondary structure of globular proteins. *J. Mol. Biol.* 120, 97-120.

Gonzalez-Mondragon E, Zubillaga RA, Saavedra E, Chanez-Cardenas ME, Perez-Montfort R, Hernandez-Arana A. 2004. Conserved cysteine 126 in triosephosphate isomerase is required not for enzymatic activity but for proper folding and stability. *Biochemistry* 43, 3255-3263.

Gromiha, M.M. 1999. A simple method for predicting transmembrane α helices with better accuracy. *Protein Eng.* 12, 557-561.

Gromiha MM. 2003a. Influence of cation–π interactions in different folding types of membrane proteins. *Biophys. Chem.* 103, 251-258.

Gromiha MM. 2003. Factors Influencing the Thermal Stability of Buried Protein Mutants. *Polymer* 44, 4061-4066.

Gromiha, M.M, Ponnuswamy, P.K. 1993. Prediction of transmembrane beta-strands from hydrophobic characteristics of proteins. *Int. J. Pept. Protein Res.* 42, 420-431.

Gromiha, M.M, Ponnuswamy, P.K. 1995. Prediction of protein secondary structures from their hydrophobic characteristics. *Int. J. Peptide Protein Res.* 45, 225-240.

Gromiha, M.M, Selvaraj, S. 1997. Influence of medium and long Range Interactions in different structural classes of globular proteins *J. Biol. Phys.*23, 151-162.

Gromiha, M.M, Selvaraj, S. 1998. Protein secondary structure prediction in different structural classes. *Protein Eng.* 11, 249-251.

Gromiha, M.M, Selvaraj, S. 1999. Importance of long-range interactions in protein folding. *Biophys. Chem.* 77, 49-68.

Gromiha MM Selvaraj S. 2001a. Comparison between long-range interactions and contact order in determining the folding rates of two-state proteins: application of long-range order to folding rate prediction. *J. Mol. Biol.* 310: 27-32.

Gromiha, M.M, Selvaraj, S. 2001b. Role of medium and long-range interactions in discriminating globular and membrane proteins. *Int. J. Biol. Macromol.* 29, 25-34.

Gromiha, MM, Selvaraj, S (Ed.) 2002a. *Recent Research Developments in Protein Folding, Stability and Design, Research Signpost*, Trivandrum, India.

Gromiha, M.M, Selvaraj, S. 2002b. Important amino acid properties for determining the transition state structures of two-state protein mutants. *FEBS Lett.* 526: 129-134.

Gromiha MM, Suwa M. 2003. Variation of amino acid properties in all-β globular and outer membrane protein structures. *Int. J. Biol. Macromol.* 32: 93-98.

Gromiha, M.M, Selvaraj, S. 2004. Inter-residue interactions in protein folding and stability. Prog. Biophys. *Mol. Biol.* 86, 235-277.

Gromiha, M.M, Majumdar, R, Ponnuswamy, P.K. 1997. Identification of membrane spanning beta strands in bacterial porins. *Protein Eng.* 10, 497-500.

Gromiha, M.M., Oobatake, M., Kono, H., Uedaira, H, Sarai, A. 1999. Role of structural and sequence information in the prediction of protein stability changes: comparison between buried and partially buried mutations. *Protein Eng.* 12: 549-555.

Gromiha MM, Oobatake M, Kono H, Uedaira H, Sarai A. 2002. Importance of mutant position in Ramachandran plot for predicting protein stability of surface mutations. *Biopolymers* 64, 210-220.

Gromiha MM, Pujadas G, Magyar C, Selvaraj S, Simon I. 2004. Locating the stabilizing residues in (alpha/beta)8 barrel proteins based on hydrophobicity, long-range interactions, and sequence conservation. *Proteins* 55, 316-329.

Gromiha MM, Ahmad S, Suwa M. 2005. Application of residue distribution along the sequence for discriminating outer membrane proteins. Comput Biol Chem. 29, 135-142.

Ito, M., Matsuo, Y, Nishikawa, K. 1997. Prediction of protein secondary structure using the 3D-1D compatibility algorithm. *CABIOS* 13, 415-423.

Kneller, D.G., Cohen, F.E, Langridge, R. 1990. Improvements in protein secondary structure prediction by an enhanced neural network. *J. Mol. Biol.* 214, 171-182.

Kragelund BB, Osmark P, Neergaard TB, Schiodt J, Kristiansen K, Kundsen J, Poulsen FM. The formation of a native-like structure containing eight conserved hydrophobic residues is rate-limiting in two-state protein folding of ACBP. *Nature Struct Biol* 1999;6:594-601.

Kumarevel, T.S., Gromiha, M.M, Ponnuswamy, M.N. 2000. Structural class prediction: an application of residue distribution along the sequence. *Biophys. Chem.* 88, 81-101.

Kursula I, Partanen S, Lambeir AM, Wierenga RK. 2002. The importance of the conserved Arg191-Asp227 salt bridge of triosephosphate isomerase for folding, stability, and catalysis. *FEBS Lett* 518, 39-42.

MacArthur MW, Thornton JM. 1991. Influence of proline residues on protein conformation. *J Mol Biol.* 218, 397-412.

Matthews, B.W. 1993. Structural and genetic analysis of protein stability. *Ann. Rev. Biochem.* 62, 139-160.

Miyazawa S, Jernigan, R.L. 1999. Evaluation of short-range interactions as secondary structure energies for protein fold and sequence recognition. *Proteins* 36, 347-356.

Northey JG, Di Nardo AA, Davidson AR. Hydrophobic core packing in the SH3 domain folding transition state. *Nature Struct Biol* 2002;9:126- 130.

Plaxco, K.W., Simons, K.T, Baker, D. 1998. Contact order, transition state placement and the refolding rates of single domain proteins. *J. Mol. Biol.* 277, 985-994.

Ponnuswamy, P.K, Gromiha, M.M. 1993. Prediction of transmembrane helices from hydrophobic characteristics of proteins. *Int. J. Pept. Protein Res.* 42, 326-341.

Ponnuswamy, P.K, Gromiha, M.M. 1994. On the conformational stability of folded proteins. *J. Theor. Biol.* 166, 63-74.

Punta M, Rost B. 2005. Protein folding rates estimated from contact predictions. *J Mol Biol.* 348, 507-512.

Qian, N, Sejnowski, T.J. 1988. Predicting the secondary structure of globular proteins using neural network models. *J. Mol. Biol.* 202, 865-884.

Rost, B, Sandor, C. 1994. Combining evolutionary information and neural networks to predict protein secondary structure. *Proteins* 19, 55-72.

Selvaraj S, Gromiha MM. 2003. Role of hydrophobic clusters and long-range contact networks in the folding of (alpha/beta)8 barrel proteins. *Biophys J.* 84,1919-1925.

Selvaraj S, Gromiha MM. 2004. Importance of hydrophobic cluster formation through long-range contacts in the folding transition state of two-state proteins. *Proteins* 55, 1023-1035.

Tanaka, S, Scheraga, H.A. 1975. Model of protein folding: inclusion of short-, medium-, and long-range interactions.*Proc. Natl. Acad. Sci.* 72, 3802-3806.

INDEX

A

B

C

D

E

F

G

H

I

J

K

L

M

N

Q

R

S

T

U

V